David Kent
Roy Woodward
Keith Pledger
John Hackney
Graham Newman

HEINEMANN MATHEMATICS B

Upper Course

These are the different types of pages and symbols used in this book:

These pages develop mathematical skills, concepts and facts in a wide variety of realistic contexts.

These pages develop mathematical problem-solving skills.

▶ **Do Worksheet 1**　　This shows when you need to use a Worksheet.

● **Remember**　　This is a reminder of the key information essential for the work of the pages.

▼ **Challenge**　　Challenges are more demanding activities designed to stimulate further thought and discussion.

Heinemann

Contents

PART 2

PART 3

Keep up the standard 1

Some of the largest cities in the world have populations of between 6 000 000 and 9 000 000 people.

It often makes it clearer to say that the populations are between 6 million and 9 million.

If the population of London was approximately 5 200 000 it is clearer to write 5·2 million.

1 Write these numbers in 'number of millions' using decimals where necessary:

(a) 3 400 000   (b) 7 500 000   (c) 2 000 000

(d) 8 950 000   (e) 6 250 000   (f) 5 030 000

2 Write these numbers in 'number of thousands' giving your answers correct to 1 decimal place:

(a) 4325   (b) 6478   (c) 9812

(d) 1888   (e) 5992   (f) 2009

10^6 means $10 \times 10 \times 10 \times 10 \times 10 \times 10$ or 1 million.

There are now three ways of writing the population of London
5 200 000 or 5·2 million or $5 \cdot 2 \times 10^6$

3 Write these numbers as decimals, correct to 2 decimal places $\times 10^6$:

(a) 3 435 000   (b) 7 895 000   (c) 2 738 987

(d) 9 438 231   (e) 3 669 087   (f) 2 000 006

4 Write these numbers as powers of 10:

(a) 1 hundred   (b) 1 thousand

(c) ten thousand   (d) ten

(e) 1 million   (f) one

(g) hundred thousand   (h) one million million

Any number can be written in the form of $a \times 10^n$
For example, $8000 = 8 \times 1000 = 8 \times 10^3$

5 Write each of these in the form 8×10^n:

(a) 800   (b) 8 000 000

(c) 800 000 000   (d) 8

(e) 800 000   (f) 8 000 000 000 000

When 5 200 000 is written as $5 \cdot 2 \times 10^6$ it is said to be in **standard index form**.

A number expressed in terms of $a \times 10^n$ where a is a decimal number between 1 and 10 and n is an integer is in standard index form.

$89 \cdot 6 \times 10^4$ is not in standard index form because the 'number' must be between 1 and 10.

$89 \cdot 6 \times 10^4$ can be written in standard index form by rewriting as $8 \cdot 96 \times 10^5$.

The term standard index form is sometimes shortened to **standard form**.

6 Copy and complete this table:

10^6	10^5	10^4	10^3	10^2	10^1	10^0	Standard form
		7	2	0	0	0	$7 \cdot 2 \times 10^4$
				6	4	0	
8	5	0	0	0	0	0	
			0	3	8	0	
					9	2	
						7	

7 Write these numbers in standard index form correct to the approximation given:

(a) 16·5 (2 dp)   (b) 24·8 (1 dp)

(c) 5678 (3 dp)   (d) 6453·2 (3 sf)

(e) 675 430 (2 dp)   (f) 86·92 (3 sf)

(g) 98 670 000 (3 dp)   (h) 9 870 000 (1 dp)

8 Change these numbers from standard form into ordinary form:

(a) $4 \cdot 3 \times 10^3$ (b) $6 \cdot 8 \times 10^7$

(c) $5 \cdot 43 \times 10^5$ (d) $3 \cdot 46 \times 10^2$

(e) $7 \cdot 98 \times 10$ (f) $1 \cdot 2 \times 10^0$

9 Evaluate these expressions giving your answer in standard form:

(a) $400 \times 56 \cdot 8$ (b) $2 \cdot 4 \times 2 \cdot 6$

(c) $300 \times 3 \cdot 8 \times 5 \cdot 5$ (d) $70 \times 2 \cdot 5 \times 0 \cdot 89$

(e) $0 \cdot 5 \times 0 \cdot 5 \times 280$ (f) $1000 \times 0 \cdot 01 \times 2$

(g) $10 \cdot 5 + 34 \cdot 8$ (h) $1456 \cdot 8 - 23 \cdot 6$

(i) $345 \cdot 2 \times 35 - 234$ (j) $178 \cdot 3 - 2 \cdot 5$

(k) $3 \cdot 4 \times 10^4 + 45 \cdot 7$ (l) $5 \cdot 6 \times 10^5 - 1246$

When an experimental nuclear reactor starts up, electric currents as low as 0·000 000 000 007 amps are measured.
Just as it is convenient to write large numbers in standard index form it is also convenient to write very small numbers in standard index form.

To write 0·063 in standard form, first write 0·063 as a fraction where the numerator is a number between 1 and 10.

$$0·063 = \frac{6·3}{100}$$

Then express the denominator in terms of powers of ten:

$$= 6·3 \times \frac{1}{100} = 6·3 \times 10^{-2}$$

So $0·063 = 6·3 \times 10^{-2}$ expressed in standard form.

1 Copy and complete this table:

10^0	10^{-1}	10^{-2}	10^{-3}	10^{-4}	10^{-5}	Standard form
0	2	4	0	0	0	$2·4 \times 10^{-1}$
0	0	5	7	0	0	
0	0	0	0	2	3	
0	0	0	8	5		
0	0	0	7			
0	5	7	8			
0	0	0	0	0	7	
0	0	2	5			

2 Write these numbers in standard index form correct to the approximation given:
(a) 0·5678 (2 dp)
(b) 0·0045 (1 dp)
(c) 0·009 81 (2 sf)
(d) 0·000 065 (1 dp)
(e) 0·000 078 6 (2 dp)
(f) 0·000 678 (2 dp)
(g) 0·3007 (2 dp)
(h) 0·098 (1 sf)
(i) 0·967 (1 dp)
(j) 0·000 008 76 (1 dp)

3 Change these numbers back to ordinary form:
(a) $3·4 \times 10^{-2}$
(b) $8·8 \times 10^{-1}$
(c) $7·95 \times 10^{-5}$
(d) $1·024 \times 10^{-4}$
(e) $4·011 \times 10^{-1}$
(f) $9·87 \times 10^{-6}$
(g) $5·6 \times 10^{-7}$
(h) $8·8 \times 10^{-10}$

4 Write 0·000 000 000 07 in standard index form.

Work out the answer to $(2·95 \times 10^5) \times (4·0 \times 10^3)$ giving your answer in standard index form.

$$2·95 \times 10^5 \times 4·0 \times 10^3$$
$$= 2·95 \times 4·0 \times 10^5 \times 10^3$$
$$= 11·8 \times 10^8$$
$$= 1·18 \times 10^9 \text{ in standard index form}$$

5 Using a calculator evaluate the following giving your answer in standard index form:
(a) $(6·4 \times 10^8) \times (1·2 \times 10^3)$
(b) $(7·2 \times 10^{-3}) \times (5 \times 10^{-5})$
(c) $(5·14 \times 10^{-5}) \times (2·4 \times 10^2)$
(d) $\dfrac{4·5 \times 10^4}{2·3 \times 10^2}$
(e) $\dfrac{5·6 \times 10^{-3}}{8·8 \times 10^4}$
(f) $\dfrac{3·4 \times 10^{24}}{1·2 \times 10^{-4}}$
(g) $\dfrac{6·4 \times 10^6}{6·4 \times 10^4}$
(h) $(3·4 \times 10^4)^2$
(i) $(2·2 \times 10^{-2})^3$

6 Evaluate these expressions giving your answer in standard form:
(a) $400 \times 600 \times 700$
(b) $0·007 \times 0·005$
(c) $\dfrac{0·09 \times 360}{120}$
(d) $\dfrac{67\,000 \times 0·0086}{42 \times 0·5}$
(e) $\dfrac{65 \times 120}{800}$
(f) $\dfrac{5·52 \times 8·008}{1000}$
(g) $(12·4)^3$
(h) $(36·4 \times 24·2)^{-2}$

7 Work out how many seconds there are in 1 year giving your answer in standard form correct to one decimal place.

8

Planet	Diameter (km)	Mass (kg)
Mercury	$4·86 \times 10^3$	$2·35 \times 10^{23}$
Venus	$1·21 \times 10^4$	$5·29 \times 10^{24}$
Earth	$1·27 \times 10^4$	$5·88 \times 10^{24}$
Mars	$6·79 \times 10^3$	$5·88 \times 10^{23}$
Jupiter	$1·43 \times 10^8$	$1·86 \times 10^{27}$
Saturn	$1·20 \times 10^8$	$5·58 \times 10^{26}$

(a) Which planet has the greatest mass?
(b) Which planet has the smallest diameter?
(c) How many times bigger is the diameter of Saturn than the diameter of the Earth?
(d) How many times smaller is the mass of Mars than the mass of the Earth?

More interesting 1

Colin invests £250 in a building society account that pays 6% interest per annum. He wants to know how much his investment will be worth after 5 years.

This would be an easy problem if the building society paid **simple interest**.

6% interest on £250 for 1 year = £15
6% interest on £250 for 5 years = £15 × 5
= £75

Colin's investment after 5 years will be worth £250 + £75 = £325

1 How much would Colin's investment have been worth if the building society had paid a simple interest rate of 8·4%?

Colin knows, however, that at the end of the second year he will get 6% interest on both his original investment and 6% interest on the first year's interest. This is called **compound interest**, meaning interest on the interest.

To work out how much his investment is worth Colin draws up a table to show the year by year growth.

Initial investment = £250

End of the	Capital	Interest	Total
1st year	250	250 × 0·06	£265
2nd year	265	265 × 0·06	£280·90
3rd year	280·90	280·90 × 0·06	£297·75
4th year	297·75	297·75 × 0·06	£315·62
5th year	315·62	315·62 × 0·06	£334·56

After 5 years the investment has grown to £334·56 to the nearest penny compared with £325 with simple interest.

2 Copy the above table and using the memory facilities on your calculator extend the table to work out to how much the £250 investment would have grown after 10 years.

3 How does the £250 invested at 6% compound interest for 10 years compare with £250 invested at 6% simple interest?

4 How many years will it take for £250 invested at an interest rate of 6% to double in value?

5 On 1st January Surjit invests £1000 in an investment account that pays an interest rate of 8·3% Calculate the value of her account:
(a) at the end of the first year
(b) at the end of the 5th year
(c) at the end of the 8th year.

6 How long will it take to the nearest 0·1 of a year for the £1000 invested at an interest rate of 8·3% to double in value if:
(a) compound interest is paid
(b) simple interest is paid.

£1000 is invested in the Bank of Narvana. This bank pays an annual interest rate such that an investment doubles in value every 2 years.

7 Colin thinks that the interest rate paid per annum by the bank must be 50%, but Surjit disagrees. Explain why Colin must be wrong.

No, it can't be 50%!

8 Calculate the percentage growth if:
(a) an interest rate of 50% is paid on £1000 for 2 years.
(b) an interest rate of 40% is paid on £1000 for 2 years.
(c) Starting with your answers for **(a)** and **(b)** use a trial and improvement method to calculate the annual interest paid by the Bank of Narvana. Give your answer to the nearest 0·1%.

Surjit wants to work out the annual interest rate for an investment to treble every 2 years. Here is part of the method she used.

Let the initial investment be P and the annual interest rate r (as a decimal) Then the value of the investment:

after 1 year will be $\quad P + rP$

after 2 years will be $\quad P + rP + r(P + rP)$

If the investment trebles every 2 years then
$$3P = P + rP + r(P + rP)$$

9 (a) Show that the above expression simplifies to $3 = (1 + r)^2$

(b) Solve this equation to find, correct to the nearest 0·1%, the interest paid for an investment to treble every 2 years.

10 Using P for the initial investment and r for the interest rate, obtain and simplify an expression for an investment to double every 2 years.

11 Use your expression to prove or disprove your answer to question **4**.

12 Write down an expression to find the annual interest rate for an investment to grow m times every 2 years.

13 Use your expression to calculate the interest rate for an investment to increase:

(a) 4 times every 2 years

(b) 6 times every 2 years

(c) m times every 2 years.

14 (a) Write down, in terms of the initial investment P and the interest rate r, a full expression to calculate the value of the investment after 3 years.

(b) If this investment doubles every 3 years show that the expression simplifies to $2 = (1 + r)^3$

15 (a) Suggest an expression connecting a growth rate of m times and an interest rate r for a period of 3 years.

(b) An investment increases 1·5 times every 3 years. Calculate the interest rate as a percentage.

16 Suggest an expression connecting a growth rate of m times and an interest rate r for a period of n years.

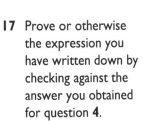

$$2 = (1 + r)^3$$
$$3 = (1 + r)^2$$

17 Prove or otherwise the expression you have written down by checking against the answer you obtained for question **4**.

18 An insurance policy guarantees a six-fold increase of an investment over a period of 20 years. Calculate, to the nearest 0·1% the interest rate paid by the insurance company.

19 By what factor of increase will an investment grow if paid a compound interest rate of 12·5% over a period of 10 years?

20 Andrew borrows £4600 in order to buy a car. The finance company charges an annual interest rate of 16·5%. After making all his payments Andrew calculates that he has paid £11 500 in total back to the finance company. Using a trial and improvement method or otherwise, calculate the length of the loan.

Put your calculator away and add these fractions. $\dfrac{1}{4} + \dfrac{2}{3}$

Here is a simple way of adding fractions.

A Multiply the two denominators 4×3

B Cross multiply 1×3

C Cross multiply 4×2

D Add the numerators

$$\dfrac{1}{4} + \dfrac{2}{3} = \dfrac{3 + 8}{12} = \dfrac{11}{12}$$

1 Use this method to add these fractions. Do not cancel down or change to a mixed number.

(a) $\dfrac{1}{2} + \dfrac{3}{4}$ **(b)** $\dfrac{2}{3} + \dfrac{3}{5}$ **(c)** $\dfrac{3}{4} + \dfrac{2}{5}$

(d) $\dfrac{3}{5} + \dfrac{2}{7}$ **(e)** $\dfrac{5}{6} + \dfrac{4}{7}$ **(f)** $\dfrac{5}{8} + \dfrac{7}{9}$

A similar method can be used to subtract fractions

$$\dfrac{2}{3} - \dfrac{1}{4} = \dfrac{8 - 3}{12} = \dfrac{5}{12}$$

2 Subtract these fractions:
(Try to do them in your head.)

(a) $\dfrac{3}{4} - \dfrac{2}{3}$ **(b)** $\dfrac{5}{6} - \dfrac{1}{2}$ **(c)** $\dfrac{3}{4} - \dfrac{4}{7}$

Algebraic fractions can be added or subtracted in a similar way.

$$\dfrac{1}{x} + \dfrac{2}{y} = \dfrac{y + 2x}{xy}$$

3 Write these fractions with a common denominator:

(a) $\dfrac{1}{a} - \dfrac{1}{b}$ **(b)** $\dfrac{a}{c} + \dfrac{b}{d}$ **(c)** $\dfrac{2}{a} + \dfrac{a}{2}$

(d) $\dfrac{1}{a} - \dfrac{1}{b}$ **(e)** $\dfrac{1}{a} - \dfrac{b^2}{c}$ **(f)** $\dfrac{3}{2a} + \dfrac{5}{b^2}$

In electrical engineering it is often necessary to find the equivalent resistor of two resistors in parallel.

The formula for this is
$$\dfrac{1}{R_e} = \dfrac{1}{R_1} + \dfrac{1}{R_2}$$

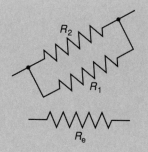

4 (a) Express $\dfrac{1}{R_1} + \dfrac{1}{R_2}$ as a single fraction.

(b) Find the value of R_e when $R_1 = 0.3$ and $R_2 = 0.6$

(c) Rearrange the formula $\dfrac{1}{R_e} = \dfrac{1}{R_1} + \dfrac{1}{R_2}$ to make R_e the subject.

(d) Calculate the value of R_1 when $R_2 = 0.8$ and $R_e = 0.2$

5 $\dfrac{1}{a} = \dfrac{1}{b} - \dfrac{1}{c}$ and $b = Kc$

(a) Show that $\dfrac{1}{a} = \dfrac{1 - K}{Kc}$

(b) Rearrange the formula to make a the subject.

(c) Find a when $b = 5.6$ and $c = 3.5$

6 (a) Add these fractions: $\dfrac{x}{4} + \dfrac{x}{5}$

(b) Use your answer to solve the equation $\dfrac{x}{4} + \dfrac{x}{5} = 4.5$

7 (a) Subtract $\dfrac{x}{3} - \dfrac{x}{5}$

(b) Solve the equation $\dfrac{x}{3} - \dfrac{x}{5} = 2$

8 Show that $\dfrac{1}{a} + \dfrac{1}{b} + \dfrac{1}{c} = \dfrac{ab + ac + bc}{abc}$

Express as a single fraction $\dfrac{3}{(x+1)} + \dfrac{2}{(x+4)}$

These type of fractions can be added using the same method as before:

- Multiply the denominators
- Cross multiply 1
- Cross multiply 2
- Simplify as far as possible

$$\dfrac{3}{(x+1)} + \dfrac{2}{(x+4)} = \dfrac{3(x+4) + 2(x+1)}{(x+1)(x+4)}$$

$$= \dfrac{3x + 12 + 2x + 2}{(x+1)(x+4)}$$

$$= \dfrac{5x + 14}{x^2 + 5x + 4}$$

9 Express each of these as a single fraction:

(a) $\dfrac{2}{x} + \dfrac{1}{x+1}$

(b) $\dfrac{3}{y} + \dfrac{2}{x-y}$

(c) $\dfrac{5}{x+3} - \dfrac{2}{x}$

(d) $\dfrac{2}{x-3} + \dfrac{3}{x+1}$

(e) $\dfrac{x+2}{5} + \dfrac{2}{7}$

(f) $\dfrac{x-5}{3} - \dfrac{4}{5}$

(g) $\dfrac{x+5}{3} + \dfrac{x-2}{4}$

(h) $\dfrac{x+1}{2} + \dfrac{3}{x-2}$

(i) $\dfrac{2x+1}{x-1} - \dfrac{3x-2}{x+1}$

(j) $\dfrac{x+4}{y-5} + \dfrac{x-4}{y+4}$

Supposing we are given $\dfrac{1}{(x+1)(x-2)}$ and asked to put this back into two separate fractions. This is the reverse of what we have been doing.

The denominators must be $(x+1)$ and $(x-2)$ but what about the numerators? To start with let

$$\dfrac{1}{(x+1)(x-2)} = \dfrac{A}{(x+1)} + \dfrac{B}{(x-2)}$$

The problem is to find the values of A and B.

To find A and B add together the right-hand side of the expression.

$$\dfrac{1}{(x+1)(x-2)} = \dfrac{A}{(x+1)} + \dfrac{B}{(x-2)}$$

$$= \dfrac{A(x-2) + B(x+1)}{(x+1)(x-2)}$$

$$= \dfrac{Ax - 2A + Bx + B}{(x+1)(x-2)}$$

$$\dfrac{1}{(x+1)(x-2)} = \dfrac{x(A+B) - 2A + B}{(x+1)(x-2)}$$

Now since these two expressions are the same thing it means that the denominators are equal **and the numerators are equal**. Therefore

$$1 = x(A+B) - 2A + B$$

on the left-hand side the only numerical term is 1, therefore

$$1 = -2A + B$$

and on the left-hand side there are no x terms, therefore

$$0 = A + B$$

This gives the two simultaneous equations

$$1 = -2A + B$$
$$0 = A + B$$

$$B = \dfrac{1}{3} \text{ and } A = \dfrac{-1}{3}$$

So $\dfrac{1}{(x+1)(x-2)} = \dfrac{-\frac{1}{3}}{(x+1)} + \dfrac{\frac{1}{3}}{(x-2)}$

$$= \dfrac{-1}{3(x+1)} + \dfrac{1}{3(x-2)}$$

10 By adding $\dfrac{-1}{3(x+1)} + \dfrac{1}{3(x-2)}$ check that the values of A and B are correct.

11 By writing each of these expressions in the form $\dfrac{A}{x+a} + \dfrac{B}{x+b}$ split the following into two separate fractions and find the values of A and B:

(a) $\dfrac{2}{(x-1)(x+3)}$

(b) $\dfrac{4}{(x+2)(x+5)}$

(c) $\dfrac{3x}{(x+2)(x-3)}$

(d) $\dfrac{2x+1}{(x+5)(x+4)}$

Draw a graph I

For the first part of a question Jean has to draw a graph of $y = 2x^2 - x - 4$.

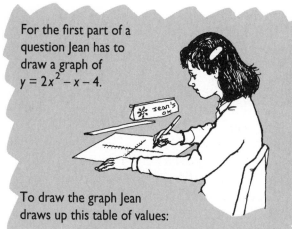

To draw the graph Jean draws up this table of values:

x	$^-2$	$^-1$	0	1	2	3
y	6	$^-1$	$^-4$	$^-3$	2	11

By plotting the points Jean draws this graph:

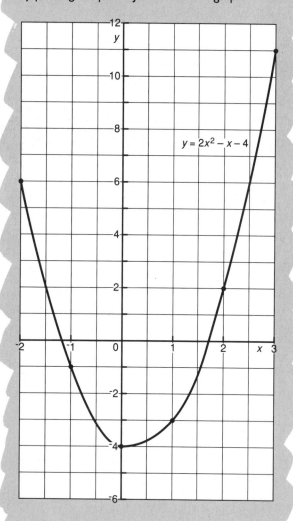

$y = 2x^2 - x - 4$

For the second part of the question Jean has to use the graph to solve these equations
(a) $2x^2 - x - 4 = 0$
(b) $2x^2 - x - 4 = 4$

To solve the equation $2x^2 - x - 4 = 0$ Jean knows that she needs to find the values of x when $y = 0$. In this case this will be where the curve cuts the x-axis.

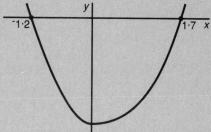

From the graph Jean can see that the values of x where the curve cuts the x-axis are $^-1\cdot2$ and $1\cdot7$.

The solutions to the equation $2x^2 - x - 4 = 0$ are therefore $x = {}^-1\cdot2$ and $1\cdot7$.

1 Check that these two values $x = {}^-1\cdot2$ and $x = 1\cdot7$ are the approximate solution to the equation $2x^2 - x - 4 = 0$ by substituting each value in turn into the equation.

To solve the equation $2x^2 - x - 4 = 4$

This time the value of y is 4. Draw the line $y = 4$ until it cuts the curve $y = 2x^2 - x - 4$. The x coordinates at the point of intersection give the solution to the equation $2x^2 - x - 4 = 4$

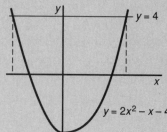

$y = 2x^2 - x - 4$

You need Worksheet I.

2 (a) Use the graph to solve the equation
$2x^2 - x - 4 = 4$
(b) Check your answer by substituting each value in turn into the equation.

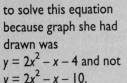

For the third part of the question Jean has to solve the equation
$2x^2 - x - 10 = 0$

At first she thought that she couldn't use her graph to solve this equation because graph she had drawn was
$y = 2x^2 - x - 4$ and not
$y = 2x^2 - x - 10$.

The equation can be solved but first it **must be re-arranged** in the form of $2x^2 - x - 4 = n$ where n is a number.

• Start with $2x^2 - x - 10 = 0$

• Add 6 to
  each side $2x^2 - x - 10 + 6 = 6$

• To give $2x^2 - x - 4 = 6$

This shows that the equation $2x^2 - x - 10 = 0$ is the same as $2x^2 - x - 4 = 6$ and since it is now in the form of $2x^2 - x - 4$ it can be solved directly from the graph.

You need graph paper.

3 What values of y will Jean need to use in order to solve the equation $2x^2 - x - 4 = 6$?

4 Solve the equation $2x^2 - x - 4 = 6$

5 (a) Re-arrange the equation $2x^2 - x - 1 = 0$ in the form $2x^2 - x - 4 = n$ where n is a number.
(b) Write down the value of the number n.
(c) Use the graph to solve the equation $2x^2 - x - 1 = 0$.

6 (a) Show how the graph can be used to solve the equation $2x^2 - x = 0$
(b) Solve the equation $2x^2 - x = 0$

7 (a) Draw a graph of $y = x^2 - 8$ for values of x between $x = {}^-4$ and $x = 4$.
(b) Use your graph to solve these equations
  (i) $x^2 - 8 = 0$ **(ii)** $x^2 - 8 = 3$
  (iii) $x^2 - 5 = 0$ **(iv)** $x^2 + 1 = 20$

8 (a) Copy and complete this table of results for $y = 2 - 2x - 3x^2$:

x	$^-4$	$^-3$	$^-1$	0	1	2	3
y	$^-38$			2			$^-31$

(b) On graph paper draw the graph of $y = 2 - 2x - 3x^2$.
(c) Use your graph to solve these equations:
  (i) $2 - 2x - 3x^2 = 0$
  (ii) $7 - 2x - 3x^2 = 3$

9 Use the graph you have drawn for question **8** to solve these equations:
(a) $2(2 - 2x - 3x^2) = 0$
(b) $2(2 - 2x - 3x^2) = 3$
(c) $6 - 6x - 9x^2 = 5$
(d) $9x^2 + 6x - 6 = {}^-5$

10 (a) Draw a graph of $y = x^2 - 2x - 3$ for values of x between $^-3$ and 3.
(b) Solve, graphically the equation $x^2 - 2x - 3 = 0$

This graph can be used to solve the equation $x^2 - 3x - 3 = 0$ but first it must be re-arranged in the form of $x^2 - 2x - 3$, the graph that has been drawn.

• Start with $\qquad x^2 - 3x - 3 = 0$

• Add x to
  each side $\qquad x^2 - 3x + x - 3 = 0 + x$

• To give $\qquad x^2 - 2x - 3 = x$

On your graph draw the line $y = x$. The point where the lines intercept can be used to solve the equation.

11 (a) Write down the coordinates of the points of interception of the two lines.
(b) Use this information to solve the equation $x^2 - 3x - 3 = 0$.

12 (a) Show how the graph of $y = x^2 - 2x - 3$ can be used to solve the equations
  (i) $x^2 - x - 3 = 0$
  (ii) $x^2 - 3x - 4 = 0$
(b) Now solve the two equations, checking your answers in both cases.

The factors of the matter

Suzanne is trying to factorise this quadratic expression.

$x^2 + 12x + 20$

She knows that:

$x^2 + 12x + 20$

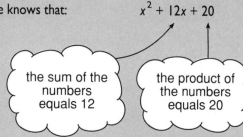

the sum of the numbers equals 12

the product of the numbers equals 20

Product of the numbers	The sum of the numbers
$1 \times 20 = 20$	$1 + 20 = 21$
$2 \times 10 = 20$	$2 + 10 = 12$
$4 \times 5 = 20$	$4 + 5 = 9$

Which means $x^2 + 12x + 20 = (x + 2)(x + 10)$

1 Factorise these quadratic expressions:

(a) $x^2 + 2x + 1$
(b) $x^2 + 7x + 10$
(c) $x^2 - 7x + 12$
(d) $x^2 - 5x - 50$
(e) $x^2 - 9x + 20$

2 Factorise these quadratic expressions:

(a) $3x^2 - 17x + 10$
(b) $2x^2 + 7x - 4$
(c) $4x^2 - 24x + 20$
(d) $6x^2 - 17x - 14$
(e) $4x^2 + 5x - 21$

This quadratic equation can be solved by factorising the expression

$2x^2 - 7x + 3 = 0$

Factorising to ⟶ $(2x - 1)(x - 3) = 0$

This means $2x - 1 = 0$
$x = 0.5$

or $x - 3 = 0$
$x = 3$

The solutions are $x = 0.5$ or $x = 3$.

3 Factorise these quadratic equations and then solve them:

(a) $x^2 + 11x + 30 = 0$
(b) $x^2 + 14x + 48 = 0$
(c) $x^2 + 12x + 27 = 0$
(d) $x^2 - 12x + 35 = 0$
(e) $x^2 + 11x - 60 = 0$
(f) $x^2 - 9x - 36 = 0$
(g) $x^2 - x - 56 = 0$
(h) $x^2 + 5x = 0$
(i) $x^2 - 36 = 0$

4 Solve these equations:

(a) $2x^2 - 5x + 3 = 0$
(b) $3x^2 + 4x + 1 = 0$
(c) $4x^2 - 11x - 3 = 0$
(d) $4x^2 - 20x + 25 = 0$
(e) $6x^2 + 13x - 5 = 0$
(f) $8x^2 + 14x - 15 = 0$

The solutions to a quadratic equation are 2 and ⁻5. Find the equation.

If 2 is the solution then
$x = 2$ or
$x - 2 = 0$

If ⁻5 is the solution then
$x = {}^-5$ or
$x + 5 = 0$

giving $(x - 2)(x + 5) = x^2 + 3x - 10$

The solutions to a quadratic equation are called the **roots of the equation**.

5 Write down the equation whose roots are:

(a) 2 and 4   (b) 3 and ⁻4
(c) ⁻3 and ⁻7   (d) ⁻4 and 4
(e) 0 and 8   (f) 3 and 3

6 The roots of an equation are 0·5 and ⁻0·25.

(a) Write down an equation with these roots.
(b) If the equation with these roots has integer coefficients write down the equation.

7 Use your results from question **5** to find two relationships between the roots of a quadratic equation and its coefficients.

The diagram shows **one white** and **two black** squares set out in a row.

w	b	b

This can be symbolised as $w + 2b$

The second diagram shows a row of **three lots of one white and two black squares**.

w	b	b	w	b	b	w	b	b

This can be symbolised as $3(w + 2b)$

The second row can be re-arranged so that all the white squares are side by side and all the black squares are side by side as

w	w	w	b	b	b	b	b	b

This can now be symbolised as $3w + 6b$ and is called **a linear form**.

Because the second and third row are made up of the same squares we can say that they are equivalent and write this symbolically as:

$3(w + 2b) = 3w + 6b$

The second row could also be set out as:

b	w	w	b	b	b	b	w	b

This could be symbolised as:

$b + 2w + 4b + w + b$

which is again **a linear form equivalent to** $3(w + 2b)$

1 Show that the original expression $w + 2b$ can be arranged into only 3 equivalent linear forms.

2 Find the total number of linear forms equivalent to:
   (a) $w + 3b$ **(b)** $2w + 3b$

3 Find all the linear forms equivalent to $3(w + 2b)$.

4 Investigate the number of linear forms equivalent to $n(\alpha x + \beta y)$ where α, β and n are positive integers.

In your report you are advised to:
● **state and record any observations**
● **form and test any conjectures**
● **use appropriate forms of symbolism**
● **make and explain any generalisations**
● **justify your results**
● **try to offer any forms of proof.**

A square peg in . . .

One of the most powerful and versatile techniques used to investigate quadratic functions is called **completing the square**.

This square has a corner missing. The area of the shaded part must be the total area minus the missing corner.

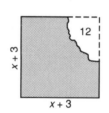

$$\text{Area} = (x + 2)^2 - 10 = x^2 + 4x + 4 - 10$$
$$= x^2 + 4x - 6$$

or written the other way round

$$x^2 + 4x - 6 = (x + 2)^2 - 10$$

1 Show that the area of the shaded section is $x^2 + 6x - 3$

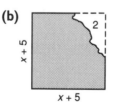

2 Write down an expression for finding the area of these shapes and in each case simplify the expression you have written.

(a)

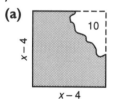

(b)

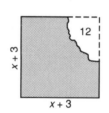

(c)

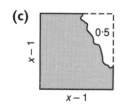

(d)

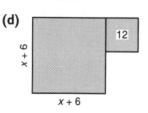

(e)

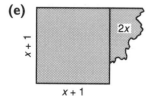

A quadratic function written in the form of $(x + a)^2 + b$ is in its 'completed the square form'.

$$(x + 2)^2 - 10$$

is the 'completed the square form' of

$$x^2 + 4x - 6$$

3 (a) Copy and complete this table of results for questions **1** and **2**:

Simplified expression	Completed the square form
$x^2 + 4x - 6$	$(x + 2)^2 - 10$
$x^2 + 6x - 3$	

(b) Can you spot how to transform a quadratic function into its completed the square form? To help you here is a worked example
$$x^2 - 10x + 4 = (x - 5)^2 - 25 + 4$$
$$= (x - 5)^2 - 21$$

(c) Write $x^2 + 10x - 4$ in its completed the square form.

4 Write each of these quadratic expressions in their completed the square form:
(a) $x^2 + 8x - 10$
(b) $x^2 + 12x - 5$
(c) $x^2 - 12x - 5$
(d) $x^2 - 6x + 20$
(e) $x^2 + 3x + 2 \cdot 25$
(f) $x^2 - 7x + 10$

$$2x^2 + 4x + 8 = 2(x^2 + 2x + 4)$$
$$= 2((x + 1)^2 - 1 + 4)$$
$$= 2((x + 1)^2 + 3)$$
$$= 2(x + 1)^2 + 6$$
The completed the square form

5 Write in the completed the square form:
(a) $2x^2 + 6x - 14$
(b) $3x^2 - 12x - 15$
(c) $2x^2 - 7x - 6$
(d) $4x^2 + 2x - 20$
(e) $5x^2 + 12x + 15$

This is a graph of $y = x^2 - 4x + 3$.

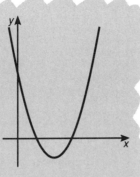

By writing the function in its completed the square form the coordinates of its lowest point can be found.

$$y = x^2 - 4x + 3 = (x - 2)^2 - 4 + 3$$
$$= (x - 2)^2 - 1$$
$$y = (x - 2)^2 - 1$$

Now $(x - 2)^2$ cannot be negative therefore the minimum value of $(x - 2)^2 - 1$ is $^-1$ and the value of x when this occurs is when $(x - 2) = 0$ or $x = 2$.

The coordinates of the minimum point of $y = x^2 - 4x + 3$ are $(2, {}^-1)$.

6 This is a graph of $y = x^2 - 6x + 10$.

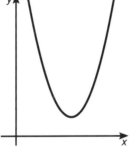

(a) Find the coordinates of the minimum point.

(b) What can you say about the equation $x^2 - 6x + 10 = 0$?

7 (a) Write the function $x^2 - 2x + 3$ in its completed the square form.

(b) Prove that $x^2 - 2x + 3 \geq 2$ for all values of x.

8 This is a graph of $y = -x^2 + 2x - 5$.
Show that its maximum value occurs at the point $(1, {}^-4)$.

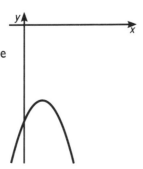

9 (a) Factorise the expression $x^2 + 7x + 12$.

(b) Use your answer to solve the equation $x^2 + 7x + 12 = 0$.

Completing the square is a useful method of solving quadratic equations.

$$x^2 + 7x + 12 = 0$$
$$(x + 3 \cdot 5)^2 - 12 \cdot 25 + 12 = 0$$
$$(x + 3 \cdot 5)^2 - 0 \cdot 25 = 0$$
$$(x + 3 \cdot 5)^2 = 0 \cdot 25$$
$$x + 3 \cdot 5 = \sqrt{0 \cdot 25}$$
$$x + 3 \cdot 5 = 0 \cdot 5 \text{ or } {}^-0 \cdot 5$$
$$x = 0 \cdot 5 - 3 \cdot 5 = {}^-3$$
$$\text{or } x = -0 \cdot 5 - 3 \cdot 5 = {}^-4$$

10 (a) Solve these quadratic equations by completing the square:

(i) $x^2 + 8x + 12 = 0$

(ii) $x^2 - 10x + 21 = 0$

(iii) $x^2 + 6x - 16 = 0$

(iv) $x^2 + 12x + 20 = 0$

(b) Now check your answers by factorising each expression.

11 Solve the equation $2x^2 - 4x + 1 = 0$ by:

(a) dividing each term by 2

(b) completing the square

(c) taking the square root of both sides. Give both answers correct to 3 decimal places.

12 Solve the equations:

(a) $2x^2 - 13x + 15 = 0$

(b) $3x^2 - 11x + 8 = 0$

▼ **Challenge**

13 By completing the square try to find a general solution to the equation $x^2 + bx + c = 0$ and, for the very brave, a general solution to the equation $ax^2 + bx + c = 0$.

To the *n*th degree – revisited

Jackie has been asked to find the *n*th term of this sequence:

Term	Value
1st	4
2nd	15
3rd	32
4th	55
5th	84

She knows that it is a good idea to start to look at difference. She re-writes the table to get:

Term	Value	1st difference	2nd difference	3rd difference
1st	4			
2nd	15	11	6	
3rd	32	17	6	0
4th	55	23	6	0
5th	84	29		

To find the *n*th term Jackie re-writes the table but adding the value of $n = 0$ term. This is done by using the differences and working backwards. The $n = 0$ term is called the constant term and sometimes is zero.

Term	Value	1st difference	2nd difference	3rd difference
$n = 0$	⁻1			
1st	4	5	6	
2nd	15	11	6	0
3rd	32	17	6	0
4th	55	23	6	0
5th	84	29		

These $n = 0$ values are put into this formula

$$\left(\begin{array}{c}\text{value} \\ \text{of } n = 0\end{array}\right)$$

$$+ \ n(\text{1st difference})$$

$$+ \ \frac{n(n-1)}{2} \ (\text{2nd difference})$$

$$+ \ \frac{n(n-1)(n-2)}{6} \ (\text{3rd difference})$$

The *n*th term $= -1 + 5n + \dfrac{6n(n-1)}{2} + 0$

$$= -1 + 5n + 3n^2 - 3n$$
$$= 3n^2 + 2n - 1$$

This is called the **Gregory-Newton formula**.

1 (a) Copy and complete this table:

Term	Value	1st difference	2nd difference
$n = 0$	⁻1		
1st	2	3	0
2nd	5		
3rd	8		
4th	11		
5th	14		

(b) Use the Gregory-Newton formula to show that the *n*th term is $3n - 1$.

2 A sequence of numbers has these values:

Term	1st	2nd	3rd	4th	5th
Value	3	8	15	24	35

(a) Copy the table and include the 1st differences, 2nd differences and 3rd differences.

(b) Show that the value of the $n = 0$ term is 0.

(c) Find a formula for the *n*th term.

3 Use the Gregory-Newton formula to find the *n*th term of:

(a)

Term	Value
$n = 0$	
1st	1
2nd	3
3rd	6
4th	10

(b)

Term	Value
1st	0
2nd	3
3rd	10
4th	21
5th	36

(c)

Term	Value
1st	3
2nd	1
3rd	⁻5
4th	⁻15
5th	⁻29

(d)

Term	Value
1st	⁻1
2nd	5
3rd	29
4th	83
5th	179

In its simplest form Pythagoras' theorem states that for any right-angled triangle:

The square on the hypotenuse is equal to the sum of the squares on the other two sides.

Visually this can be shown as:

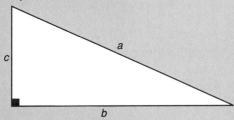

and in symbols is usually written as:

$$a^2 = b^2 + c^2$$

Worked example I

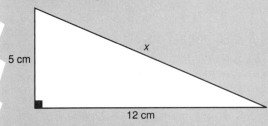

Calculate the length of the side marked x.
Solution
$$x^2 = 5^2 + 12^2$$
$$x^2 = 25 + 144$$
$$x^2 = 169$$
so $x = 13$ cm

Worked example 2

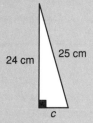

Calculate the length of the side marked c.
Solution
$$25^2 = 24^2 + c^2$$
so $625 = 576 + c^2$
or $c^2 = 625 - 576$
$$c^2 = 49$$
$$c = 7 \text{ cm}$$

Worked example 3

The coordinates of two points P and Q are (3, 5) and (7, 11) respectively. Calculate the length of the line PQ.
Solution

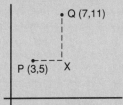

PX = 4 units and QX = 6 units
By Pythagoras
$$PQ^2 = PX^2 + QX^2$$
so $PQ^2 = 4^2 + 6^2$
$$PQ^2 = 16 + 36$$
$$PQ^2 = 52$$
$$PQ = 7.21 \text{ units, written correct to two}$$
decimal places.

I Calculate each of the lengths marked x. All lengths are in centimetres.

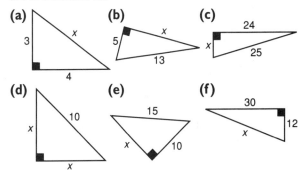

2 A walker walks 7 km due north, turns and walks a further 10 km due east. He then turns again and walks in a straight line back to the starting point. Calculate the total distance walked.

3 In a triangle XYZ the angle at X is 90°, the length of XY is 12 cm and the area of the triangle is 36 cm². Calculate the length of YZ, correct to two decimal places.

4 The lengths of the three sides of a triangle are 5 cm, 7 cm and 10 cm. Determine, with justification, whether or not the triangle is right-angled.

5 A triangle is right-angled. Two of its sides are of length 9 cm and 12 cm. What are the possible lengths of the third side?

6 Calculate each of the lengths marked with a letter. All lengths are in centimetres.

(a) **(b)** **(c)**

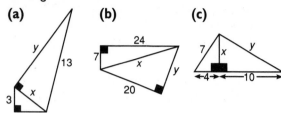

7 ABCDEFGH is a cuboid.
AB = 8 cm, AD = 5 cm and AF = 4 cm.
Calculate:

(a) the length of AG   **(b)** the length of AH.

8 A cuboid has dimensions x cm by y cm by z cm. Find an expression, in terms of x, y and z for the length of the longest diagonal of the cuboid.

9 Calculate the length of the longest straight rod that will fit inside a box which measures 5 cm by 12 cm by 8 cm.

10 A triangle PQR has PQ = PR = 8 cm and QR = 6 cm. Calculate:

(a) the length of the perpendicular from P to QR
(b) the area of the triangle.

11 An isosceles triangle has sides of length x cm, x cm and y cm. Find an expression, in terms of x and y for the area of this triangle.

12 ABCDV is a square-based pyramid with V vertically above the centre of the base ABCD.

AB = 10 cm and VA = 16 cm.
Calculate the vertical height of V above the base ABCD.

13 An equilateral triangle has all three sides of length 6 cm. Calculate the area of the triangle.

14 An equilateral triangle has all three sides of length x cm. Show that the area of this triangle is $\frac{1}{4}\sqrt{3}x^2$ cm².

15 The lengths of the sides of the triangle below are $2x - 3$ units, $x + 3$ units and x units.

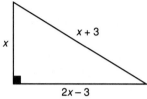

(a) Show that $2x^2 - 9x = 0$
(b) Solve this equation.

16 The lengths of the sides of the rectangle ABCD are AB = $x + 1$ units, AD = $x - 2$ units.
The length of the diagonal AC = $3x + 1$ units

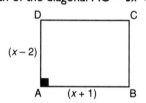

(a) Show that $7x^2 + 8x - 4 = 0$
(b) Solve the above equation.
(c) Write down the dimensions of the rectangle and the length of its diagonal.

17 The lengths of the three sides of a right-angled triangle are $x - 1$, x and $x + 1$ centimetres. Find the value of x.

18 A vertical pole TP, with base T, is held in place by two tight ropes AP and BP.

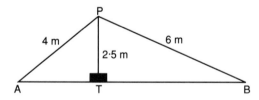

The length of AP = 4 m and the length of BP = 6m.
The height of the pole is 2·5 m.
Calculate the distance AB.

19 A spoon of length 14 cm rests inside a cylindrical mug which has a diameter of 8 cm and height 11 cm.

Calculate the length of the spoon which will protrude over the end of the cup.

20 Prove that a right-angled triangle cannot have the lengths of its sides in the ratio $1:2:3$.

21 Any three numbers x, y and z for which
$$x^2 + y^2 = z^2$$
is called a **pythagorean triple**.
Prove that for all values of n and m
$$n^2 - m^2, \quad 2nm \quad \text{and} \quad n^2 + m^2$$
is a pythagorean triple.

22 A piece of thin wire, AB is 20 centimetres long.

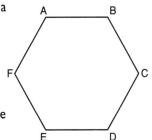

It is bent at a point X, where $AX = x$ cm and the angle $AXB = 90°$.

(a) Obtain an expression in x for the distance AB.

(b) Comment on the statement that AB will be a minimum when $x = 5$ cm.

23 The diagram shows a regular hexagon ABCDEF.
The length of each side is 1 unit.
Calculate:

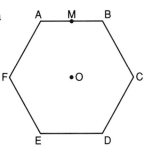

(a) the length of the diagonal AC

(b) the length of the diagonal AD.

24 The diagram shows a regular hexagon ABCDEF.
The length of each side is 2 units.
O is the centre of the hexagon.
M is the mid-point of AB.

(a) Calculate the distance OM.

(b) Hence or otherwise calculate the area of ABCDEF.

25 A cone has a circular base of radius 5 cm. The vertex V is 12 cm above the centre of the base. Calculate the length, l, of the slant height of the cone.

26 ABC is a right-angled triangle with sides of length a, b and c units as shown.
Show that $c = (a + b)(a - b)$

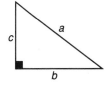

27 The diagonal of a square is exactly 12 cm in length. Calculate the lengths of the sides of the square.

28 The volume, in cubic centimetres of a cube is numerically equal to its surface area in square centimetres. Show that the length of one of the longest diagonals of the cube is greater than 10 cm but less than 10·5 cm.

29 Calculate the distance from the origin $(0, 0, 0)$ to the point with coordinates $(3, 4, 12)$.

30 Calculate the distance between the point P with coordinates $(2, 3, 1)$ and the point Q with coordinates $(10, 9, 11)$.

31 The lengths of the sides of a triangle are 5 cm, 7 cm and 8 cm. State, with justification, whether the triangle contains a right angle, an obtuse angle or three acute angles.

32 The lengths of the sides of a triangle are a, b and c units. Write down a general condition connecting a, b and c which will guarantee that the triangle contains an obtuse angle.

33 The diagram shows a circle of radius 5 cm, centred on the point with coordinates $(1, 2)$.

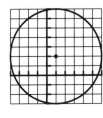

The coordinates of a general point P on the circle are (x, y).

(a) Show that the equation of the locus of P is
$$(x - 1)^2 + (y - 2)^2 = 25$$

(b) Show that this equation can be written in the form
$$x^2 - 2x + y^2 - 4y - 20 = 0$$

(c) Find the values of x when $y = 6$.

34 A circle has radius r and centre the point with coordinates (a, b).
Find the equation of this circle.

Trigonometry 1

In any right-angled triangle, the basic trigonometric ratios are defined by:

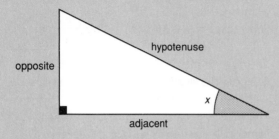

$$\text{Sin } x = \frac{\text{opposite}}{\text{hypotenuse}} \text{ or opposite} = \text{hypotenuse} \times \text{Sin } x$$

$$\text{Cos } x = \frac{\text{adjacent}}{\text{hypotenuse}} \text{ or adjacent} = \text{hypotenuse} \times \text{Cos } x$$

$$\text{Tan } x = \frac{\text{opposite}}{\text{adjacent}} \text{ or opposite} = \text{adjacent} \times \text{Tan } x$$

Some people find it helpful to remember this as

SOH   CAH   TOA

Worked example 1

Calculate the length of the side marked x in this triangle.

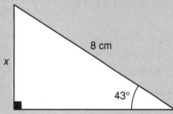

Solution

For this triangle we have the angle of $43°$ and the hypotenuse is 8 cm. We want to find x, which is opposite the $43°$. So we use **Sine**.

opposite = hypotenuse $\times$ Sin 43

> ● **Remember**
> To work out Sin 43 you input 43 to your calculator and then press the Sin button.

$x = 8 \times 0.6820$

$x = 5.46$ cm, this answer being given to two decimal places.

Worked example 2

A vertical pole of height 10 metres casts a shadow of length 25 metres on horizontal ground. Find the angle of elevation of the sun.

Solution

The picture of this situation is:

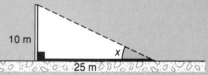

We want the angle marked x. We have the opposite and adjacent sides for this angle, so we use **Tan**.

$$\text{Tan } x = \frac{\text{opposite}}{\text{adjacent}} = \frac{10}{25} = 0.4$$

$x = 21.8°$, correct to one decimal place.

> ● **Remember**
> To find this angle when you have Tan $x = 0.4$ you input 0.4 into your calculator, press the 2nd function (or inv) button and then press the Tan button.

Worked example 3

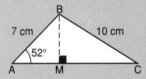

ABC is a triangle and M is the foot of the perpendicular from B to AC. AB = 7 cm, BC = 10 cm and the angle at A = $52°$.

Calculate:

(a) AM   **(b)** BM   **(c)** the angle at C.

Solution

(a) AM = $7 \times$ Cos 52
          = 4.31 cm, correct to two decimal places.

(b) $(BM)^2 = (AB)^2 - (AM)^2$ (by Pythagoras)
          $(BM)^2 = 7^2 - 4.31^2$
                = 49 − 18.5761
                = 30.4239
          BM = 5.52 cm, correct to two decimal places.

(c) $\text{Sin } C = \frac{BM}{BC} = \frac{5.52}{10}$

   Sin C = 0.552

   C = $33.5°$, correct to one decimal place.

1 In each of the triangles all the lengths are in centimetres. Calculate the length of the sides or angles marked with letters.

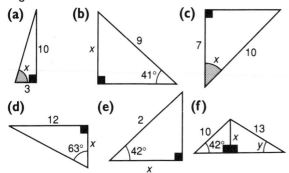

(a)   (b)   (c)

(d)   (e)   (f)

2 A man sets out from his home, H and walks 8 km due north to a point P. At P he turns and walks for a further 5 km due east to reach a shop S. Calculate the bearing of S from H.

3 PQR is a triangle and M is the foot of the perpendicular from Q to PR.
PQ = 10 cm, PR = 20 cm and the angle at P = 47°. Calculate:

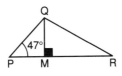

(a) the length of QM   (b) the length of PM
(c) the length of RM   (d) the angle at R.

4 In the village of Whatling the vertical church spire is 70 metres high. At a certain time of day it casts a shadow of length 280 metres on horizontal ground.

(a) Calculate the angle of elevation of the sun at that time.

At a later time of day the angle of elevation of the sun is 23°.

(b) Calculate the length of the shadow at that later time.

5 The diagram represents the cross-section, ABCD of a cuboid-shaped crate on the trailer of a lorry. The crate is held in place by a tight rope EDCF, secured at E and F.

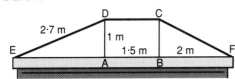

Calculate:

(a) the distance EA   (b) the angle BF̂C
(c) the length of the rope EDCF.

6 The diagram shows the cross-section of the front of a car. The bonnet has been opened and held in place by a support of length 32 cm. The bonnet is of length 1·15 metres.

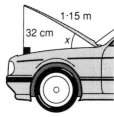

Calculate the angle, marked x, through which the bonnet has been turned.

7 A mother, M, is at the top of a vertical cliff MA. The top of the cliff is 42 m above sea level. The mother sees her daughter, D, in the sea at an angle of depression 9·1°.
Calculate the distance of the daughter from the bottom of the cliff.

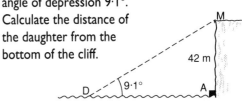

8 The diagram shows a map of the villages Audley (A), Whatling (W), Springfield (S) and Melford (M). Springfield is 10 km from Audley on a bearing of 032°. Melford, Springfield and Whatling are in a line which runs due east–west.

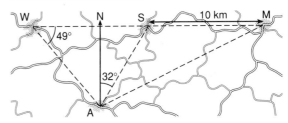

(a) Calculate the distance of W from S.
(b) Calculate the distance of W from A.

Springfield is 10 km due west of Melford.
(c) Calculate the angle SM̂A.
(d) Calculate the bearing of M from A.

9 ABC is an isosceles triangle with AB = AC = 15 cm. The angle at A is 40°. Calculate the length of BC.

10 ABCD is a rectangle with AD = 6 cm and BD = 15 cm.
Calculate:

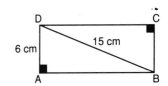

(a) the length of AB
(b) the angle AB̂D
(c) the angle AD̂B.

Mensuration I

You need to know and be able to apply each of the following formulae.

Rectangle

Area $= ab$
Perimeter $= 2(a + b)$
Length of a diagonal $= \sqrt{a^2 + b^2}$

Triangle

Area $= \frac{1}{2}$ base $\times$ vertical height

$= \frac{1}{2}bh$

Perimeter $= a + b + c$

Note, for any triangle there is a formula, known as Heron's formula which states that if we write

$s = \frac{1}{2}(a + b + c) =$ semi-perimeter

then

Area $= \sqrt{s(s - a)(s - b)(s - c)}$

You do not need to know this formula for examination purposes, but it can sometimes be useful.

There is another formula for the area of a triangle which is dealt with in *Trigonometry 2* on page 55.

Parallelogram

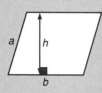

Area $=$ base $\times$ vertical height
$= bh$
Perimeter $= 2(a + b)$

Circle

Area $= \pi r^2 = \frac{1}{4}\pi d^2$
Circumference $= 2\pi r = \pi d$

The formulae for a circle are not usually given on the formulae sheet in examinations.

Trapezium

Area $= \frac{1}{2}$ (sum of parallel sides) $\times$ vertical height

$= \frac{1}{2}(a + b)h$

Perimeter $= a + b + c + d$

Cuboid

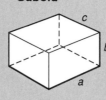

Volume $= abc$

Surface area $= 2(ab + ac + bc)$

Total distance around the edges
$= 4(a + b + c)$

Cube

A cube is a special case of a cuboid with $a = b = c$

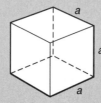

Volume $= a^3$

Surface area $= 6a^2$

Total distance around the edges $= 12a$

Prism

A prism has a plane shape as its (horizontal) base and vertical edges which go from the base to the top face. The top face must be exactly the same as the base.

Volume $=$ area of base $\times$ vertical height

Surface area $=$
$(2 \times$ area of base$)$ + areas of other faces

Cylinder

Volume $=$ area of base $\times$ vertical height

Volume $= \pi r^2 h$ or $\frac{1}{4}\pi d^2 h$

Surface area $=$
area of curved surface + two circles

Surface area $= 2\pi rh + 2\pi r^2$

Note, a cylinder can be regarded as a very special case of a prism.

Sphere

Volume $= \dfrac{4\pi r^3}{3}$

Surface area $= 4\pi r^2$

1 The diagram shows a plan
of an ornamental garden.
It is in the shape of a
rectangle with a semicircle.
Calculate:

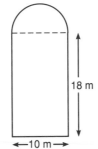

(a) the perimeter of the garden
(b) the area of the garden.

The garden is to be made into a lawn. Each packet of
grass seed is sufficient for 5 m^2 of lawn.

(c) Calculate the number of packets of grass seed
required to make this lawn.

2 A rectangular flower bed is to be enclosed by a wall
on one side and a wire fence on the other three sides.
The total length of wire fencing is 20 m. Let the length
of each side perpendicular to the wall be x metres and
the area of the flower bed be A square metres.

(a) Show that $A = 20x - 2x^2$
(b) Draw the graph of A against x for values of x
from 0 to 10.
(c) From your graph estimate:
  (i) the value of A when $x = 7.5$ m
  (ii) the values of x when $A = 40$ m^2

3 A cylinder has base radius of 5 cm and vertical height
12 cm. Calculate:

(a) the surface area of the cylinder
(b) the volume of the cylinder
(c) the length of the side of a cube which has
volume equal to the volume of the cylinder.

4 Calculate the area of a triangle with sides of length
3 cm, 5 cm and 7 cm.

5 Calculate the volume
of the wedge shown.

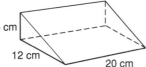

6 The Earth can be regarded as a sphere of radius
6378 km.

(a) Calculate the volume of the Earth, correct to
3 decimal places.
(b) Give your answer to (a) in standard form.
It is estimated that two thirds of the Earth's
surface is covered by water.
(c) Calculate the area of the Earth's surface covered
by water, giving your answer correct to three
significant figures.

7 A scoop, in the shape
of a wedge, is made by
cutting two equal squares
of length x cm from the
corners of a rectangular
sheet of thin metal which
measures 30 cm by 20 cm.

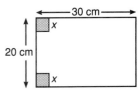

(a) Show that V, the volume of the scoop in cm^3,
can be expressed as
$V = x(30 - x)(10 - x)$
(b) Draw a graph of V against x for values of x from
0 to 10.
(c) Use your graph to estimate:
  (i) the value of V when $x = 7.5$ cm
  (ii) the value of x when $V = 350$ cm^3
  (iii) the maximum value of V and the value of x
  which gives this maximum value.

8 The diagram shows the
cross-section of a prism
of height 20 cm.

This cross-section is a trapezium with parallel sides
of lengths 5 cm and 9 cm. The perpendicular
distance between the two parallel sides is 10 cm.
Calculate:

(a) the volume of the prism
(b) the radius of a sphere with volume equal to
that of the prism.

9 The volume of a sphere in cubic centimetres is
numerically equal to its surface area in square
centimetres. Show that the radius of the sphere is
equal to 3 cm.

10 The diagrams show a sketch of a house and its
cross-section.

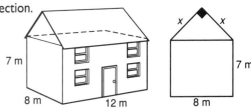

The house consists of a cuboid and a wedge-shaped
roof. Show that:

(a) $x = 5.66$ m, correct to two decimal places
(b) the height of the house is 11 m.
(c) Calculate the volume of the house.

● **Remember**

The word **locus** means the path taken by some **moving points subject to a given rule**. The plural of locus is **loci**.

1 O is a fixed point. A variable point P moves in two-dimensional space such that OP = 5 cm.
(a) Sketch the locus of P.
(b) Comment on this locus.

2 Comment on the variation to question **1** if the variable point P is subjected to the same rule but the point can move in three-dimensional space.

3 **You need a set square or similar.**
A and B are two points, fixed in the plane of two-dimensional space with AB = 10 cm.

In the same space, P is a variable point which moves according to the rule the angle $A\hat{P}B = 90°$.
(a) Draw the locus of P.
(b) Comment on the locus.

4 Repeat question 3 but make the angle $A\hat{P}B = 60°$.

5 Repeat questions 2 and 3 but make the angle $P\hat{A}B$ any size of your own choosing. Comment on your result.

6 A walker leaves a village centre V and travels due north for 12 km to reach a style S. At S the walker turns onto a bearing of 075° and walks for a further 10 km until he reaches a farmhouse F. At F the walker turns again and walks in a straight line back to V.
(a) Make an accurate scale drawing of the walker's journey.
(b) From your scale drawing measure:
  (i) the total distance walked
  (ii) the bearing of F from V.

7 In a two-dimensional coordinate system a fixed point A has coordinates (2, 3).

In the same system a variable point P has general coordinates (x, y).

The locus of P is defined by the rule PA = 7 units.
(a) Show that the equation of the locus of P is given by $(x - 2)^2 + (y - 3)^2 = 49$
(b) Show that the above relationship in part **(a)** reduces to $x^2 - 4x + y^2 - 6y - 36 = 0$
(c) Can x and y ever be integers? Explain.

8

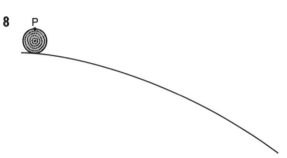

The above diagram represents a modelling situation of a circular log which is about to roll down a parabolic curve.

A point P has been marked on the circumference of the circular cross-section of the log.

Sketch the locus of the point P throughout the movement.

9 The diagram below shows two fixed circles. The smaller of these circles has been shaded.

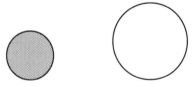

A third, variable circle is introduced and is such that it always just touches the two fixed circles.

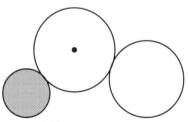

Sketch the locus of the centre of the variable circle.

Silicon chips are made from a wafer of silicon. 500 are made at one time. It is estimated that the probability of a chip being faulty is $\frac{3}{20}$. How many chips in each batch of 500 are estimated to be faulty?

$\frac{3}{20} \times 500 = 75$ faulty chips

1 The probability of Derek being late for work is $\frac{2}{5}$. Over a period of 40 days, how many times would you expect Derek to be:

  (a) late   **(b)** on time?

2 The probability of rain during June is $\frac{2}{5}$. June has 30 days. On how many days will it:

  (a) rain   **(b)** be dry?

3 The probability of Mario getting up in the morning on time is $\frac{5}{7}$. Out of 49 days, on how many occasions will Mario be:

  (a) up on time   **(b)** late getting up?

4 The probability of getting a bruised apple in a particular batch is $\frac{1}{8}$. How many bruised apples will there be in a batch of 200 apples?

5 The probability that Adam will break the yolk when cracking an egg is $\frac{2}{5}$. He needs to crack open 30 eggs. How many yolks might you expect him to break?

6 Twenty vehicles out of every 100 passing a census point are found to be HGV. 5000 vehicles pass this point each day. How many HGV vehicles would you expect to pass this point each day?

7 Out of 20 people at a disco 13 are female. What is the probability that a person at the disco chosen at random will be:

  (a) female   **(b)** male?

8 The probability that a light bulb is made satisfactory is $\frac{7}{8}$. Two thousand light bulbs are made in a day. How many will be:

  (a) satisfactory   **(b)** faulty?

The original estimate of $\frac{3}{20}$ for faulty silicon chips could have been arrived at by a number of means.

• By using existing records. Perhaps 150 000 chips were found to be faulty out of every 1 million manufactured.
• By examination of a sample about 3 out of 20 were found to have faults.
• By subjective estimate – a scientist/technician might have arrived at this estimate based on experience, though it is unlikely in this context.

A multiple choice question gives five alternative answers. Only one is correct. What is the probability of choosing:

  (a) the right answer   **(b)** a wrong answer

Probability of event =

$$\frac{\text{number of ways in which the event can occur}}{\text{number of ways in which all events can occur}}$$

  (a) P(picking the right answer) $= \frac{1}{5}$

  (b) P(picking the wrong answer) $= 1 - \frac{1}{5} = \frac{4}{5}$

9 What is the probability of spinning this spinner and getting:

  (a) 2   **(b)** 3?

10 Ten coins are in a bag. Four of them are 5p coins, and six are 10p coins. You pick a coin at random. What is the probability that you will pick:

  (a) a 5p coin   **(b)** a 10p coin?

11 It is estimated that the word 'the' is used 15 times in every 300 words. If you pick a word at random from the page of a newspaper, what is the probability that you will pick:

  (a) 'the'   **(b)** a word other than 'the'.

12 In a box there are 16 chocolates. Five are dark chocolate, and the rest are milk chocolate. One is picked at random. What is the probability that the one picked out is:

  (a) dark chocolate   **(b)** milk chocolate?

Events are **mutually exclusive** when those events are all **different** outcomes, and have no influence on each other.

There are three white, two red, and four yellow roses in this bunch. A rose is picked by its stem, at random, from the bunch. What is the probability of the rose being:

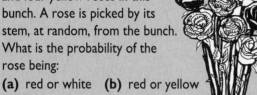

(a) red or white   **(b)** red or yellow
(c) white or yellow?

P(red rose) = $\frac{2}{9}$

P(white rose) = $\frac{3}{9} = \frac{1}{3}$

P(yellow rose) = $\frac{4}{9}$

(a) P(a red or a white rose) = $\frac{2}{9} + \frac{3}{9} = \frac{5}{9}$

(b) P(a red or a yellow rose) = $\frac{2}{9} + \frac{4}{9} = \frac{6}{9} = \frac{2}{3}$

(c) P(a white or a yellow rose) = $\frac{3}{9} + \frac{4}{9} = \frac{7}{9}$

> If the probability needed includes more than one mutually exclusive event: the probabilities of those events are added.

1 One month of the year is to be chosen at random. What is the probability of picking a month beginning with the letter:

   (a) J   **(b)** J or M   **(c)** J or F   **(d)** A or J or M?

2 A bag contains several numbered counters:

One counter is picked out at random from the bag. What is the probability of picking a counter which is:

(a) 2 or 15
(b) a multiple of 3 or 4
(c) a square or prime number
(d) 3, 5, or even number?

3 A snooker table has 15 red balls, and one ball each of yellow, blue, green, brown, pink and black. One ball is picked at random. What is the probability of picking:

  (a) a red   **(b)** a red or a pink
  (c) any colour   **(d)** a pink or a blue?

4 This spinner is spun. What is the probability of throwing:

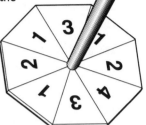

  (a) 2 or 3
  (b) 1 or 4
  (c) a even number
  (d) a number more than 4.

5 A letter is chosen at random from the letters in the word MATHEMATICAL. Calculate the probability that the letter is:

  (a) M or T
  (b) M or A
  (c) A or E
  (d) M or A or T.

6 A computer is programmed to generate the letters A, B, C, D, E, F according to the following probabilities:

P(A) = $\frac{3}{40}$, P(B) = $\frac{7}{40}$, P(C) = $\frac{9}{40}$,

P(D) = $\frac{5}{40}$, P(E) = $\frac{13}{40}$, P(F) = $\frac{3}{40}$,

The computer is asked to select a letter.
Find the probability that the letter selected is:

  (a) A or B   **(b)** D or F   **(c)** C or E
  (d) A or B or C **(e)** D or E or F **(f)** A or B or D.

7 A dice is biased so the probabilities of throwing the numbers are shown in the table.

Number	1	2	3	4	5	6
Probability	$\frac{1}{12}$	$\frac{2}{12}$	$\frac{2}{12}$	$\frac{2}{12}$	$\frac{2}{12}$	$\frac{3}{12}$

What is the probability of throwing:

  (a) an odd number
  (b) a number more than 2
  (c) a number less than 6
  (d) a prime number?

> ● **Remember**
>
> **Dispersion** is a measure of **spread**.

The **standard deviation** is the most frequently used measure of spread. Other measures of spread are the **range** and **interquartile range**.

Standard deviation is based on the mean and measures the deviation from the mean.

The standard deviation is useful to compare two different sets of data.

The standard deviation, s, can be calculated using either of the two formulae:

$$s = \sqrt{\frac{\Sigma(x-\bar{x})^2}{n}} \text{ or } s = \sqrt{\frac{\Sigma x^2}{n} - \bar{x}^2}$$

where $\bar{x}$ is the mean and calculated using the formulae: $\bar{x} = \frac{\Sigma x}{n}$

Use both methods to calculate the standard deviation of the set of data.
(10, 12, 15, 16, 18, 19).

Method 1

- Work out the mean
$$\bar{x} = \frac{10 + 12 + 15 + 16 + 18 + 19}{6} = \frac{90}{6} = 15$$

- Use the table to help calculate s.

x	$x - \bar{x}$	$(x - \bar{x})^2$
10	⁻5	25
12	⁻3	9
15	0	0
16	1	1
18	3	9
19	4	16
Totals	0	60

$$s = \sqrt{\frac{\Sigma(x-\bar{x})^2}{n}} = \sqrt{\frac{60}{6}} = \sqrt{10} = 3\cdot16 \text{ to 2dp}$$

Method 2

- Work out the mean $\bar{x} = \frac{\Sigma x}{n} = \frac{90}{6} = 15$
- Use the table to help calculate s.

x	x^2
10	100
12	144
15	225
16	256
18	324
19	361
Total	$\Sigma x^2 = 1410$

$$s = \sqrt{\frac{\Sigma x^2}{n} - \bar{x}}$$
$$= \sqrt{\frac{1410}{6} - 15^2}$$
$$= \sqrt{235 - 225}$$
$$= \sqrt{10}$$
$$= 3\cdot16 \text{ to 2 dp}$$

It can be seen that both methods give the same answer. However, according to the type of data one method is usually easier to calculate than the other.

In the example above method 1 seems most suitable.

1 For each set of data calculate the mean and standard deviation using both methods 1 and 2. State which is the easier method.

   (a) (1, 2, 3, 4, 7, 8)
   (b) (9, 3, 11, 4, 5, 3, 7)
   (c) (5·3, 4·9, 5·2, 4·4, 5·5, 6·0, 5·8, 4·5)
   (d) (210·91, 220·84, 173·11, 38·01, 195·12, 212·04, 233·12, 187·15, 224·16, 172·65)
   (e) (3·16, 3·03, 3·94, 3·46, 3·38, 3·80, 3·12, 2·97, 3·03, 3·62)
   (f) (10, 11, 10, 11, 12, 10, 10, 10, 11, 10)

2 Calculate the mean and standard deviation for both sets of data below.

   (a) (4, 5, 6, 7, 8)
   (b) (16, 17, 18, 19, 20)
   What do you notice about the two means?
   Comment on the standard deviation of the two sets of data.
   Write a short summary comparing the two sets of data including reference to mean and standard deviation.

Histograms

- **Remember** Histograms are statistical diagrams where the areas contained by the bars drawn are proportional to the frequencies.

  The height of each bar, called the **frequency density**, is calculated using the rule:

  $$\text{frequency density} = \frac{\text{frequency}}{\text{width of class}}$$

You need graph paper

1 **(a)** Copy and complete the table below:

Height	Frequency	Width of class	Frequency density
$140 \leq x < 150$	10	10	1
$150 \leq x < 160$	16		
$160 \leq x < 165$	34		
$165 \leq x < 169$	46	4	11·5
$169 \leq x < 175$	52		
$175 \leq x < 181$	21		
$181 \leq x < 190$	11	9	1·22
$190 \leq x < 205$	6		
$205 \leq x < 225$	4		

(b) Draw the histogram on 2 mm graph paper. Remember to provide a key, label the axis and give the histogram a title.

2 The mass of 200 potatoes are shown in the frequency distribution below:

Mass (g) x	Frequency f
$0 \leq x < 150$	14
$15 \leq x < 250$	26
$250 \leq x < 300$	72
$300 \leq x < 350$	54
$350 \leq x < 450$	28
$450 \leq x < 600$	6

Draw a histogram for this distribution.

3 The age of 176 employees were recorded as shown in the frequency distribution.

Age (years) x	Frequency f
$16 \leq x < 21$	18
$21 \leq x < 30$	35
$30 \leq x < 50$	72
$50 \leq x < 60$	35
$60 \leq x < 75$	16

Illustrate this frequency distribution with a histogram.

You may wish to find out the **frequency class**, **widths** and **total sample** from a histogram that is already drawn.

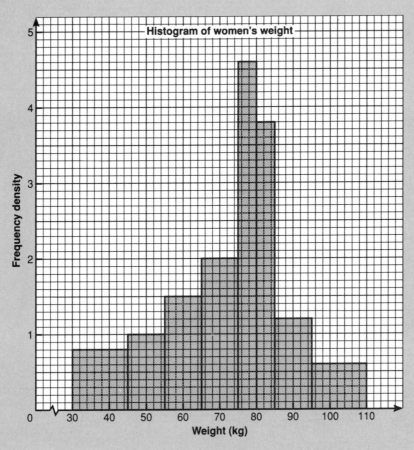

Use the rule:
frequency = frequency density × class width

Draw up and complete the table.

Class interval weight (kg)	Frequency density	Class width	Frequency f
$30 \leq x < 45$	0·8	15	12
$45 \leq x < 55$	1·0	10	10
$55 \leq x < 65$	1·5	10	15
$65 \leq x < 75$	2·0	10	20
$75 \leq x < 80$	4·6	5	23
$80 \leq x < 85$	3·8	5	19
$85 \leq x < 95$	1·2	10	12
$95 \leq x < 110$	0·6	15	9
		Total	$\Sigma f = 120$

The table illustrates the class width and frequency. The total number in the sample $\Sigma f = 120$ women.

4

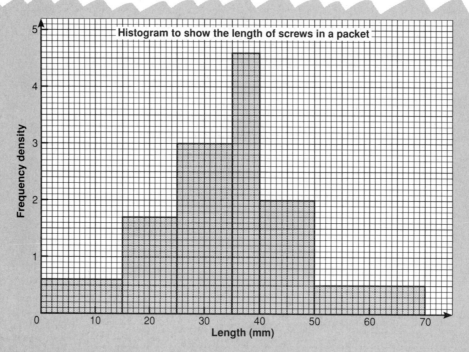

From this histogram draw up a table to show the class interval, frequency density, class width and frequency.

What is the total number of screws in the sample?

5

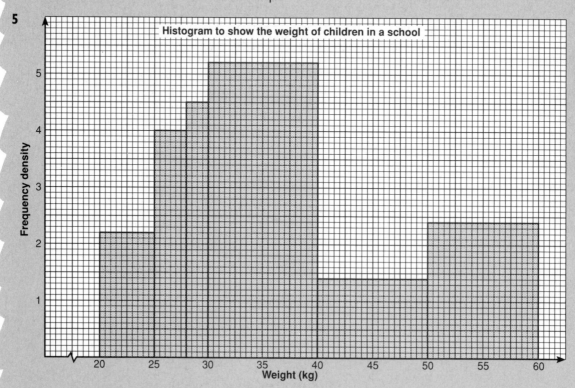

The weights of children in a village school are shown above.
How many children are there altogether?

6

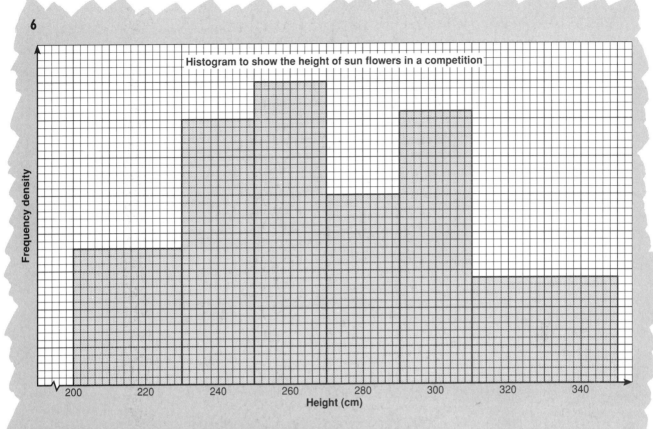

If there are 35 sunflowers in the class interval 230–250 work out the frequency density axis. Copy and complete the histogram. How many sunflowers were there in the competition?

7 Here are the weights of 36 leaves measured in a survey in grams:

1·1	2·6	8·1	3·3	0·8	3·2
2·0	2·6	2·5	6·1	8·4	2·3
1·9	3·1	1·1	1·3	3·2	7·6
1·8	5·7	4·4	2·9	2·6	5·4
1·7	9·7	3·5	3·1	1·9	3·7
5·3	6·4	7·1	1·5	4·1	2·8

Draw up and complete a frequency table using the class intervals 0 to 1·5, 1·6 to 2·0, 2·1 to 3·0, 3·1 to 6·0, 6·1 to 10.

Work out the frequency density and draw a histogram.

Beyond any doubt: proof

Proof is one of the most complicated concepts in all of mathematics. The history of mathematics is rich with attempts to prove some results which have been known for many years but which no-one has been able to **prove beyond any doubt**.

Goldbach's conjecture

In 1742 there was an exchange of letters between C. Goldbach and L. Euler – Euler is considered to be one of the most distinguished mathematicians of all time – in which Goldbach put forward the simple conjecture that 'Every even positive whole number greater than 2 can be written as the sum of two prime numbers'.
For instance,

$48 = 41 + 7$, both of which are prime
$100 = 97 + 3$, and again 97 and 3 are both prime.

Despite the efforts of Euler and many other great mathematicians over a period which is now in excess of 250 years, this simple conjecture has remained unproven.

The four colour problem

For centuries, map makers have known that we can colour the countries of the world on a map in such a way that no two adjacent countries are coloured in the same colour using at most four colours – and this is despite any possible changes in the boundaries of these countries.

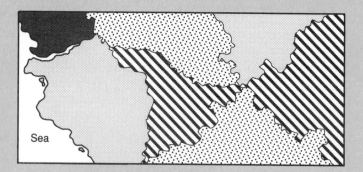

Sea

A proof of this result eluded society until a few years ago when mathematicians finally proved the Four Colour Theorem using a great deal of high powered computer time.

Euclid's parallel postulate

Euclid was a Greek mathematician of around 300BC who is generally regarded as the father figure of Geometry. In his parallel postulate Euclid stated that:
Given a (infinite) straight line L and a point P,
not on the line, there is only one line which
passes through P but does not intersect L.
For over 2000 years mathematicians tried to
prove this seemingly 'obvious' result but to no
avail. Then in the early part of the last century, Nikolai Ivanovich Lobachevski demonstrated that it was possible to define space in such a way that the parallel postulate was not true. This opened up a whole new branch of Geometry called Non-Euclidean Geometry.

•P

———————————————————— L

The obvious is not always true.

We shall now demonstrate four of the classically accepted methods of proof.

Direct proof

Prove that the angles of any triangle add up to 180°.

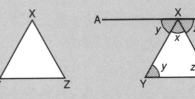

We draw a line AB through X and parallel to YZ.
Then, because AB and YZ are parallel

Angle $A\hat{X}Y$ = Angle $Z\hat{Y}X$ = y (alternate angles)
and Angle $B\hat{X}Z$ = Angle $Y\hat{Z}X$ = z for the same reason.

But AB is a straight line so the three angles at X, of $A\hat{X}Y$, $Y\hat{X}Z$ and $B\hat{X}Z$ must add up to 180°.

So $y + x + z = 180°$
This completes the proof.

Proof by contradiction

We shall prove that $\sqrt{2}$ is irrational using the method of contradiction. To do this we assume the counter of the result, that is we assume that $\sqrt{2}$ is rational.

So we can set $\sqrt{2} = \frac{a}{b}$ where this is a fraction in its lowest terms, with a and b being positive integers.

If $\frac{a}{b} = \sqrt{2}$ then it follows that $\frac{a^2}{b^2} = 2$ or $a^2 = 2b^2$

We now examine the three cases where
(i) a and b are both odd
(ii) a is odd and b is even
(iii) a is even and b is odd.

We do not need to consider the case where a and b are both even because our original fraction has been reduced to its lowest terms.

We can safely state that $\text{odd}^2 = \text{odd}$ and $\text{even}^2 = \text{even}$.

Remembering that $a^2 = 2b^2$ is a consequence of our assumption

case **(i)** gives $\text{odd}^2 = 2 \times \text{odd}^2$
    i.e.   odd = even   **Impossible.**

case **(ii)** gives $\text{odd}^2 = 2 \times \text{even}^2$
    i.e.   odd = even   **Impossible.**

case **(iii)** gives $\text{even}^2 = 2 \times \text{odd}^2$

which looks possible but if a is even then we must be able to say that $a = 2n$ for some value of n. Then $a^2 = 4n^2$, so $a^2 = 2b^2$ gives $4n^2 = 2b^2$ or $2n^2 = b^2$ and this means that $2n^2$ must be even whilst b^2 is odd, so again we have even = odd. **Again impossible.**

So it is not possible to have $a^2 = 2b^2$
which can only mean that our assumption that $\sqrt{2} = \frac{a}{b}$ is wrong.

Thus we have contradicted this assumption. So it follows that $\sqrt{2}$ cannot be written in such a way, so it is irrational.

Proof by induction

Prove that every whole number multiple of 5 ends with either a 0 or a 5.

We need to prove that for any whole number n, the last digit of $5n$ is either a 0 or a 5.

We start by assuming that this is true for some whole number which we shall write as k, that is, we have assumed that the last digit of $5k = 0$ or 5 or in symbols $LD(5k) = 0$ or 5

Now we will examine what happens if we increase k by 1 to $k + 1$ so we are examining the last digit of $5(k + 1)$

But $LD(5(k + 1)) = LD(5k + 5)$
$= LD(5k) + 5$

and we have assumed that $LD(5k) = 0$ or 5

so $LD(5(k + 1) = 0 + 5$ or $5 + 5$
$= 5$ or 0 (not 10 because we are considering only the last digit)

So if $5k$ ends in a 0 or 5 it then follows that $5(k + 1)$ also ends in a 0 or 5.

But it is clearly true that when $k = 1$, i.e. $5k = 5$ then this ends in a 5. So our assertion is true in the first case, so it must then be true in the second case, third case and all subsequent cases.

This completes the proof.

Proof by exhaustion

Prove that there are 24 ways of arranging the four letters A, B, C and D in a row.

To do this exhaustively, we merely show all 24 arrangements as:

ABCD BACD CABD DABC
ABDC BADC CADB DACB
ACBD BCAD CBAD DBAC   This array shows
ACDB BCDA CBDA DBCA   all 24 possibilities.
ADBC BDAC CDAB DCAB
ADCB BDCA CDBA DCBA

Clearly this method can be tedious and lack elegance.

Mathematics has many utilitarian values, the subject has many useful purposes. These utilitarian values are important but there is also a side to mathematics which makes it a very creative art form which has fascinated and stimulated minds over thousands of years. This can be nowhere more true than in the search for proof. For your problem solving and investigative work the establishing of a proof is something which demands the highest level of skill.

You are now given some exercises aimed at helping to develop this skill.

1 Prove by some means other than exhaustion, that there are 24 ways of arranging 4 letters in a row. Extend your method to prove that there are 120 ways of arranging 5 letters in a row.

2 Prove that a squared whole number cannot end in any of the digits 2, 3, 7 or 8.

3 Prove that the equation
$x^2 = n! + 7$
has only one integer solution in x.
(Note $n!$ means $1 \times 2 \times 3 \times 4 \times 5 \times \ldots n$, so $4! = 1 \times 2 \times 3 \times 4 = 24$, etc.)

4 Prove that $1 + 2 + 3 + 4 + \ldots + n = \frac{1}{2}n(n + 1)$

5 Starting with the fact that any odd whole number can be written in the form $2n + 1$, where n is a whole number, prove that the sum of two odd numbers is an even number.

6 Using the same starting point as question **5**, or otherwise, prove that the square of any odd number is also odd.

7 It is known that:
$1 = 1^2$
$1 + 3 = 4 = 2^2$
$1 + 3 + 5 = 9 = 3^2$
$1 + 3 + 5 + 7 = 16 = 4^2$
From this known information, form a general result and prove it.

8 Prove:
   (a) by exhaustion
   (b) by some other method
   that the equation $xy + x + y = 36$ has no positive integer solutions in x and y unless either $x = 0$ or $y = 0$.

9 Prove that $1 + 2 + 2^2 + 2^3 + 2^4 + \ldots + 2^{n-1} = 2^n$

10 Given that n is a positive integer, prove that $n^2 - n$ is even.

11 Given that n is a positive integer, prove that $n^3 - n$ is a multiple of 6.

12 Prove that when n is a whole number greater than 4 then 2^n is greater than n^2.

13 Prove that the sum of any two consecutive triangular numbers is a square number.

14 A regular polygon has n vertices. A diagonal is a line joining any two vertices which is not a side of the polygon. Prove that the polygon has $\frac{1}{2}n(n - 3)$ diagonals.

The sum of the series
$$1 + 2 + 2^2 + 2^3 + 2^4 + 2^5$$
is
$$1 + 2 + 4 + 8 + 16 + 32 = 63$$
So the sum of the series is **63**.

Similarly, the sum of the series
$$1 + 2 + 2^2 + 2^3 + 2^4 + 2^5 + 2^6$$
is
$$1 + 2 + 4 + 8 + 16 + 32 + 64 = 127$$
So the sum of this series is **127**.

1   Investigate the sum of the series
$$1 + 2 + 2^2 + 2^3 + \ldots + 2^n$$
for various values of n.
Justify or prove any general result.

2   Investigate the sum of the series
$$1 + x + x^2 + x^3 + \ldots + x^n$$
for various values of both x and n.
Justify or prove any general result.

3   In this case, y is a positive fraction, so $y < 1$.
The series $1 + y + y^2 + y^3 \ldots$ goes on for ever.
Obtain, with an explanation, the sum of this so-called **infinite** series.

4   In this case, r is a positive fraction, so $r < 1$, and the series
$$1 + 2r + 3r^2 + 4r^3 + \ldots \text{ goes on for ever.}$$
Obtain, with an explanation, the sum of this infinite series.

5   Use the results of your above enquiries to obtain, with justification,
the sum of each of these series.
(a) $1 + 5 + 5^2 + 5^3 + \ldots + 5^{20}$
(b) $1 + \frac{1}{2} + \left(\frac{1}{2}\right)^2 + \left(\frac{1}{2}\right)^3 + \ldots$ as it goes on forever.
(c) $1 + \frac{3}{4} + \left(\frac{3}{4}\right)^2 + \left(\frac{3}{4}\right)^3 + \ldots$ as it goes on forever.
(d) $1 + 2\left(\frac{1}{4}\right) + 3\left(\frac{1}{4}\right)^2 + 4\left(\frac{1}{4}\right)^3 + \ldots$ as it goes on forever.
Give a justification for all of your results.

The cover of a book is 31 cm high and 21 cm wide. Both measurements are to the nearest centimetre.

Since both measurements are to the nearest centimetre the maximum possible height, called the **upper bound**, of the book is 31·5 cm and the minimum height, called the **lower bound**, is 30·5 cm.

The **interval approximation** for the height of the book is between 30·5 cm and 31·5 cm.

1 Write down, for the width of the book:
  (a) the upper bound
  (b) the lower bound
  (c) the interval approximation.

2 (a) Calculate the interval approximation for the perimeter of the cover of the book.
  (b) Write down what you notice about the interval approximation for the perimeter.

3 A length of wood is measured and found to be x cm long to the nearest centimetre. In terms of x write down:
  (a) the upper bound
  (b) the lower bound.

4 If 10 equal lengths of wood are placed end to end, explain how to find:

  (a) the upper bound of the 10 lengths
  (b) the lower bound of the 10 lengths
  (c) the interval approximation.

5 Write down the interval approximation if:
  (a) 100 lengths of wood are placed end to end
  (b) y lengths of wood are placed end to end.

6 This diagram shows the floor of a rectangular room. The dimensions are to the nearest metre. Write down:

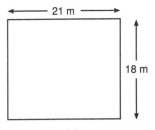

  (a) the lower bound of the area of the room
  (d) the upper bound of the area of the room
  (c) the interval approximation for the area of the room.
  (d) Comment on your answer for **(c)**.

7 Victor works on a machine that makes bricks. The length of the brick is 22·0 cm, the width, 10·0 cm and the height, 8·0 cm. All measurements are to the nearest 0·05 cm. Write down:

  (a) the interval approximation of the three measurements of the brick
  (b) the size of each interval (the upper bound minus the lower bound)
  (c) the interval approximation of the areas of the three different faces of the brick
  (d) the size of each interval
  (e) the interval approximation of the total surface area of one brick
  (f) the size of this interval
  (g) the interval approximation of the volume of one brick
  (h) the size of this interval.

8 Comment on the answer you get when you multiply two or more approximations together.

9 Can you suggest a method of obtaining a better interval approximation for the volume of the brick in question **7**?

Sequences 1

Wendy has been asked, 'Which of these sequences is the odd one out?'

1, 2, 3, 4, 5, 6, . . .
2, 4, 8, 16, 32, . . .
3, 6, 9, 12, 15, . . .
25, 20, 15, 10, 5, . . .
‾19, ‾15, ‾11, ‾7, ‾3, . . .

1 Which one do you think is the 'odd one out' and why?

When answering these types of questions the important thing is not the sequence that you pick but the reason why you picked it.

In fact, for various reasons, they all could be the 'odd one out'.

2 Give a reason why each sequence could be the 'odd one out'.

A sequence in which you go from term to term by adding the same number each time is called an **arithmetic sequence**.

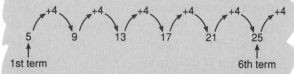

1st term   6th term

To get to the 6th term start with 5 and add on 4 five times.

To get to the 10th term start with 5 and add on 4 nine times.

3 Some of the sequences that Wendy looked at are arithmetic sequences.
(a) Write down the arithmetic sequences.
(b) Write down the number that is added on each time.
(c) In each case write down the 8th term.

The number that you add each time is called the **common difference**. This can be a negative *or* positive number.

In question **3** you should have found four arithmetic sequences.

Wendy has been asked to investigate this arithmetic sequence:

Term	1st	2nd	3rd	4th
Value	5	11	17	23

The first thing that Wendy notices is that the common difference is 6.

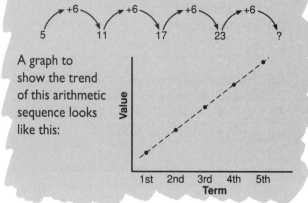

A graph to show the trend of this arithmetic sequence looks like this:

4 (a) Explain why a graph of position against value to show the trend of any arithmetic sequence would give a straight line.
  (b) Work out the value of the 10th term.

5 Which of these cannot be a graph to show the trend of an arithmetic sequence?

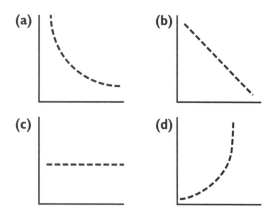

Back to the sequence Wendy was investigating

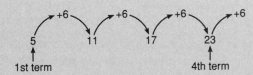

The 4th term is $5 + 6 + 6 + 6 = 23$ or
$$5 + (6 \times 3) = 23$$

Because the common difference is 6 Wendy also thinks that the nth term must be of the form:

$(6 \times n) \pm$ something.

6 (a) Suggest a relationship between the nth term and the common difference.

(b) Test your suggestion against the 1st term and the 4th term.

Here is a second arithmetic sequence:

Term	1st	2nd	3rd	4th	5th
Value	5	12	19	26	33

7 Find:

(a) the common difference

(b) the value of the 20th term

(c) the nth term.

8 Generate an arithmetic sequence of 8 terms for:

(a)

(b)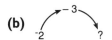

(c)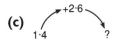

(d)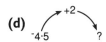

(e)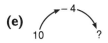

9 Write down an expression for the nth term for all the sequences you generated in question **8**.

10 For each of these arithmetic sequences find the common difference, the 10th term, the 101st term and the nth term:

(a) 7, 11, 15, 19, 23, . . .

(b) 5, 8, 11, 14, 17, . . .

(c) 11, 8, 5, 2, −1, −4, . . .

(d) −17, −12, −7, −2, . . .

(e) −6, −10, −14, −18, . . .

11 The 3rd term of an arithmetic sequence is 10 and the 6th term is 22.

| ? | ? | 10 | ? | ? | 22 |

(a) Write down the difference between the values of the 3rd and the 6th terms.

(b) Use this information to work out the common difference.

(c) Write down an expression for the nth term.

12 The 5th term of an arithmetic sequence is 32 and the 13th term is 72.

| ? | ? | ? | ? | 32 | ? | ? | ? | ? | ? | ? | ? | 72 |

5th term   13th term

Write down:

(a) the common difference

(b) the 21st term

(c) the nth term.

13 The nth term of an arithmetic sequence is 7 and the $(n + 7)$th term is 42. Write down the sequence of numbers between these two terms.

14 The 3rd term of an arithmetic sequence is 7 and the 7th term is 44.
Calculate:

(a) the first term of the sequence

(b) the common difference.

Sequences 2

Jagjit is looking at the five sequences used to introduce *Sequences 1*.

1, 2, 3, 4, 5, 6, . . .
2, 4, 8, 16, 32, . . .
3, 6, 9, 12, 15, . . .
25, 20, 15, 10, 5, . . .
⁻19, ⁻15, ⁻11, ⁻7, ⁻3, . . .

We know that four of the sequences are arithmetic sequences. The one that isn't is:

2, 4, 8, 16, 32, . . .

1 (a) Write down the next two numbers in this sequence.

(b) Write down how this sequence is generated.

A sequence in which you go from term to term by multiplying by the same number is called a **geometric sequence**.

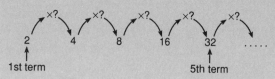

2 What number do you multiply by to get the next term in the above sequence?

The number that you multiply by each time is called the **common ratio**. A graph to show the trend of this type of geometric sequence looks like this:

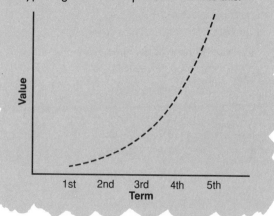

The common ratio can be a negative number as well as a positive number.

3 Copy these axes and sketch a graph to show the trend of this type of geometrical sequence.

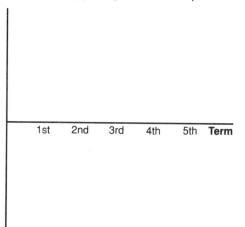

1st   2nd   3rd   4th   5th   **Term**

4 Which of these cannot be a graph to show the trend of a geometrical sequence?

(a)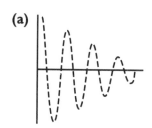

(b)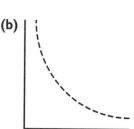

(c)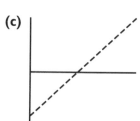

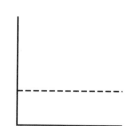

(e)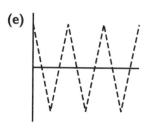

Jagjit has been asked to investigate this geometric sequence:

Term	1st	2nd	3rd	4th	5th
Value	2	6	18	54	162

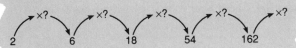

5 Write down:

(a) the common ratio

(b) the value of the next two terms of the sequence.

Jagjit notices that each term in the sequence can be expressed in terms of the first term and the common ratio.

Term	Value	Relationship
1st	2	2
2nd	6	2×3^1
3rd	18	2×3^2
4th	54	2×3^3
5th	162	2×3^4

6 Write in terms of the common ratio:

(a) the 20th term

(b) the 101st term

(c) the nth term

(d) the first term.

7 Generate a sequence of 5 terms for:

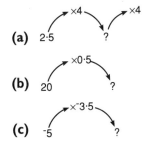

(a) 2·5

(b) 20

(c) ⁻5

8 For each of these geometric sequences write down the common ratio and in terms of the common ratio, the 21st term, the 50th term and the nth term:

(a) 3, 6, 12, 24, 48, . . . (b) 5, 20, 80, 320, . . .

(c) 5, 30, 180, 1080, . . . (d) 256, 64, 16, 4, . . .

(e) 81, 27, 9, 3, 1, . . . (f) 4, ⁻8, 16, ⁻32, 64, . . .

(g) 1, ⁻1, 1, ⁻1, 1 ⁻1, . . .

9 A geometric sequence has a first term of 7 and a common ratio of 2.

Write down:

(a) the 5th term

(b) the 8th term

(c) the nth term.

10 A geometric sequence starts 3, 12, 48, . . .
Find:

(a) the common ratio

(b) the value of the 8th term

(c) the nth term.

11 A geometric sequence is given as:

$a, ar, ar^2, ar^3, ar^4, ar^5, \ldots$

If the first term is 1·5 and the 3rd term is 6, write down:

(a) the value of a

(b) an equation involving the 3rd term

(c) the common ratio

(d) the 12th term

(e) the nth term.

12 A second sequence also starts:

$a, ar, ar^2, ar^3, ar^4, ar^5, \ldots$

If the 3rd term is 4·5 and the 6th term is 121·5, write down:

(a) an equation involving the 3rd term

(b) an equation involving the 6th term

(c) the common ratio

(d) the 1st term

(e) the 8th term.

13 The 3rd term of a geometrical sequence is 2, and the 5th term is 18.

?	?	2	?	18	?	?

Find:

(a) two possible values for the common ratio

(b) the 4th term in each case

(c) the nth term in each case.

How many terms?

Danny has to work out how many terms there are in this arithmetic sequence:
3, 7, 15, 19, . . . 35, 39
Danny quickly noticed that the common difference of the sequence is 4.

By adding 4 to the 19 and then another 4 and so on Danny worked out that the series must contain 10 terms.

1 Write down how many terms this arithmetic sequence contains:
3, 7, 11, 15, 19, . . . 55, 59, 63

Clearly this is not a very efficient way of working out the number of terms in a sequence. Consider the above sequence if the last term had been 1287. It would have taken a long time to work out the total number of terms.

This next piece of work tries to find a more efficient method.

2 (a) Work out the difference between the last term and the first term for the sequence in question 1.
   (b) Divide your answer for part (a) by the common difference.
   (c) Suggest a possible relationship between your answer for part (b) and the number of terms in the sequence.

3 Check the relationship that you suggested in question 2 against this arithmetic sequence:
4, 6, 8, 10, 12, 14, 16, 18, 20, 22, 24, 26

Here is another arithmetic sequence:
6, 11, 16, 21, 26, . . . 71, 76, 81

4 (a) Show, by calculation, that the sequence has 16 terms.
   (b) Check your answer by writing down the complete sequence.

5 Find the number of terms in each of these arithmetic sequences:
   (a) 2, 4, 6, 8, . . . 42, 44, 48
   (b) 53, 50, 47, . . . 14, 11, 8, 5
   (c) 2·6, 3·1, 3·6, . . . 27·6, 28·1
   (d) 13, 2, $^-$9, . . . $^-$119, $^-$130, $^-$141

6 Find, in terms of n, the number of terms in these arithmetic sequences:
   (a) $a, (a + 1), (a + 2), \ldots (a +(n − 1))$
   (b) $a, (a + 2), (a + 4), \ldots (a +(n − 1)2)$
   (c) $a, (a + 3), (a + 6), \ldots (a +(n − 1)3)$

7 Show algebraically that this arithmetic sequence contains n terms.
   $a, (a + d), (a + 2d), \ldots (a +(n − 1)d)$

8 The first term of an arithmetic sequence is 3 and the last term is 799. If the sequence contains 200 terms, find:
   (a) the common difference
   (b) the 21st term.

9 An arithmetic sequence of 40 terms has a common difference of 1·25. If the last term is $^-$13·5, find:
   (a) the first term
   (b) the 10th term.

10 Danny starts work at a local building firm.
   His starting salary is £12 000 per annum and rises by annual increments of £800 to a maximum of £19 200. Find:
   (a) how long it takes Danny to reach the maximum salary
   (b) Danny's salary after 6 years.

Andrew is trying to solve this quadratic equation.

$$x^2 + 3x - 2 = 0$$

Unfortunately he is having difficulty in finding the factors:

$$x^2 + 3x - 2 = 0$$

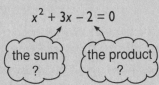

the sum ?   the product ?

Product of the numbers
$$1 \times {}^-2 = {}^-2$$
$$^-1 \times 2 = {}^-2$$

The sum of the numbers
$$1 + {}^-2 = {}^-1$$
$$^-1 + 2 = 1$$

Many years ago a formula was derived to solve quadratic equations. A simplified version of this equation is:

$$x = \frac{-b + \sqrt{b^2 - 4c}}{2} \quad \text{and} \quad x = \frac{-b - \sqrt{b^2 - 4c}}{2}$$

where b and c are the coefficients of the quadratic equation $x^2 + bx + c = 0$

For the equation $x^2 + 3x - 2 = 0$
$b = 3$ and $c = {}^-2$

To solve the equation substitute the values of b and c into the formula.

$$x = \frac{-3 + \sqrt{3^2 - (4 \times {}^-2)}}{2} \quad \text{or} \quad \frac{-3 - \sqrt{3^2 - (4 \times {}^-2)}}{2}$$

$$= \frac{-3 + \sqrt{9+8}}{2} \qquad \frac{-3 - \sqrt{9+8}}{2}$$

$$= \frac{-3 + \sqrt{17}}{2} \qquad \frac{-3 - \sqrt{17}}{2}$$

$$= \frac{-3 + 4 \cdot 123}{2} \qquad \frac{-3 - 4 \cdot 123}{2}$$

$$= 0 \cdot 562 \qquad \text{or} \quad -3 \cdot 562$$

The roots of the equation $x^2 + 3x - 2 = 0$ are $x = 0 \cdot 562$ and $x = {}^-3 \cdot 562$ correct to 3 dp.

No wonder Andrew had difficulty in trying to factorise $x^2 + 3x - 2$!

1 Solve the equation $x^2 + 7x + 12 = 0$ by:
 (a) factorising
 (b) using the formula.

2 Solve these quadratic equations giving your answer correct to 3 decimal places where appropriate:
 (a) $x^2 + 5x + 3 = 0$
 (b) $x^2 + 6x - 3 = 0$
 (c) $x^2 + 7x + 2 = 0$
 (d) $x^2 - 4x - 5 = 0$
 (e) $x^2 - 10x + 4 = 0$
 (f) $x^2 + 6x - 1 = 0$
 (g) $x^2 - 4x - 8 = 0$
 (h) $x^2 - 12 = 0$
 (i) $x^2 + 8x + 16 = 0$

No sooner had Andrew mastered the quadratic formula than he was given this quadratic equation to solve:

$$2x^2 - 6x + 2 = 0$$

The formula only works if the quadratic equation contains a single x^2 term.
Andrew has two choices.
He can: try to find a new formula or modify the equation.
He decides to modify the equation by dividing every term by 2 to give:

$$x^2 - 3x + 1 = 0$$

3 Use the formula to solve Andrew's new equation.

4 Solve these quadratic equations:
 (a) $2x^2 + 8x - 4 = 0$
 (b) $3x^2 - 12x - 6 = 0$
 (c) $2x^2 - 9x + 2 = 0$
 (d) $5x^2 + 35x + 20 = 0$
 (e) $2x^2 - 7x - 5 = 0$
 (f) $5x^2 - 12x + 3 = 0$

5 Andrew is trying to solve the quadratic equation $4x^2 - 12x + 24 = 0$.
 (a) Use the formula to solve the equations.
 (b) Try to give a geometrical explanation of the result.

In mathematics and science it is often necessary to find the rate of change of one variable with respect to another.

This graph shows the time taken to travel a certain distance. The rate of change of distance with respect to time gives the speed.

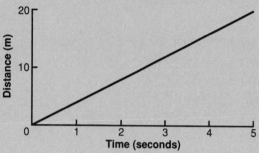

With a straight line graph the speed is the

$$\frac{\text{distance travelled}}{\text{time taken}} = \frac{20 \text{ metres}}{5 \text{ seconds}}$$
$$= 4 \text{ metres per second}$$

With this distance time graph the distance travelled is equal to the time squared.
$d = t^2$

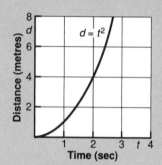

This graph does not have a constant gradient. However the gradient at a point on the line can be found by drawing a tangent line to the curve at the point we are interested in and calculating the gradient of the tangent line.

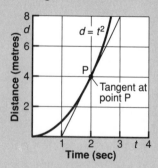

1 (a) Calculate the gradient of the tangent line at the point P.

(b) What information is your answer giving you?

You need graph paper.

2 The following diagram shows the progress of a particle moving along a straight line.

(a) Make a copy of the diagram.

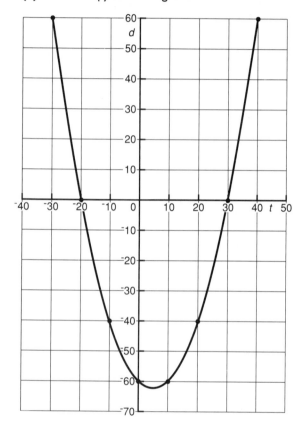

(b) By drawing a tangent at the point $t = 20$, find the velocity of the particle at that point.

(c) Write down the equation of the line of symmetry of the curve.

(d) Work out the velocity of the particle at the point $t = {}^-10$.

(e) Comment on your answer.

3 (a) Draw a graph of $y = x^2 - 4$ for values of x between $^-4$ and 4.

(b) By drawing a tangent line at the point $x = 1$ find the gradient of the curve at that point.

(c) Find also the gradient of the curve at the point $x = {}^-3$.

4 These results show the distance travelled by a racing car for the first 30 seconds of a test run.

Time (seconds)	0	5	10	15	20	25	30
Distance (metres)	0	7·5	40	97·5	180	287	420

(a) Using a scale of 2 cm to 5 seconds horizontally and 1 cm to 25 m vertically draw a graph to show the progress of the car.

(b) Draw a tangent at the point $t = 10$ and work out the gradient at this point.

(c) Work out the velocity of the car at the point $t = 20$.

5 The velocity of the car on a second test run was recorded as:

Time (seconds)	0	10	20	30	40	50
Velocity (m/sec)	0	40	60	60	40	0

(a) On graph paper draw a graph to show this information.

(b) What is the maximum velocity that the car reached?

(c) Draw a tangent at the point $t = 40$ and calculate the gradient at this point.

(d) What information is part **(c)** giving you?

(e) Write down the coordinates of the point on the graph where the gradient is zero.

6 Part of information of the velocity of a particle moving along a straight line is given in this table:

Time (seconds)	0	1	2	3	4	5	6
Velocity (cm/sec)	0	⁻1	0	3			24

(a) Work out the missing two values in the table.

(b) On graph paper plot the point and by drawing a suitable tangent line work out the acceleration of the particle after 4 seconds.

For this next piece of work you are going to investigate the gradient function of the curve $y = x^2$.

7 On graph paper draw a graph of $y = x^2$ for values of x from ⁻4 to 4. Use 2 cm to 1 unit on the x-axis and 2 cm to 2 units on the y-axis.
Draw the curve as accurately as you can.

8 (a) Draw tangent lines at the points $x = 1$, $x = 2$ and $x = 3$ and in each case work out the gradient at these points.

(b) What is the gradient at the point $x = 0$?

9 (a) Write down the equation of the line of symmetry of your graph.

(b) Explain why it is not necessary to draw tangent lines to work out the gradient at the points $x = ⁻1$, $x = ⁻2$ and $x = ⁻3$.

(c) Write down the gradients of the curve at the points $x = ⁻1$, $x = ⁻2$ and $x = ⁻3$.

10 On a second piece of graph paper draw a pair of coordinate axes. Use 2 cm to 1 unit on the x-axis, numbered ⁻3 to 3 and 2 cm to 1 unit on the y-axis numbered ⁻6 to 6.

11 (a) Plot the graph of x-value against the gradient of $y = x^2$ at each point for $x = ⁻3$ to $x = 3$.

(b) Draw the line of best fit through the points that you have plotted.

(c) Write the equation of the line you have just drawn.

Draw a graph 2

Do you remember in *Draw a graph 1* Jean was asked to solve the equation $2x^2 - x - 4 = 0$ using a graphical method? Well Derek is in the same class and also needs to solve the equation $2x^2 - x - 4 = 0$ by a graphical method.

Derek, however, decodes to use a different method. He re-arranges the equation like this:

$$2x^2 - x - 4 = 0$$
$$2x^2 = x + 4$$

Derek draws two graphs: $y = 2x^2$ and $y = x + 4$.

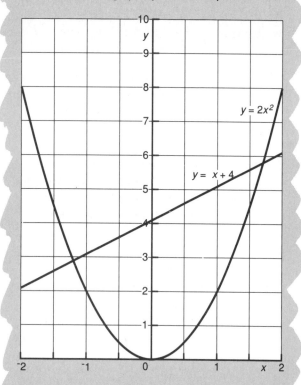

The two lines intercept where the two y values are equal. This means the point(s) of interception will be where

$$2x^2 = x + 4$$

and the x values can be read directly off the graph.

At the point where the two lines cross $x = {}^-1\cdot2$ and $x = 1\cdot7$ (as before).

You need graph paper.

1 Solve graphically the equation
$x^2 - x - 1 = 0$ as follows.

(a) Draw a graph of $y = x^2$ for values of x between $x = {}^-3$ and $x = 3$.

(b) On the same axes draw a graph of $y = x + 1$.

(c) Write down the coordinates of the points of intersection of the two lines.

(d) Use this information to solve the equation $x^2 - x - 1 = 0$

2 Solve graphically the equation $6 + x - x^2 = 0$ by drawing a graph of $y = x^2$ and a second linear graph on the same axes.

(a) Write the equation of the line of the second graph to be drawn.

(b) Draw both graphs on the same pair of axes. The x-axis is to run from $^-3$ to 4.

(c) Use the graph to solve the equation $6 + x - x^2 = 0$

(d) By adding a third line to the graphs solve the equation $4 + x - x^2 = 0$.

3 This diagram shows a graph of $y = 9 + 3x - 2x^2$ and a graph of $y = x + 5$.

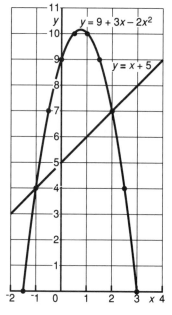

(a) Write down the x-values at the point where the two lines cross.

(b) Write down and simplify the equation to which these values of x are solutions.

4 Solve, graphically, the equation

$$\frac{x^2 - 6}{x} = 1 \text{ by drawing:}$$

(a) the graph of $y = x$ and the graph of a quadratic function

(b) the graphs of $y = x^2$ and the graph of a linear function.

Nakeeta, Leroy and Jill are trying to solve the equation $x^3 + 2x^2 - 2x - 1 = 0$. They decide to solve the equation by a graphical method.

Nakeeta's method is to draw up a table and draw a graph of $y = x^3 + 2x^2 - 2x - 1$.

5 (a) Copy and complete this table that Nakeeta drew:

x	$^-3$	$^-2$	$^-1$	0	1	2	3
y	$^-4$			$^-1$		11	

(b) On graph paper plot the points and join them up with a smooth curve.

(c) Use your graph to solve the equation $x^3 + 2x^2 - 2x - 1 = 0$.

Leroy decided to re-arrange the equation
$x^3 + 2x^2 - 2x - 1 = 0$
as $\qquad x^3 = -2x^2 + 2x + 1$
and draw graphs of $y = x^3$ and $y = -2x^2 + 2x + 1$.

6 (a) Copy and complete these tables for Leroy:
$y = x^3$

x	$^-3$	$^-2$	$^-1$	0	1	2	3
y	$^-27$	$^-8$			1	11	

$y = -2x^2 + 2x + 1$

x	$^-3$	$^-2$	$^-1$	0	1	2	3
y	$^-23$			1			$^-11$

(b) On your graph paper draw both graphs.

(c) Use your graph to check the solution to the equation $x^3 + 2x^2 - 2x - 1 = 0$ obtained in question **5**.

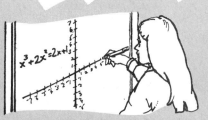

Jill solved the equation using a third method. She re-arranged the equation
$x^3 + 2x^2 - 2x - 1 = 0$ to
$\qquad x^3 + 2x^2 = 2x + 1$
She then drew the graphs of $y = x^3 + 2x^2$ and $y = 2x + 1$ to find the points of intersection.

7 (a) On the same axes draw graphs of $y = x^3 + 2x^2$ and $y = 2x + 1$.

(b) Use this graph to solve the equation $x^3 + 2x^2 - 2x - 1 = 0$.

8 There is another way to solve the equation $x^3 + 2x^2 - 2x - 1 = 0$ by drawing two graphs on the same axes. Write down, but do not draw, the equation of the two lines you could use.

9 Solve the equation $x^3 - 5x + 3 = 0$ by:

(a) drawing the graph of $y = x^3 - 5x + 3$

(b) re-arranging the equation and drawing the two graphs on the same axes.

(c) Compare your answers and comment any differences.

10 (a) Solve these equations by graphical methods, using in each case two different methods:
(i) $x^3 - x^2 - x = 2$
(ii) $2x^3 - 3x - 6 = 0$

(b) Compare your answers and comment on any differences.

11 (a) Solve graphically the equation
$x^3 - 2x + 1 = 0$

by re-arranging the equation and drawing two graphs on the same axes.

(b) Use your graph to solve:
(i) $x^3 - 2x - 1 = 0$
(ii) $x^3 - 2x = -3$

(c) By drawing one more line on your graph solve the equation $x^3 - 3x - 1 = 0$.

The quadratic formula 2

In *The quadratic formula 1* Andrew was trying to solve this equation
$$2x^2 - 6x + 2 = 0$$
He had the choice of either
- modifying the formula
- modifying the equation

In *The quadratic formula 1* Andrew decided to modify the equation.

This time the formula will be modified to be able to solve quadratic equations of the form

Modified formula

$$ax^2 + bx + c = 0 \qquad x = \frac{b \pm \sqrt{b^2 - 4ac}}{2a}$$

where a and b are numbers called the coefficients of x^2 and x, and c is the constant term.

To solve the equation $2x^2 + 5x - 3 = 0$

For this equation $a = 2$, $b = 5$, and $c = {}^-3$.

Substituting these values into the formula

$$x = \frac{-5 \pm \sqrt{5^2 - (4 \times 2 \times {}^-3)}}{2 \times 2}$$

$$= \frac{-5 \pm \sqrt{25 - (-24)}}{4}$$

$$= \frac{-5 \pm \sqrt{49}}{4}$$

$$= \frac{-5 \pm 7}{4}$$

$$= {}^-3 \text{ or } x = 0 \cdot 5$$

1 Solve the equation $x^2 - 3x - 10 = 0$ by:
   (a) factorising
   (b) the modified quadratic formula.

2 For the equation $3x^2 - 8x + 3 = 0$:
   (a) write down the values of a, b and c
   (b) solve the equation giving your answer correct to 2 decimal places.

3 Solve the equation $2x^2 + 4x - 6 = 0$ by:
   (a) factorising
   (b) dividing each term by 2 and using the formula
   $$x = \frac{-b \pm \sqrt{b^2 - 4c}}{2}$$
   (c) the modified quadratic formula.

4 Solve these quadratic equations giving your answers correct to 3 decimal places:
   (a) $4x^2 - 3x - 4 = 0$
   (b) $3x^2 + 7x - 3 = 0$
   (c) $2x^2 - 7x - 3 = 0$
   (d) $6x^2 - 6x - 6 = 0$
   (e) $3x^2 + 5x + 1 = 0$
   (f) $8x^2 + 12x - 2 = 0$

To solve this equation it is better to rearrange it in the form
$$x + 5 = -\frac{6}{x}$$

$$ax^2 - bx - c = 0$$

Multiplying by x
$$x(x + 5) = -6$$
$$x^2 + 5x = -6$$
$$x^2 + 5x + 6 = 0$$

Factorising
$$(x + 2)(x + 3) = 0$$

$$x = {}^-2 \text{ or } {}^-3$$

5 Solve these equations:
   (a) $\dfrac{x^2 - 8}{6} = -x$
   (b) $2x + \dfrac{1}{x} = 5 - \dfrac{1}{x}$
   (c) $\dfrac{x - 2}{4} = \dfrac{x + 2}{x}$
   (d) $\dfrac{x}{6} + \dfrac{3}{2x} = 1$
   (e) $\dfrac{x + 1}{x - 1} = 2x + 1$

A snooker table with no middle pockets is in the shape of a 4 by 5 rectangular grid.
The ball always enters at the bottom left-hand corner and moves at 45° to the edges of the table.
It rebounds around the table until it exits at one of the corners.

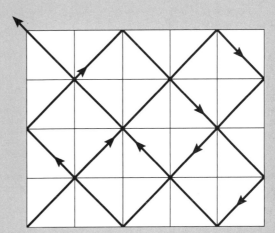

In the case shown the ball
• makes 7 rebounds before it exits the table
• exits at the top left-hand corner
• always turns in a clockwise direction.

The second diagram shows the similar situation for a 2 by 6 grid.

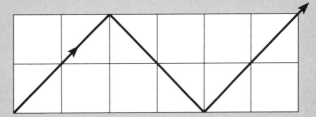

In this case the ball
• makes only 2 rebounds
• exits at the top right-hand corner
• makes one clockwise turn and one anti-clockwise turn, that is, it has one change of direction.

1 Familiarise yourself with the problem by examining grids of sizes:
   (a) 3 by 6   **(b)** 3 by 5   **(c)** 3 by 8   **(d)** 4 by 10   **(e)** 5 by 5
   In each case you are advised to record:
   • the number of rebounds
   • the exit corner
   • the number of changes of direction.

2 Conduct an enquiry for a general grid of size *n* by *m*.
   Try to make observations and form conjectures and generalisations about:
   • the number of rebounds
   • the exit corners
   • the number of changes of direction.

In your report you are advised to:
● **make and record observations**
● **state and test any conjectures**
● **offer appropriate forms of symbolic communication**
● **form and explain any generalisations**
● **offer any proofs of your results.**

Spring the trap

This diagram shows part of the curve $y = 10 - 0.1x^2$ for values of x from 0 to 8.

Brian needs to find the area under this curve.

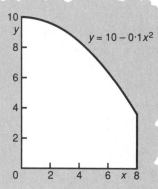

The heights of each rectangle can be calculated from the equation of the curve
$y = 10 - 0.1x^2$
The heights and areas of the larger rectangles are shown in this table:

Rectangle	Height	Width	Area
a	$10 - 0 = 10$	2	20
b	$10 - (0.1 \times 2^2) = 9.6$	2	19.2
c	$10 - (0.1 \times 4^2) = 8.4$	2	16.8
d	$10 - (0.1 \times 6^2) = 6.4$	2	12.8

Total area $= 20 + 19.2 + 16.8 + 12.8$
$= 68.8$ square units

He decides to split the area into vertical strips of equal width.

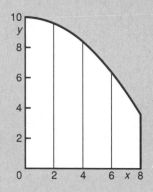

The heights and areas of the smaller rectangles are shown in this table:

Rectangle	Height	Width	Area
e	$10 - (0.1 \times 2^2) = 9.6$	2	19.2
f	$10 - (0.1 \times 4^2) = 8.4$	2	16.8
g	$10 - (0.1 \times 6^2) = 6.4$	2	12.8
h	$10 - (0.1 \times 8^2) = 3.6$	2	7.2

Total area $= 19.2 + 16.8 + 12.8 + 7.2$
$= 56$ square units

This means that $56 <$ true area < 68.8

A good approximation of the true area would be to take the mean of these two values:
$$\frac{56 + 68.8}{2} = 62.4 \text{ square units}$$

Rectangular strips are drawn as shown. The area of these strips will be larger than the true area.

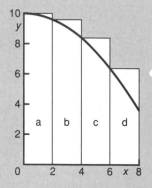

1 (a) Calculate the total larger area under this curve.
(b) Calculate the total smaller area.
(c) Write down an approximation of the true area.

These rectangular strips drawn as shown will give a total smaller than the true area.

The true area will be 'trapped' between the smaller area and the larger area.

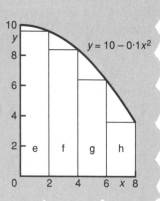

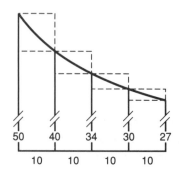

The total area of the larger rectangles is called the **upper bound** and the total of the smaller rectangles is called the **lower bound**.

2 Calculate:
  (a) the upper bound area under the curve
  (b) the lower bound area under the curve
  (c) an approximation of the true area under the curve.

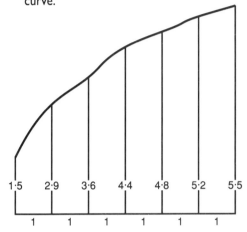

| 1·5 | 2·9 | 3·6 | 4·4 | 4·8 | 5·2 | 5·5 |
| 1 | 1 | 1 | 1 | 1 | 1 |

3 This diagram shows part of the curve $y = 2 + 0.5x^2$ between $x = 0$ and $x = 6$.

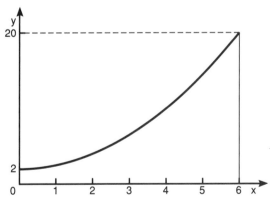

Draw a diagram and calculate the upper bound area, the lower bound area and an approximation of the true area under the curve when the width of the rectangles are:

(a) 3 units wide

(b) 2 units wide

(c) 1 unit wide

(d) Which approximation is the closest to the true area under the curve and why?

The approximation to the true area under the graph gets closer and closer by using narrower and narrower strips. As the width of the strips gets closer and closer to zero then the approximation gets closer and closer to the true value.

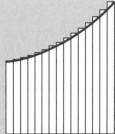

Unfortunately if the width chosen is very small then there will be an equally large number of calculations to make. This can be very tedious and extremely time-consuming.

Fortunately this type of calculation is ideally suited for computers.

This 'no-frills' program will work out the approximate area under a curve with the computer doing all the tedious calculations for you.

```
CLS
10  INPUT "LOWER VALUE OF X" LX
20  INPUT "UPPER VALUE OF X" UX
30  INPUT "WIDTH OF RECTANGLE" W
40  FOR X = LX TO UX-W STEP W
50  Y1 = 2 + 0.5*X*X
60  Y2 = 2 + 0.5*(X + W)*(X + W)
70  A = W*Y1: LT = LT + A
80  B = W*Y2: YT = YT + B
90  NEXT
100 PRINT "UPPER BOUND AREA "YT
110 PRINT "LOWER BOUND AREA "LT
120 PRINT "APPROXIMATE AREA "(YT + LT)/2
```

4 (a) Use a computer and the above program to check your answers to question **3**.

(b) Calculate an approximation to the area under the curve of $y = 2 + 0.5x^2$ with rectangles of these widths:
   (i) 0·5   (ii) 0·2   (iii) 0·1

(c) Suggest a limit that the approximate area is approaching.

5 By changing lines 50 and 60 in the program calculate the area under curve between $x = 1$ and $x = 4$ of the function $y = x^2 + 4$.

The trapezium rule

Another method of finding the area under a curve is to use the **trapezium rule**.

Here is part of the curve $y = 10 - 0.1x^2$ again.

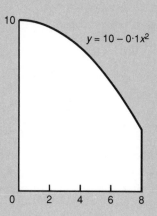

This time the curve is split into four trapezia.

The total area of all the trapezia gives a good approximation to the true area.

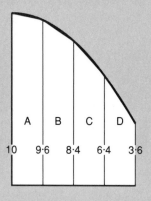

$$\text{Area of A} = \frac{2(10 + 9.6)}{2} = 19.6$$

$$\text{Area of B} = \frac{2(9.6 + 8.4)}{2} = 18.0$$

$$\text{Area of C} = \frac{2(8.4 + 6.4)}{2} = 14.8$$

$$\text{Area of D} = \frac{2(6.4 + 3.6)}{2} = 10.0$$

Total area $= 19.6 + 18.0 + 14.8 + 10.0$

$= 62.4$ square units

As you can see the trapezium gives a good method of finding the area under a curve.

1 Here is the same curve as in question 1 of *Spring the trap* but this time the area under the curve has been split into trapezia.

   (a) Calculate the area under the curve.

   (b) Compare your answer with the one calculated in question 1 *Spring the trap*.

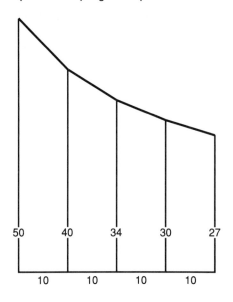

2 Use the trapezium rule to calculate the approximate area under this curve.

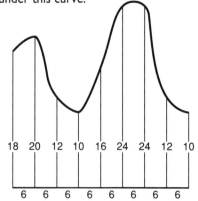

3 This table shows the x and y values for the curve $y = x^2$.

x	0	0.5	1	1.5	2.0	2.5	3.0
y	0	0.25	1	2.25	4.0	6.25	9.0

   (a) Make a sketch of $y = x^2$ between $x = 0$ and $x = 3$ divided into trapezia.

   (b) Use the trapezium rule to find an approximation for the area under the curve.

The area of this shape is to be expressed using the trapezium rule.

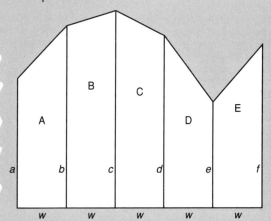

Area of A $= \dfrac{w(a + b)}{2}$

Area of B $= \dfrac{w(b + c)}{2}$

Area of C $= \dfrac{w(c + d)}{2}$

Area of D $= \dfrac{w(d + e)}{2}$

Area of E $= \dfrac{w(e + f)}{2}$

Since $\dfrac{w}{2}$ is a common factor the total area can be found by

Area $= \dfrac{w}{2}(a + b + b + c + c + d + d + e + e + f)$

$= \dfrac{w}{2}(a + 2b + 2c + 2d + 2e + f)$

which can lead to a general expression for the trapezium rule. The area under a curve is equal to:

$\dfrac{\text{Width}}{2}$ (1st height + last height + 2(sum of other heights)

Using the previous example of $y = 0 \cdot 1x^2$

Area $= \dfrac{2}{2}(10 + 3 \cdot 6 + 2(9 \cdot 6 + 8 \cdot 4 + 6 \cdot 4))$

$= (10 + 3 \cdot 6 + 48 \cdot 8)$

$= 62 \cdot 4$ square units (as before)

4 Use the trapezium rule to check your answers to questions **2** and **3**.

This diagram shows the cross section of a model railway tunnel.

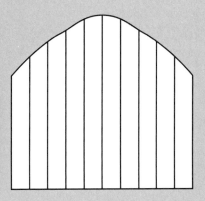

5 By taking measurements from the drawing calculate, using the trapezium rule the approximate area under the curve shown.

6 (a) Solve, by factorising, the equation $x^2 - 2x - 8 = 0$.
   (b) Calculate, using the trapezium rule the area bounded by the curve $y = x^2 - 2x - 8$ and the x-axis (as shaded).

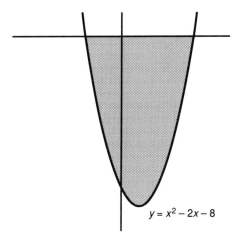

$y = x^2 - 2x - 8$

● **Remember**

A **vector** is basically a translation, a movement from one point to another.

The diagram above shows the vector $\overline{AB} = \begin{pmatrix} 3 \\ 2 \end{pmatrix}$, written in component form.

Equal vectors

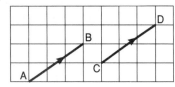

In the above diagram the two vectors $\overline{AB}$ and $\overline{CD}$ are equal, even though they have different starting and finishing points.

Multiplication of a vector

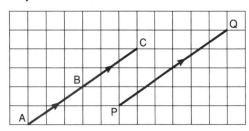

In the above diagram $\overline{AC}$ and $\overline{CD}$ are both equal to $2\overline{AB}$.

Note, for any number k, $k\overline{AB}$ will be parallel to $\overline{AB}$.

Addition and subtraction of two vectors

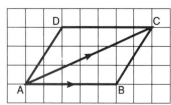

In the above diagram

$$\overline{AC} = \overline{AB} + \overline{BC} \quad \text{and} \quad \overline{DB} = \overline{AB} - \overline{BC}$$

This is often known as the **parallelogram rule for addition and subtraction**.

---

1 $\overline{AB} = \begin{pmatrix} 3 \\ -1 \end{pmatrix} \quad \overline{BC} = \begin{pmatrix} -2 \\ 5 \end{pmatrix}$

(a) Calculate $\overline{AB} + \overline{BC}$.

(b) Calculate $\overline{AB} - \overline{BC}$.

(c) Calculate:
  (i) $2\overline{AB}$ (ii) $3\overline{BC}$ (iii) $-4\overline{AC}$

(d) Calculate the length of $\overline{BC}$.

(e) Calculate the acute angle between AB and the x-axis.

2 $\overline{PQ} = \begin{pmatrix} 4 \\ 3 \end{pmatrix} \quad \overline{QR} = \begin{pmatrix} 2 \\ 5 \end{pmatrix} \quad \overline{TS} = \begin{pmatrix} 3 \\ 4 \end{pmatrix}$

(a) Show that $\overline{PR}$ is parallel to $\overline{TS}$.

(b) Calculate the lengths of:
  (i) $\overline{TS}$ (ii) $\overline{PR}$

3 $\mathbf{x} = \begin{pmatrix} -3 \\ 4 \end{pmatrix} \quad \mathbf{y} = \begin{pmatrix} 8 \\ 6 \end{pmatrix}$

(a) Show that $\mathbf{x}$ and $\mathbf{y}$ are perpendicular.

(b) Calculate $3\mathbf{x} - \frac{1}{2}\mathbf{y}$.

(c) Calculate the area of the square whose side is equal in length to the length of $3\mathbf{x} - \frac{1}{2}\mathbf{y}$.

4 A square ABCD has mid-point M, where the coordinates of M are (3,1).

The vector $\overline{MA} = \begin{pmatrix} 3 \\ 2 \end{pmatrix}$ so A is (6,3).

Find:

(a) the coordinates of the other three vertices of the square

(b) the area of the square

(c) the size of the acute angle between AC and the y-axis.

5 The vertices P, Q, R and S of a rectangle are at the points with coordinates (1,1), (5,2), (3,10) and (a,b) respectively.

(a) Find the values of a and b.

A transformation, T, of the plane is defined by

$$T: \begin{pmatrix} x \\ y \end{pmatrix} \rightarrow \begin{pmatrix} x \\ y \end{pmatrix} + \begin{pmatrix} -3 \\ 2 \end{pmatrix}$$

Under T, the image of PQRS is P'Q'R'S'.

(b) Find the coordinates of P', Q', R' and S'.

Physical vectors

A vector is a quantity having both **size** (or magnitude or length) and **direction**.

In the physical world, examples of vectors are: **force, velocity, acceleration** and others.

Such quantities obey the same rules of addition, subtraction and multiplication by a number (often known as a **scalar**) as given previously.

Example

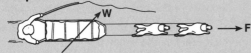

The diagram shows a sleigh being pulled by a team of dogs on a windy day.

The force the dogs are exerting is represented by a force **F**, the effect of the wind is represented by another force **W**.

Draw a diagram of the resultant force acting on the sleigh.

Solution
The word **resultant** means the **overall effect** of the two forces. It is merely the **vector addition** of **F** and **W**.
This vector addition can be shown by the parallelogram law of addition.

So we have

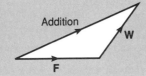

6 An object is being pulled by two forces.
The first force is directed due north and is of a magnitude 12 Newtons. The second force has a magnitude of 5 Newtons but acts in a direction due East.

(a) Draw a scale diagram representing the two forces and show the resultant force acting on the object.

(b) **Calculate** the magnitude of the resultant force.

(c) **Calculate** the bearing of the line of action of this resultant force.

(d) Confirm your answers to (b) and (c) by the scale drawing.

Abstract representations of vectors

Sometimes a vector can be represented in a **purely abstract** form.

The diagram above represents one such abstract vector, which has been symbolised as **a**.

The parallelogram laws and such, still hold true for such abstract vectors.

So, diagrammatically we have

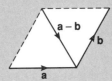

7 WXYZ is a rectangle. The vectors representing $\overline{WX}$ and $\overline{XY}$ are **x** and **y** respectively. C is the centre of the rectangle and M is the mid-point of WX.

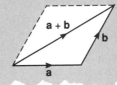

In terms of **x** and **y**, write down the vectors for:
(a) $\overline{ZY}$ (b) $\overline{YZ}$ (c) $\overline{ZW}$ (d) $\overline{MC}$ (e) $\overline{CY}$

8 PQRSTU is a regular hexagon.

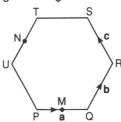

PQ = **a**   QR = **b**   RS = **c**

(a) In terms of **a**, **b** and **c**, write down the vector representations of:
(i) $\overline{ST}$ (ii) $\overline{TS}$ (iii) $\overline{TU}$ (iv) $\overline{PU}$ (v) $\overline{PR}$
(vi) $\overline{PS}$

M is the mid-point of PQ and N is the mid-point of TU.

(b) In terms of **a**, **b** and **c**, find the vector representation of:
(i) $\overline{MR}$ (ii) $\overline{MT}$ (iii) $\overline{MN}$

9 The diagram shows a quadrilateral OPQR.

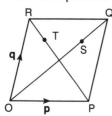

OP = **p**   OR = **q**

In the quadrilateral RQ = OP and PQ = OR.

(a) Write down the mathematical name for the quadrilateral OPQR.

(b) In terms of **p** and **q** write down the vectors representing:
(i) $\overline{OQ}$ **(i)** $\overline{RP}$

S and T are points on OQ and PR respectively such that OS = λOQ and PT = μPR where λ and μ are fractions.

(c) In terms of **p**, **q**, λ and μ write down the vector representations of:
(i) $\overline{OS}$ **(ii)** $\overline{RT}$ **(iii)** $\overline{OT}$

(d) Given that $\overline{OS} = \overline{OT}$, find the values of λ and μ.

10 An aeroplane's velocity in still air is 500 km per hour on a bearing of 050°.
The wind is blowing at 120 km per hour on a bearing of 060°.

Draw an accurate vector diagram to show the actual velocity of the aeroplane.

11

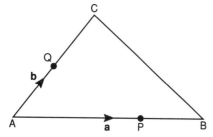

In the triangle ABC the points P and Q lie on AB and AC respectively.

$\overline{AB}$ = **a**, $\overline{AC}$ = **b** and AP : PB = AQ : QC = 3 : 1

(a) In terms of **a** and **b** express the vectors:
(i) $\overline{BC}$ **(ii)** $\overline{AP}$ **(iii)** $\overline{AQ}$ **(iv)** $\overline{PQ}$

(b) Deduce as many geometrical facts as you can about PQ and BC.

12 In still water a boat can travel with a uniform velocity of 25 kilometres per hour.

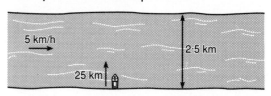

At 12.00 noon the boat sets out to cross a river which is 2.5 km wide. The current in the river has a velocity of 5 km per hour.

(a) Draw a vector diagram to show the actual velocity of the boat as it crosses the river.

(b) On your diagram mark the point where the boat reaches the other side of the river.

13 ABCDE is a pentagon.

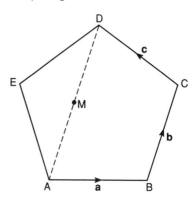

$\overline{AB}$ = **a** $\overline{BC}$ = **b** and $\overline{CD}$ = **c**.

(a) In terms of **a**, **b** and **c** write down the vectors representing:
(i) $\overline{AC}$ **(ii)** $\overline{AD}$

M is the mid-point of AD.

(b) In terms of **a**, **b** and **c** write down the vectors representing:
(i) $\overline{AM}$ **(ii)** $\overline{MC}$ **(iii)** $\overline{BM}$

14 Two vectors OA and OB are defined by:

$$\overline{OA} = \binom{4}{7} \qquad \overline{OB} = \binom{-7}{4}$$

where O is the origin of coordinates.

(a) On squared paper, draw a diagram of the two vectors.

(b) Describe completely the single transformation which maps $\overline{OB}$ onto $\overline{OA}$.

(c) Calculate the lengths of:
(i) OA   **(ii)** AB

The formula for the area of a circle, radius r, is
Area $= \pi r^2$
The formula for the circumference of a circle, radius r, is
Circumference $= 2\pi r$
In these two formulae
π is just the number nearly equal to $3 \cdot 14$ and is called **dimensionless**.
In the formula for the circumference
2 is also **dimensionless**.
But in each formula
r has the dimensions of length, it is of **dimension 1**, and
r^2 has **dimension 2**.

> All formulae for:
> **length or distance have dimension 1**
> **area have dimension 2**
> **volume have dimension 3.**

Looking only at the dimensions can never tell you whether a formula is correct – but
it can act as a guide towards the correct formula.

Worked example 1
Yasmin is using a formula sheet to work out the volume of a sphere. Unfortunately the sheet became blurred when it was passed through a photocopier so she cannot read it properly.

Her sheet looks like:

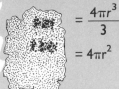

$$\cdots = \frac{4\pi r^3}{3}$$
$$\cdots = 4\pi r^2$$

Which of these formulae should she use to calculate the volume?

Solution
The dimension of $4\pi r^2$ is 2, whilst the dimensions of $\dfrac{4\pi r^3}{3}$ is 3.

Since the dimension of a volume is 3, Yasmin should use the formula $\dfrac{4\pi r^3}{3}$.

1 The formulae for the volume and curved surface area of a cylinder are:
$\pi r^2 h$ and $2\pi rh$.

  (a) By considering dimensions, explain why the first of these must be for the volume and the second for the curved surface area.

  (b) Examine the implications when you are told that π is dimensionless but $2\pi rh$ gives the volume of a particular solid shape.

2 The volume of a particular solid is given by the formula
$V = \lambda a^x b^y$, where
λ is dimension less, a and b have dimensions of length and x and y are positive integers.
Find the possible values of x and y.

3 In the following expressions the Greek letters represent dimensionless constants and the Arabic numerals also represent dimensionless quantities. The other letters represent lengths.

A	B	C	D	E
λabc	$3\mu xy$	$2\pi(a + b)$	πab	$\frac{1}{2}\eta xy^2$

F	G	H	I
$\pi a + 2b + c$	$\pi a^2 + b$	$x^3 + 3x^2$	$\tau x^3 + 3y^2 z$

Each expression can either:
represent a length, represent an area, represent a volume or be nonsense.
Categorise the expressions accordingly.

4 Comment on the accuracy of the following argument.
When the area of a square is equal to the perimeter of a square it follows that, by letting the side of the square be x then
$$x^2 = 4x$$
so $x = 4$
hence the length of the side of the square is x units.

5 It is known that a and b both have dimensions of length. **Comment as fully as possible** on the statement that $a^2 + b$ cannot represent an area.

6 For any triangle with sides of length a, b and c, Heron's formula states that the area is given by

$$\sqrt{s(s - a)(s - b)(s - c)}$$

where $s = \frac{1}{2}(a + b + c)$.
Check that this formula is dimensionally sound.

Trigonometry 2

The area of a triangle

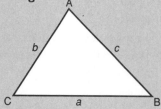

$$\text{Area} = \tfrac{1}{2}\,ab\,\text{Sin C}$$

The Sine rule

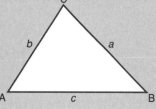

$$\frac{\text{Sin A}}{a} = \frac{\text{Sin B}}{b} = \frac{\text{Sin C}}{c}$$

or

$$\frac{a}{\text{Sin A}} = \frac{b}{\text{Sin B}} = \frac{c}{\text{Sin C}}$$

The Cosine rule

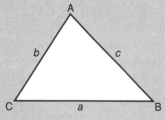

$$c^2 = a^2 + b^2 - 2ab\,\text{Cos C}$$

or

$$\text{Cos C} = \frac{a^2 + b^2 - c^2}{2ab}$$

The formula
$$c^2 = a^2 + b^2 - 2ab\,\text{Cos C}$$
is perhaps best remembered as
c^2 = Pythagoras minus a bit
  the bit being **$2ab\,\text{Cos C}$**

> Note: You will be provided with the Sine rule
> and Cosine rule formulae in your
> examinations. However, it is well worth
> trying to remember them.

Worked example 1

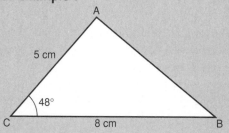

Calculate:

(a) the area of the triangle
(b) the length of AB
(c) the angle at B, given that it is acute.

Solution

(a) Area of triangle $= \tfrac{1}{2} ab\,\text{Sin C}$

$$= \tfrac{1}{2} \times 5 \times 8 \times \text{Sin } 48$$
$$= \tfrac{1}{2} \times 40 \times 0{\cdot}7431$$
$$= 20 \times 0{\cdot}7431$$
$$= 14{\cdot}86 \text{ cm}^2$$

This answer has been given to two
decimal places.

(b) By the Cosine rule
$$(AB)^2 = 5^2 + 8^2 - 2 \times 5 \times 8 \times \text{Cos } 48$$
$$= 25 + 64 - 80 \times \text{Cos } 48$$
$$= 89 - 80 \times 0{\cdot}6691$$
$$= 89 - 53{\cdot}5304$$
$$= 35{\cdot}4696$$

so
AB $= 5{\cdot}96$ cm correct to two decimal places.

(c) Using the Sine rule

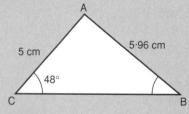

$$\frac{\text{Sin B}}{5} = \frac{\text{Sin } 48}{5{\cdot}96}$$

so
$$\text{Sin B} = \frac{5 \times \text{Sin } 48}{5{\cdot}96} = \frac{5 \times 0{\cdot}7431}{5{\cdot}96}$$

$$\text{Sin B} = 0{\cdot}6234$$
$$B = 38{\cdot}59°, \text{ correct to two decimal places.}$$

Worked example 2

A ship sets sail from a harbour H and travels 32 km due north to a marker buoy B. At B the ship turns on a bearing of 300 degrees and travels a further 25 km before stopping at S. Calculate the straight line distance from H to the place where the ship stops.

Solution
The diagram is:

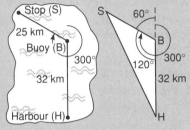

By the Cosine rule

$(HS)^2 = 32^2 + 25^2 - 2 \times 32 \times 25 \times \text{Cos } 120$

$= 1024 + 625 - (^-800)$

$= 1024 + 625 + 800$

$= 2449$

$HS = 49.5 \text{ km}$

1

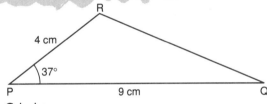

Calculate:

(a) the area of the triangle

(b) the length of the side QR

(c) the angle at:
   (i) Q   (ii) R

2 Re-work question 1 but make PQ = 4 cm, PR = 9 cm and keep the angle at P as 37°.
Comment on your results.

3 Calculate:

(a) the length of BC

(b) the angle at C

(c) the length of AB

(d) the area of the triangle.

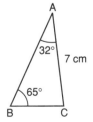

4 Use the Sine rule to show that this is **an impossible** triangle.

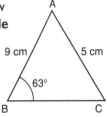

5 The diagram shows a triangle ABC.

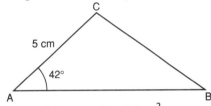

The area of this triangle is 24 cm².
AC = 5 cm.
Calculate:

(a) the length of AB

(b) the length of BC

(c) the angles at B and C.

6 In a triangle ABC, the lengths of CA and CB are 9 cm and 5 cm, respectively. The angle at A is 23°.

(a) Use the sine rule to show that to four decimal places Sin B = 0·7033

(b) Hence show that the angle at B could be either **(i)** 44·69° or **(ii)** 135·31°, correct to two decimal places.
(Note: this is sometimes called the **ambiguous** case.)

(c) Given that the angle at B is acute, find the length of AB.

7 In a triangle XYZ, XY = 11 cm, XZ = 6 cm and the angle at Y = 32°.
Calculate:

(a) the two possible values for the angle at Z

(b) the two possible values for the angle at X

(c) the two possible perimeters of the triangle.

8 A builder lays out a triangular building plot PQR. PQ = 20 metres, PR = 24 metres and the angle at P is 75°.
Calculate:

(a) the area of the building plot

(b) the length of QR

(c) the angles at Q and R.

9 A ship S, sets sail from a port P and travels 45 km due south until it reaches a lighthouse L. At L it turns onto a bearing of 130° and travels for a further distance of 52 km until it reaches a marker buoy B. At B the ship turns again and travels back to P in a straight line.
Calculate:
(a) the total distance travelled by the ship
(b) the bearing B from P
(c) the shortest distance between the ship and L on the return journey.

10 The diagram shows a sketch of a triangle ABC. The diagram has not been drawn to scale but all of its angles are acute.

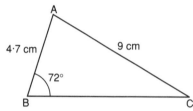

Calculate:
(a) the angle at C
(b) the angle at A
(c) the length of BC
(d) the area of the triangle.

11

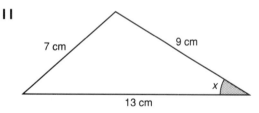

Calculate the angle marked x.

12 In a triangle ABC, AB = 9 cm, AC = 5 cm and BC = 6 cm. Calculate the three angles of the triangle.

13 The lengths of the sides of a triangle are k cm, $2k$ cm and $3k$ cm. Calculate the three angles of the triangle.

14 The lengths of the sides of a triangle are in the ratio 2 : 4 : 5. Calculate the angles of the triangle.

15 The angles at A, B and C of a triangle ABC are 50°, 60° and 70° respectively. Calculate the ratios of the sides of the triangle.

16 A walker sets out from her home H and walks 12 km on a bearing of 070° until she reaches a gate G. At G she turns on a bearing of 330° and walks for a further 8 km until she reaches a landmark L. At L she turns again and walks back home in a straight line.
Calculate:
(a) the total distance she walks.
(b) the bearing of L from H.
On her return journey she stops at a point M which is the point on the return journey nearest to G.
Calculate:
(c) the distance GM
(d) the bearing of M from G.

17

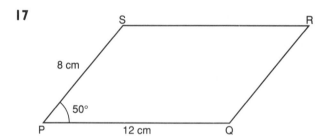

For the parallelogram PQRS calculate:
(a) its area
(b) the length of the diagonal SQ
(c) the length of the diagonal PR
(d) the angle PQ̂S
(e) the angle RQ̂S
A point M lies on SR and is such that the angle MP̂Q = 30°.
(f) Calculate the length of SM.

18 A tree is inclined at an angle of 85° to the horizontal. When the angle of elevation of the sun is 20° the tree casts a shadow of length 30 metres on horizontal ground. Calculate the height of the tree.

19 The diagram shows a vertical pole OP standing on a slope. It is held in place by two tight ropes PT and PM.

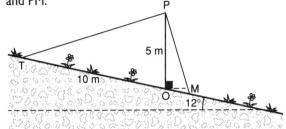

The slope is inclined at an angle of 12° to the horizontal.
Angle TP̂M = 90°
The length of the pole OP is 5 metres.
The distance OT is 10 metres.
Calculate:

(a) the length of the rope PT
(b) the angle OT̂P
(c) the length of the rope PM.

20 At 12 noon a ship S and a yacht Y set sail from a port P. The ship travels on a bearing of 043° at a constant speed of 20 km per hour. The yacht travels on a bearing of 265° at a constant speed of 15 km per hour.
Calculate:

(a) the distance between the ship and yacht at 1400 hours.
(b) the time of day when the ship and yacht are exactly 100 km apart.

21 The diagram shows a triangle ABC in which the angle at C is 120°.

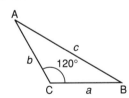

(a) Show that $c^2 = a^2 + b^2 + ab$
(b) Show that one possible solution to the above equation is $a = 3$, $b = 5$ and $c = 7$.
(c) Find at least one other solution to the equation in **(a)** for which a, b and c are integers and are not merely multiples of 3, 5 and 7.
(d) In the case where a, b and c are 3, 5 and 7 respectively, find all three angles of the triangle ABC.

22 The vertices, P, Q and R of the triangle PQR, have coordinates (1, 1), (4, 3) and (2, 7) respectively.

(a) Draw the triangle PQR
(b) Calculate the angle at P by using the Cosine rule
(c) Calculate the angle at P by any other method.

23 The diagram shows a triangle ABC.

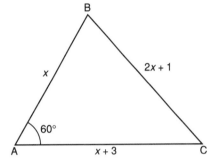

AB = x cm, AC = $x + 3$ cm and BC = $2x + 1$ cm.
The angle at A is 60°.

(a) Show that x must satisfy the equation
$3x^2 + x - 8 = 0$
(b) Obtain the solution to this equation.
(c) Find the angles at B and C.

24 At 1300 hours a trawler T leaves a port P. It travels at a constant speed of 24 km per hour on a bearing of 023°. A lighthouse L lies due east of P.
At 1400 hours the trawler is sighted by the lighthouse to be at a bearing of 320° from L.
Calculate:

(a) the distance of L from P
(b) the time of day when the trawler is due north of L.

Just the same

Two shapes which are exactly the same in every respect are called **congruent**.

Essentially being congruent means that you have two shapes, let us assume that they have been drawn. You then cut one out and you can lay it on top of the other, with no overlap and no gaps. This is a **naive** idea of **congruency**.

This chapter deals with the formal conditions needed to assure **the congruency of two triangles**.

A triangle has three sides and three angles. Clearly then, when two triangles are congruent the lengths of the sides of one are equal to the lengths of the corresponding sides of the other. Also the three angles of one are equal to the corresponding angles in the second triangle.

> Note that, having the three angles in the first triangle equal to the three angles in the second triangle will *not* be sufficient to ensure their congruency. It will merely make the triangles **similar**.

The, formal, sufficient conditions to ensure congruency

Condition 1
The three sides of one triangle are equal to the three sides of the other triangle.

Two triangles ABC and PQR will be congruent

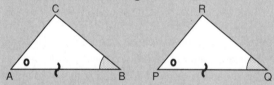

as will the two triangles LMN and XYZ.

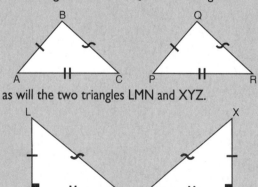

Condition 2
Two sides and the included angle in one triangle are equal to two sides and the included angle in the other.

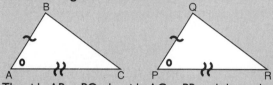

The side AB = PQ, the side AC = PR and the angle at A = the angle at P.

Please note, once you are given the lengths of two sides of a triangle and their included angle then the length of the third side is uniquely determined.

Condition 3
The length of one side and the angles at the end of that side in one triangle are equal to the length of one side and the angles at the end in the other triangle.

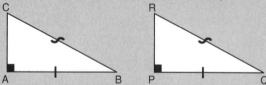

The length of AB = the length of PQ, the angle at A = the angle at P and the angle at B = the angle at Q.
This makes ABC and PQR congruent triangles.

Condition 4
When both triangles contain a right angle it is sufficient that the length of the hypotenuse and length of one other side in one triangle are equal to the length of the hypotenuse and one other side in the other triangle.

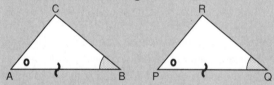

In the triangles ABC and PQR the angles at A and P are 90°, the length of BC = the length of QR and the length of AB = the length of PQ.
Again, this will be sufficient to ensure that ABC and PQR are congruent triangles.

Please note, given the hypotenuse and one other side of a right-angled triangle, then the third side is uniquely determined.

Example

In the diagram below ABCD is a parallelogram.

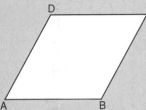

Show, giving reasons, that the triangles ABC and ADC are congruent.

AB = DC, opposite sides of a parallelogram
AD = BC, opposite sides of a parallelogram.
angle $A\hat{B}C$ = angle $A\hat{D}C$, opposite angles of a parallelogram.

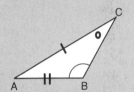 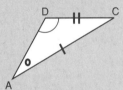

So for the two triangles ABC and ADC we have two sides and the included angle in one equal to two sides and the included angle in the other. Hence the two triangles are congruent.

I

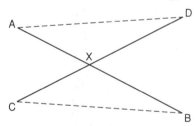

AB and CD are two line segments which meet at X. Given that AX = CX and BX = DX, show that ADX and BCX are congruent triangles.

2 In the diagram below, ABCD is a kite with AB = AD and CB = CD.

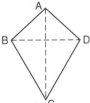

Write down, with a full explanation of your reasons, three pairs of congruent triangles.

3 In the diagram below, PQRS is a parallelogram.

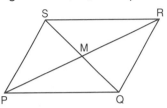

The diagonals PR and QS meet at the point M.

(a) Show that the triangles PQR and RSP are congruent.

(b) Examine, with reasons, the congruency or otherwise of the triangles:
 (i) PMQ and RMS **(ii)** PMS and RMQ.

4

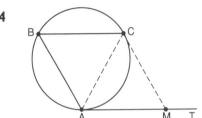

A, B and C lie on a circle. TA is a tangent to the circle at A.
The point M lies on TA and is such that angle $M\hat{A}C$ = angle $A\hat{C}B$ and MA = BC.
Show that the triangles ABC and AMC are congruent.

5 ABC and PQR are two right-angled triangles.

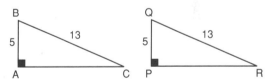

The lengths of the hypotenuse of each triangle is 13 cm. Other lengths in centimetres are shown on the diagrams. Show that ABC and PQR are two congruent triangles.

6 In the diagram below ABCD is a trapezium. AB is parallel to DC.

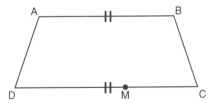

A point M lies on CD and is such that MD = AB.

Show that triangles ABM and DMA are congruent.

Similarity

● **Remember**

Two shapes are **similar** when one is an **enlargement** of the other.

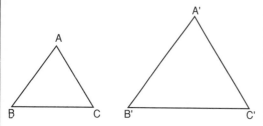

The two triangles ABC and A'B'C' are similar.

The main features of two similar triangles are:
- The pairs of corresponding angles at A and A', at B and B' and at C and C' are equal.
- The ratio of the corresponding sides are equal.

$$\text{So } \frac{A'B'}{AB} = \frac{A'C'}{AC} = \frac{B'C'}{BC}$$

with each ratio being the scale factor of the enlargement.

Example

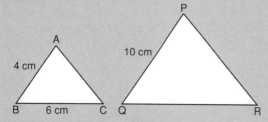

PQR is an enlargement of ABC.

Calculate:
(a) the scale factor of the enlargement
(b) the length QR.

(a) Scale factor of the enlargement $\frac{PQ}{AB}$

$$\text{scale factor} = \frac{PQ}{AB} = \frac{10}{4} = 2\frac{1}{2} \text{ or } 2 \cdot 5$$

(b) $\frac{QR}{BC} = \frac{PQ}{AB}$

$$\text{so } \frac{QR}{BC} = 2 \cdot 5 \text{ or } \frac{QR}{6} = 2 \cdot 5$$

$$QR = 6 \times 2 \cdot 5 = 15 \text{ cm}$$

1 In each pair of similar triangles calculate the lengths marked with letters. All lengths are in centimetres.

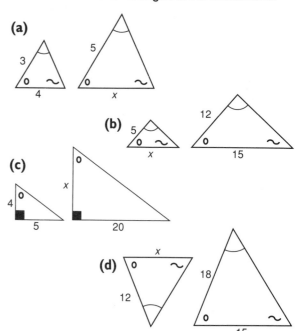

The relationship between the areas of similar figures

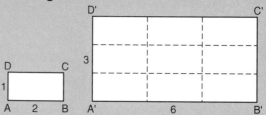

ABCD is a rectangle measuring 1 unit by 2 units. It is enlarged by **scale factor 3** to give the image A'B'C'D'.

Clearly ABCD and A'B'C'D' are similar rectangles.

The area of ABCD is 2 square units.
The area of A'B'C'D' is 18 square units.

The ratio $\dfrac{\text{area of A'B'C'D'}}{\text{area of ABCD}} = 9 = 3^2 = (\text{scale factor})^2$

● **Remember**

For any two similar figures the ratio of their areas is the square of the scale factor of the enlargement or the square of the ratio of their corresponding sides.

2 Do Worksheet 2.

3 ABC is a triangle right-angled at B. The length of
BA = 4 cm and the length of BC = 7 cm.

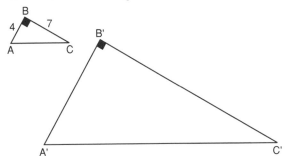

ABC is enlarged by a scale factor of 4 to give the
image A'B'C'.
Calculate the area of A'B'C'.

4 A cube of side length I cm is enlarged by a scale
factor 2·5 to give a second cube.
Calculate the surface area of the second cube.

5 A circle of radius 5 cm is enlarged by a scale factor
2·4 to give a second circle. Calculate:

(a) the area of the first circle

(b) the area of the second circle.

6 ABC and PQR are two similar triangles.

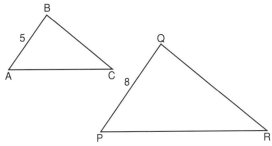

Calculate the ratio $\dfrac{\text{area of PQR}}{\text{area of ABC}}$.

7 The areas of two squares are in the ratio 16 : 1.
Find the ratio of the sides of the squares.

8 Two circles C and c are such that

$$\frac{\text{area of C}}{\text{area of c}} = 6·25$$

Given that the radius of C is R and the radius of c is

r, calculate $\dfrac{R}{r}$.

**The relationship between the volumes of
similar solids**

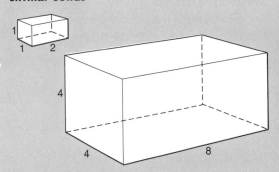

A cuboid measuring I unit by I unit by 2 units has
been enlarged by a **scale factor 4** to give a similar
cuboid which measures 4 units by 4 units by 8 units.

The volume of the smaller cuboid is 2 cubic units.
The volume of the larger cuboid is 128 cubic units.

The ratio of these volumes is

$$\frac{\text{volume of larger cuboid}}{\text{volume of smaller cuboid}} = \frac{128}{2} = 64 = 4^3$$

So the ratio of the volumes = **(scale factor)**³

9 Two spheres have radii 5 cm and 15 cm.
Calculate the ratio:

$\dfrac{\text{volume of the larger sphere}}{\text{volume of the smaller sphere}}$

10 The diagram shows two similar cola bottles.
The height of the larger bottle is 1·2 times the
height of the smaller bottle.

Calculate the ratio:

$\dfrac{\text{volume of the larger bottle}}{\text{volume of the smaller bottle}}$.

11 The volumes of the two cubes are in the ratio 27 : 1.
Calculate the ratio of:
(a) the lengths of the sides of the two cubes
(b) the surface area of the two cubes.

12 The diagram shows two similar bottles.

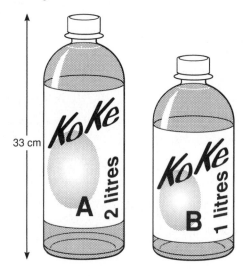

The bottle marked A has a volume of 2 litres.
The bottle marked B has a volume of 1 litre.
The height of the bottle marked A is 33 cm.

Calculate the height of the bottle marked B.

13 A die cast model of a car is made to a scale of 1 : 50.
The length of the real car is 4·3 metres.
(a) Calculate the length of the model car.
The volume of the model car is 54 cubic centimetres.
(b) Calculate the volume of the real car.

14 Two similar three-dimensional shapes A and B have surface areas S and s respectively.
It is known that $S = ks$, where k is a constant.
The volumes of A and B are V and v respectively.
Write down, with explanation, a relationship between V and v in terms of k.

15

A television company built a large scale model of a town for a film set. The model was built so that all linear measurements were $\frac{7}{8}$ of the real-life measurements. Show that on the film set:
(a) a model wall would have an area of approximately 76·5% of the area of the corresponding real-life wall
(b) a model office block would have a volume of approximately 67% of the volume of the real-life office block.

16 (a) Estimate the height of an average person aged about sixteen.
(b) Estimate the volume of an average sixteen-year-old.
A model of a sixteen-year-old is made on a scale of 1 : 12.
(c) Estimate the height of the model.
(d) Estimate the volume of the model.

The diagram represents a 3 by 4 by 5 cuboid constructed from 60 unit cubes.

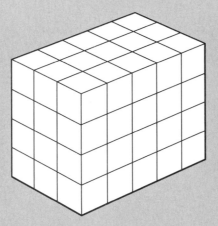

The six faces of the cuboid are painted.

Some of the 60 unit cubes will have 3 faces painted,
some will have 2 faces painted,
some will have 1 face painted,
and some will have 0 faces painted.

1 Investigate the number of faces painted for cuboids,
including cubes, of various sizes.

2 Extend the problem to consider the number of faces painted
for various shapes constructed from unit cubes.

During your investigation you are advised to:
● **make and record any observations**
● **communicate these observations clearly**
● **state and test any conjectures**
● **use appropriate forms of symbolism**
● **make and explain any conjectures**
● **offer any forms of justification or proof.**

Probability estimates are used frequently when we have **repeated (combined)** events.

This spinner is spun three times.
What is the probability of getting:
(a) three As **(b)** at least two Bs?

This problem can be solved using either tabulation, or tree diagrams.

Tabulation

(a) Results   A   A   A

Probability: $\frac{3}{5} \times \frac{3}{5} \times \frac{3}{5} = \frac{9}{125}$

(b) Results   B   B   A

Probability: $\frac{2}{5} \times \frac{2}{5} \times \frac{3}{5} = \frac{12}{125}$

Results   B   B   B

Probability: $\frac{2}{5} \times \frac{2}{5} \times \frac{2}{5} = \frac{8}{125}$

But there are three ways of arranging BBA (BBA, BAB, ABB), so the final probability estimate is:

$$3 \times \left(\frac{12}{125}\right) + \left(\frac{8}{125}\right) = \frac{44}{125}$$

Tree diagram

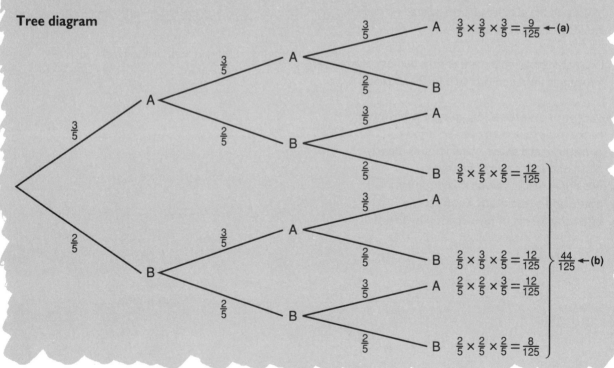

Use tabulation or tree diagrams to help you solve each of the following problems.

1 This spinner is spun twice. Find the probability that the two scores are:

(a) both odd numbers

(b) include a '1'

(c) are both the same number.

2

A coin is biased such that the probability that 'Heads' will appear is $\frac{2}{3}$. The coin is tossed three times. Find the probability that of the three throws:

(a) 'Heads' will appear three times

(b) 'Heads' will appear once

(c) 'Tails' will appear at least twice.

3 A survey reveals that during the month of January, on average, $\frac{3}{5}$ of the days receive some rain. Three days are selected at random. Calculate the probability that of the three days selected:

(a) all three days receive rain

(b) exactly two days receive rain

(c) at least two days were dry.

4 A bookshelf contains 10 books on crime, 9 SF books, and 7 on sport. Two books are each removed, their subjects noted, and then replaced on the bookself. Find the probability that the two books selected are:

(a) both SF

(b) include exactly one on sport

(c) both books on different topics?

5

The probability that a plant from a certain batch of lupin seeds will produce blue flowers is $\frac{2}{5}$. Find the probability that of the plants grown from the seeds:

(a) all three are blue

(b) at least two are blue

(c) exactly one is blue.

6 The probability of selecting a picture card from a pack of cards is $\frac{3}{13}$. Three cards are each selected, and on each occasion replaced in the pack. What is the probability that out of the three cards:

(a) two are picture cards

(b) there are no picture cards

(c) at least one is a picture card?

7

About $\frac{2}{3}$ of the cars on British roads are built outside the country, and are classed as Foreign. Three cars are selected at random in a car park. Calculate the probability that of these three cars:

(a) at least two are British

(b) all three are Foreign

(c) exactly two are Foreign.

8 A box contains two black pens, three red pens, and five blue pens. A pen is removed from the box and replaced on two separate occasions. Find the probability that:

(a) both pens are red

(b) neither pen is red

(c) both pens are of different colours.

9

An octahedral dice has the numbers 1, 2, 2, 3, 3, 3, 4, 4 on its eight faces. The dice is rolled twice. Calculate the probability that the scores recorded in the two throws:

(a) include two 3s

(b) do not include any 4s

(c) include different numbers

(d) include odd numbers only.

10 The probability of a man reaching a ferry before it sails each day is $\frac{7}{10}$. He wishes to sail on the ferry on three consecutive days. Find the probability that:

(a) he will miss the ferry on all three days

(b) he will catch the ferry twice

(c) he will catch the ferry at least once.

Without replacement

A bag contains 7 Choc bars and 3 Nutty bars.
A bar is selected at random, removed, and *not* replaced.

A tree diagram is particularly useful in the solution of this type of problem,
as it clearly shows how the probabilities change.

C = Choc
N = Nutty

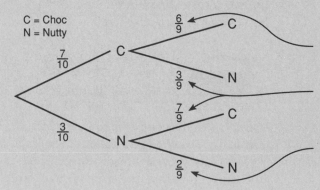

There are only 6 choc bars left here,
as one has already been removed.

All probabilities are out of 9, not 10, on
the second branches of the tree:
there are only 9 bars left, as one has been removed.

There are only 2 Nutty bars left here,
as one has already been removed.

We now have:

C and C $\frac{7}{10} \times \frac{6}{9} = \frac{7}{15}$

C and N $\frac{7}{10} \times \frac{3}{9} = \frac{7}{30}$

N and C $\frac{3}{10} \times \frac{7}{9} = \frac{7}{30}$

N and N $\frac{3}{10} \times \frac{2}{9} = \frac{1}{15}$

P(selecting two Nutty bars) is $\frac{1}{15}$

P(selecting at least one Choc bar) is $\frac{7}{30} + \frac{7}{30} + \frac{7}{15} = \frac{28}{30} = \frac{14}{15}$

The answers to these two questions cover all possibilities, since $\frac{1}{15} + \frac{14}{15} = 1$.
An easier way to work out the answer to the second question is to first ask its opposite or **complement**:.
The probability of selecting at least one Choc bar = 1 – (probability of selecting no Choc bars)

= 1 – (probability of selecting two Nutty bars)

$= 1 - \frac{1}{15} = \frac{14}{15}$

Sometimes it is easier to find the answer to a problem by finding its complement first.

Use tree diagrams to answer each of the following questions.

1 The names of the nine finalists in a competition are
drawn at random. Six are female, and three are male.
The first three names are drawn out. What is the
probability that they will:

(a) be all female

(b) include one male

(c) include at least two females?

2 A bag contains 4 red beads and 5 blue beads. Three
beads are drawn at random and not replaced. What
is the probability that these three beads:

(a) are all red

(b) include exactly two blues

(c) include at least two red beads?

3 There are 12 coins in your pocket: seven 5p coins, and five 10p coins. You remove three coins at random. What is the probability that out of the three coins:

(a) all are 5p coins

(b) the three coins add up to 20p

(c) there are at least two 10p coins?

4

A box contains six chocolates: two milk chocolates and four plain chocolates. Three chocolates are removed at random. What is the probability that, of the three chocolates:

(a) all three chocolates are plain

(b) there will be exactly two milk chocolates

(c) there will be at least two plain chocolates?

5

A cage contains 6 blue, 3 green and 3 yellow budgerigars. You catch two at random, but do not replace them. What is the probability that:

(a) both birds are blue

(b) both birds are different colours

(c) there is at least one blue bird?

6 A bookshelf has 10 books on it: 6 are fiction, 3 are factual books, and one is an atlas. Two books are removed at random, but not replaced. What is the probability that of the two books:

(a) one is the atlas

(b) both are fiction

(c) there is at least one factual book?

7 A pack of 52 playing cards has 4 aces, 12 picture cards, and 36 number cards. Two cards are chosen at random, without replacement. What is the probability that the cards:

(a) do not include a number card

(b) include both a picture and a number card

(c) include at least one ace?

8 In a class of 28, 16 are female, whilst 12 are male. Three are chosen at random, and leave the classroom in turn. Find the probability that the three who leave:

(a) are all female

(b) includes exactly one female

(c) includes at least two males.

9 A tube of 15 wine gums contains the following sweets: 8 lemon, 4 orange, and 3 lime. Two wine gums are removed at random and not replaced. What is the probability that both wine gums:

(a) do not include a lime

(b) include at least one lemon

(c) are both lemon *or* both orange?

10

There are 10 fruit juices on a shelf: 6 apple, and 4 pineapple. Three are chosen at random and removed, one at a time. What is the probability that the three fruit juices:

(a) will include exactly one apple

(b) will include at least two pineapple

(c) will include at least two apple?

11 A box contains 5 blue, 3 red, and 8 black pens. Two pens are removed at random, neither being replaced. What is the probability that of the two pens:

(a) none are black

(b) there is exactly one red

(c) there are exactly two blues *or* exactly two reds?

12 In a carton there are five oranges, six apples, and two bananas. Three fruits are chosen at random and each is removed in turn. Find the probability that the three fruits:

(a) are all apples

(b) include at least one orange

(c) include one of each fruit.

Cumulative frequency

● **Remember**

A cumulative frequency curve can be used to estimate useful statistical measures.

Median

This is the **middle** value of the distribution. The **median** is also known as the **second quartile**.

Lower quartile

This is the value **one quarter** of the way into the distribution.
The **lower quartile** is also known as the **first quartile**.

Upper quartile

This is the value **three quarters** of the way into the distribution.
The **upper quartile** is also known as the **third quartile**.

Interquartile range (a measure of dispersion)

Interquartile range (IQR)
= upper quartile − lower quartile

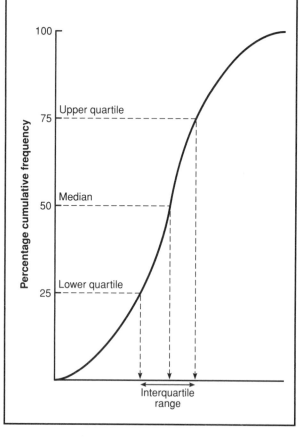

Semi-interquartile range

This is found by **dividing** the interquartile range **by 2**.

Semi-interquartile range $= \frac{1}{2}$ (upper quartile − lower quartile)

$$= \frac{1}{2} \text{(IQR)}$$

The semi-interquartile range is a measure of dispersion centred closely around the median and does not show the dispersion of the whole distribution. It shows how closely the data is spread **between** the quartiles.

As well as using a cumulative frequency curve to find the median and quartiles an **arithmetic method** can be used.

• Find the class interval that the lower quartile, median or upper quartile are in, called the **lower bound**, *Cl*.

• Find the cumulative frequency up to this class interval. Call this *CF*.

• Find the frequency of the class interval of the lower quartile, median or upper quartile. Call this *F*.

• Find the width of the class interval of the lower quartile, median or upper quartile. Call this *W*.

Then the lower quartile $= Cl + \dfrac{(\frac{1}{4}\Sigma f - CF)}{F} \times W$

similarly, the median $= Cl + \dfrac{(\frac{1}{2}\Sigma f - CF)}{F} \times W$

and the upper quartile $= Cl + \dfrac{(\frac{3}{4}\Sigma f - CF)}{F} \times W$

Notice the formulae stay the same except for the sum of the frequencies which is $\frac{1}{4}$ for the lower quartile, $\frac{1}{2}$ for the median and $\frac{3}{4}$ for the upper quartile.

Example

Find the lower quartile, median and upper quartile for the following grouped distribution.

x	f	Cumulative f
1–5	1	1
6–10	4	5
11–15	17	22
16–20	26	48
21–25	24	72
26–30	17	89
31–35	8	97
36–40	3	100
		$\Sigma f = 100$

Lower quartile

$\Sigma f = 100$, $CI = 15.5$, $CF = 22$, $F = 26$, $W = 5$

$$\text{Lower quartile} = CI + \frac{(\frac{1}{4}\Sigma f - CF)}{F} \times W$$

$$= 15.5 + \frac{(\frac{1}{4} \times 100 - 22)}{26} \times 5$$

$$= 15.5 + \frac{(25 - 22)}{26} \times 5$$

$$= 15.5 + \frac{3}{26} \times 5$$

$$= 16.08 \text{ to 2dp}$$

Median

$\Sigma f = 100$, $CI = 20.5$, $CF = 48$, $F = 24$, $W = 5$

$$\text{Median} = CI + \frac{(\frac{1}{2}\Sigma f - CF)}{F} \times W$$

$$= 20.5 + \frac{(50 - 48)}{24} \times 5$$

$$= 20.92 \text{ to 2dp}$$

Upper quartile

$\Sigma f = 100$, $CI = 25.5$, $CF = 72$, $F = 17$, $W = 5$

$$\text{Upper quartile} = CI + \frac{(\frac{3}{4}\Sigma f - CF)}{F} \times W$$

$$= 25.5 + \frac{(75 - 72)}{17} \times 5$$

$$= 26.38 \text{ to 2dp}$$

I The table below shows the ages, to the nearest year, of 1000 people.

Age (years)	Frequency
1–10	23
11–20	91
21–30	189
31–40	272
41–50	198
51–60	148
61–70	39
71–80	23
81–90	11
91–100	6

(a) Make a cumulative frequency table for this data.
(b) Draw a cumulative frequency curve.
(c) Use the cumulative frequency curve and the arithmetic method to find an estimate for the:
  • median • lower quartile • upper quartile
  • interquartile range • semi-interquartile range.

2 The table below gives the lifetime of 210 electric light bulbs to the nearest hour.

Lifetime (years)	Frequency
0 up to 200	1
200 up to 400	17
400 up to 600	42
600 up to 800	97
800 up to 1000	36
1000 up to 1200	15
1200 up to 1400	2

(a) Draw up a cumulative frequency table.

(b) Construct a cumulative frequency curve.

(c) Find estimates for the:
  • median • lower quartile • upper quartile
  • interquartile range • semi-interquartile range.

(d) Check your estimates by calculating these values using the arithmetic method.

(e) What percentage of light bulbs lasted less than 500 hours?

(f) What percentage of light bulbs lasted more than 825 hours?

3 The table below shows the examination marks scored by 200 pupils in an end-of-year examination.

Mark	Frequency
1–10	1
11–20	2
21–30	15
3 –40	29
41–50	67
51–60	35
61–70	21
71–80	15
81–90	11
91–100	4

(a) Draw up a cumulative frequency table.

(b) Construct a cumulative frequency curve.

(c) Find estimates for the:
  • median • lower quartile • upper quartile
  • interquartile range • semi-interquartile range.

(d) Check your estimates by calculating these values using the arithmetic method.

(e) What percentage of pupils scored more than 44 marks?

(f) What percentage of pupils scored between 35 and 65 marks?

4 In a different school of 200 pupils the same examination as in question **3** was taken by pupils at the end of the year. The table below shows their marks.

Mark	Frequency
1–10	0
11–20	1
21–30	5
31–40	12
41–50	17
51–60	41
61–70	59
71–80	38
81–90	21
91–100	6

(a) Use the arithmetic method to calculate the:
  • median • lower quartile • upper quartile
  • interquartile range • semi-interquartile range.

(b) Use the statistics you have calculated in questions **3** and **4** to compare and contrast the results in the examination.

Eddie is a member of a football syndicate that wins £300 000 on the football pools.

1 How much would each member of the syndicate receive if there were:

(a) 60 members

(b) 50 members

(c) 30 members?

2 A second syndicate also wins the football pools. The estimated prize is between £200 000 and £450 000. The number of people in the syndicate varies from week to week but is never less than 10 or more than 15. If the money is shared equally between the members what is:

(a) the largest possible amount that one member can receive

(b) the smallest possible amount that one member can receive?

(c) Write down the conditions necessary to calculate:

(i) the largest amount

(ii) the smallest amount.

3 Calculate:

(a) the gradient of the line A to B

(b) the gradient of the line C to D.

(c) Which line has the steeper gradient?

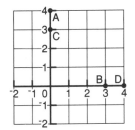

4 It is known that point A is either (6, 5) or (5, 6) and point B is either (1, 2) or (2, 1).

(a) Show this information on squared paper.

(b) Calculate the maximum possible gradient of the line joining the points A and B.

(c) Calculate the minimum possible gradient.

5 Given that m is between 10 and 12 and n is between 5 and 6 find:

(a) the largest value of mn

(b) the smallest value of mn

(c) the largest value of $\frac{m}{n}$

(d) the smallest value of $\frac{m}{n}$.

6 A car travels for 4 hours, measured to the nearest minute, at an average speed of 45 km/h rounded to the nearest kilometre.
Find:

(a) the shortest distance the car could have travelled

(b) the longest distance the car could have travelled.

7 A second car travels 50·0 km, measured to the nearest 0·1 of a kilometre in a time of 40.00 minutes measured to the nearest 0·01 of a minute.
Find:

(a) the maximum possible speed of the car

(b) the minimum possible speed of the car

(c) the difference between the maximum and minimum.

8 In question **7** a defect was discovered with the timer used in the test. The time taken to travel the 50 km could only be given as 40 minutes to the nearest minute. What effect has this on your three answers for question **7**?

9 The interval approximation for the area of a square is given as 78 cm^2 to 80 cm^2.
Calculate, correct to 2 decimal places:

(a) the upper bound of one side of the square

(b) the lower bound of one side of the square

(c) an interval approximation for the perimeter of the square.

(d) If the square is one face of a cube write down an interval approximation for the volume of the cube.

Question **15** of *More interesting 1*, page 4 asked you to suggest an expression connecting the growth rate m, interest rate r invested for 3 years. The expression you may have obtained is

$$m = (1 + \tfrac{r}{100})^3$$

where
m = the number of times the investment has grown
r = the percentage interest rate per annum.

1 Use the above formula to find r when:

(a) $m = 5$

(b) $m = 1.5$

(c) $m = 0.5$

(d) Explain the meaning of your answer for (c).

This expression can be developed for an investment of n years to

$$m = (1 + \tfrac{r}{100})^n$$

where
m = the number of times the investment has grown
r = the % interest rate paid per annum.
n = the number of years invested.

2 Find the % annual interest, to the nearest 0.1% for an investment:

(a) to double every six years

(b) to treble every five years

(c) to increase by a factor of ten every 10 years.

3 Find the number of times an investment grows, to the nearest 0.1 for an investment with:

(a) an interest rate of 5% invested for 5 years

(b) an interest rate of 6.4% invested for 12 years

(c) an interest rate of 7.6% invested for 6 months.

4 An insurance policy pays a compound interest rate of 12%. An investment grows by a factor of 10 over a certain number of years. Find, to the nearest year, the length of time the money was invested.

To find how much an investment will be worth when compound interest is paid, start with

$$m = (1 + \tfrac{r}{100})^n$$

Multiply each side by the amount invested called the **principal** P to get

$$Pm = P(1 + \tfrac{r}{100})^n$$

but Pm = the original investment multiplied by the number of times it has increased or the **actual amount** A the investment is now worth.
The formula now becomes

$$A = P(1 + \tfrac{r}{100})^n$$

where
A = the amount the investment is now worth
P = the principal (the original investment)
r = the % interest rate
n = the time, in years, the money is invested.

This formula is known as the **compound interest formula**.

If £550 is invested at an interest rate of 6% for 4 years, the amount it will have grown to is:

$$A = P(1 + \tfrac{r}{100})^n = 550(1 + \tfrac{6}{100})^4$$

$$= 550(1 + 0.06)^4$$
$$= 550(1.06)^4$$
$$= £694.36$$

The investment of £550 will have grown to £694.36.

5 Calculate the average simple interest, to the nearest 0.1%, of the investment of £550 that will grow to £694.36 in 4 years.

6 Find the amount A an investment will have grown
to when:

(a) £250 is invested at an interest rate of 8% per
annum for 8 years

(b) £1500 is invested for 12 years at an annual
interest rate of 8·6%

(c) £582 invested for 8·5 years at an interest rate of
6·25% per annum.

7 Find:

(a) the interest rate on an investment of £4000
which increases in value to £5800 over a period
of 8 years

(b) by a trial and improvement method the time it
takes, to the nearest month, for an investment of
£800 to increase to £2400 with an annual
interest rate of 8·2%.

Colin decides to invest £100 each year for 5 years
in an insurance policy. The annual compound
interest rate is 8%.

To find the total value at the end of the 5th year
the formula

$A = P(1 + \frac{r}{100})^n$ can be used.

The £100 invested at the beginning will have
5 years growth and will grow to $100(1·08)^5$.

The £100 invested in the 2nd year will have 4 years
growth and will grow to $100(1·08)^4$.

The £100 invested in the 3rd year will have 3 years
growth and will grow to $100(1·08)^3$, and so on.

£100 invested at the beginning of	Will grow to	Number of years of growth
1st year	£100(1·08)^5	5 years
2nd year	£100(1·08)^4	4 years
3rd year	£100(1·08)^3	3 years
4th year	£100(1·08)^2	2 years
5th year	£100(1·08)^1	1 years

or
$100(1·08 + 1·08^2 + 1·08^3 + 1·08^4 + 1·08^5) = £633·59$

The investment after the end of the fifth year will
be worth £633·59.

8 Stefan takes out an eight-year policy into which he
pays £150 each year starting at the beginning of the
policy. Because the policy has longer to run the
insurance company pays a compound interest rate
of 9·6%. Work out the value of Stefan's policy after:

(a) the end of the 2nd year

(b) the beginning of the 3rd year

(c) the end of the 10th year.

9 After the end of the 5th year Stefan decides to
'cash in' his policy. Because he stops the policy the
insurance company only pays out 45% of the value
at the end of the 5th year. How much money
should Stefan receive?

10 Sally takes out a six-year policy with an insurance
company. This policy costs her £200 each year
starting at the beginning of year one.
The company pays a compound interest rate of
9·6%. How much money should Sally receive at the
end of the 6th year?

11 Mark also takes out a policy but with a different
company. The annual payment is the same as Sally's
but the compound interest rate varies from year to
year. The company pays according to this table.

Year	Compound interest
1st	8%
2nd	8%
3rd	8%
4th	9·5%
5th	9·5%
6th	12%

(a) How much is Mark's policy worth at the end of
the 6th year?

(b) Which policy is the best investment and by
how much: Sally's or Mark's?

12 £2000 was invested in an investment account that
paid an annual compound interest rate of 6·8%.
After a certain number of years the investment had
grown to £5544·78. Find, to the nearest month, the
length of time the investment was held.

Come on be reasonable

The measurements of this rectangle have been given to the nearest 0·1 cm.

←——— 14·2 m ———→

16·5 m

Tony and Gaynor have been asked to calculate the area giving their answers to reasonably rounded off values:

Gaynor works out the upper and lower bound of each dimension:

Upper bound length   16·55 cm
Lower bound length   16·45 cm

Upper bound width   14·25 cm
Lower bound width   14·15 cm

She then calculates the interval approximation for the area.
$14·25 \times 16·55 = 235·8375 \text{ cm}^2$
$14·15 \times 16·45 = 232·7675 \text{ cm}^2$

Gaynor decides that a reasonable approximation for the area is 234 cm² with a rounded error of 2 cm² or 234 cm² ± 2 cm². This means

$232 \text{ cm}^2 < \text{area} < 236 \text{ cm}^2$

Tony decides not to work out the upper and lower bounds and uses the approximations as exact values. He then calculates the area as
$16·5 \times 14·2 = 234·3 \text{ cm}^2$.
He also gives an approximation of 234 cm² to the nearest cm². This means that Tony's answer is

$233·5 \text{ cm}^2 < \text{area} < 234·5 \text{ cm}^2$

which is clearly wrong since both the upper bound and the lower bound are outside Tony's interval approximation.

When making calculations with approximations the rounded off value should be appropriate to the context in which it is being used and the interval approximation as close as possible to the upper and lower bound.

1 The sides of a rectangular field are 235 m by 185 m, both measurements to the nearest metre. Calculate:
   (a) the upper bound of the area of the field
   (b) the lower bound of the area of the field
   (c) the interval approximation for the area of the field.
   (d) Give a suitable rounded off value for the area with a reasonable interval approximation.

2 A car on a test run covered a distance of 500 m, measured to the nearest metre, in a time of 15·4 seconds. Calculate:
   (a) the fastest possible speed in km/h
   (b) the slowest possible speed in km/h.
   (c) Give a reasonable rounded off value of the speed with an appropriate approximation interval.

The instructions for cooking a chicken are 'allow 35 minutes per kilogram and then add an extra 20 minutes.'

3 If the time to cook a chicken weighing x kilograms is t minutes write down a formula connecting t and x.

4 If the times given in the instructions are to the nearest minute, calculate:
   (a) the upper bound of the time to cook a chicken weighing 3·0 kg to the nearest 0·1 kg
   (b) the lower bound of the time to cook the same chicken.
   (c) Give a reasonable rounded off time to cook the chicken with an appropriate interval approximation.

5 Suzanne has 1 hour in which to cook a chicken. Calculate, giving full justification, the rounded off weight with an appropriate interval approximation for the weight of the chicken she can cook.

The triangle is one that you should recognise as having a special place in work on Pythagoras' theorem.

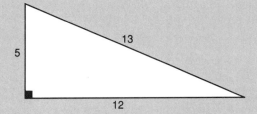

It is also special, in that its area and perimeter are **numerically** equal.

Area = $\frac{1}{2} \times 5 \times 12 = 30$ square units
Perimeter = 5 + 12 + 13 = 30 units.

1 Investigate other triangles to see which ones have their areas and perimeters numerically equal.

2 Investigate other two-dimensional shapes which have their areas and perimeters numerically equal.

The diagram shows a cube, with sides of length 6 units.

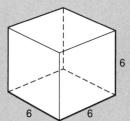

The volume of this cube is $6 \times 6 \times 6 = 216$ cubic units.

The surface area of the cube is $6 \times$ the area of the base.
So the surface area of the cube is $6 \times 36 = 216$ squares units.

So, for the cube shown above, its volume and surface area are numerically equal.

3 Investigate other cuboids which have their volumes and surface areas numerically equal.

4 Investigate other three-dimensional shapes which have their volumes and surface areas numerically equal.

5 Is it possible for a three-dimensional shape to have its volume, surface area and perimeter all numerically equal?
Justify your response.

Being rational

The vast majority of numbers we use in life are **rational**. That is to say that they can be written in the form $\frac{a}{b}$ where a and b are **whole numbers**.

So each of these numbers is rational:
$$\frac{1}{2} \quad \frac{1}{4} \quad \frac{3}{4}$$

3 which is the same as $\frac{3}{1}$

$2\frac{1}{2}$ or $2\cdot5$ which is the same as $\frac{5}{2}$

$0\cdot3333$ recurring or $0\cdot\dot{3}$ which is the same as $\frac{1}{3}$

$-3\frac{1}{2}$ or $-3\cdot5$ which is the same as $\frac{-7}{2}$ or $\frac{^-7}{2}$ or $\frac{7}{^-2}$

1 Write each of these rational numbers in the form $\frac{a}{b}$:

(a) 5   (b) $1\frac{1}{2}$ (c) 0.1   (d) 0.1111 recurring

(e) ⁻4   (f) ⁻0.3333 recurring   (g) ⁻$4\frac{1}{4}$

2 Given that x and y are both rational numbers, prove that $x + y$, $x - y$, xy and $\frac{x}{y}$ are also rational.

One particular fact about numbers is that although most of the ones we use in life are rational, there are far more numbers which are **not rational**, or which **cannot** be written in the form $\frac{a}{b}$ where a and b are whole numbers. These numbers are called **irrational**.

Perhaps the most famous irrational number of all is π, which is defined by the ratio:

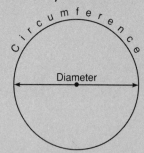

$$\pi = \frac{\text{circumference of a circle}}{\text{diameter of a circle}}$$

and which gives the formulae:
$C = \pi d$ and $C = 2\pi r$
where C is the circumference, d the diameter and r the radius of a circle.

Your calculator will have a π button which will show that
$$\pi = 3\cdot145\,926\,45$$
but this is only an approximation to π.
Other well known and often used approximations for π are
$$3\tfrac{1}{7}, \frac{22}{7}, 3\cdot14, 3\cdot142$$
and $\pi^2 = 10$ or $\pi = \sqrt{10}$

3 Given that π is irrational, show that it is impossible for both the circumference and the diameter of a circle to be equal to a whole number of centimetres.

Another very famous irrational number is $\sqrt{2}$.

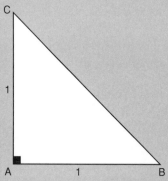

By Pythagoras' theorem, the length of BC is given by
$$BC^2 = AB^2 + AC^2$$
$$\text{so } BC^2 = 1^2 + 1^2$$
$$BC^2 = 1 + 1$$
$$BC^2 = 2$$
$$BC = \sqrt{2}$$

In other words $\sqrt{2}$ is equal to the length of the hypotenuse of an isosceles, right-angled triangle where the other two sides are each of length 1 unit.

The first five perfect square numbers are
$$1 = 1^2, \; 4 = 2^2, \; 9 = 3^2, \; 16 = 4^2, \; 25 = 5^2$$
and all of their square roots are whole numbers, as
$$\sqrt{1} = 1, \sqrt{4} = 2, \sqrt{9} = 3, \sqrt{16} = 4, \sqrt{25} = 5$$

There is a **very fundamental theorem** which says that for any whole number N, then $\sqrt{N}$ is **irrational** unless N is itself a perfect square number.

This theorem extends beyond whole numbers to say that $\sqrt{N}$ is **irrational** unless N is of the form $\dfrac{a^2}{b^2}$ where a and b are integers and in which case $\sqrt{N} = \dfrac{a}{b}$ and is then rational.

You can quote this theorem when answering questions on rational and irrational numbers.

4 Determine, with a reason, whether each of the following are rational or irrational:
(a) $\sqrt{3}$ (b) $\sqrt{5}$ (c) $\sqrt{17}$ (d) $\sqrt{36}$ (e) $\sqrt{144}$

5 Given that p is a prime number, state with a reason whether $\sqrt{p}$ is rational or irrational.

6 Given that x is a positive integer, show that $\sqrt{x^2 + 6x + 9}$ is always rational.

7

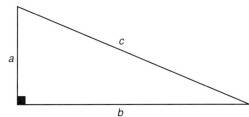

ABC is a right-angled triangle.
Find, with a full explanation, two pairs of values for a and b which will guarantee that c is:
(a) rational (b) irrational.

8 All of the following numbers are irrational.
$\sqrt{2},\ 2\sqrt{2},\ \sqrt{3}+1,\ \sqrt{3}-1,\ \dfrac{\sqrt{2}}{3}\ \sqrt{3}$
$5 + \sqrt{3},\ 5 - \sqrt{3}$
Show by making choices from the above list of numbers that it **is possible** to have two irrational numbers n and m for which
(a) nm is rational
(b) $\dfrac{m}{n}$ is rational
(c) $n + m$ is rational
(d) $n - m$ is rational
(Note, the value of n and m need not be the same in each case.)

9 Find two irrational numbers, r and s, for which:
(a) both rs and $\dfrac{r}{s}$ are rational.
(b) both of $r + s$ and $r - s$ are rational.

10 n and m are two irrational numbers for which nm is rational.
Find a general expression for each of n and m.

11 p and q are two irrational numbers for which $\dfrac{p}{q}$ is rational.
Find a general expression for each of p and q.

12 x and y are two irrational numbers for which $x + y$ is rational.
Find a general expression for each of x and y.

13 s and t are two irrational numbers for which $s - t$ is rational.
Find a general expression for each of s and t.

14 Examine whether or not it is possible for two irrational numbers a and b to exist for which all of ab, $\dfrac{a}{b}$, $a + b$ and $a - b$ are rational.

15 For any integer, N, there is a fundamental theorem, which states that $\sqrt{N}$ is irrational unless N is a perfect square number.
Generalise this theorem.

16 Determine, with an explanation, whether each of the following is rational or irrational:
(a) $\sqrt[3]{64}$ (b) $\sqrt{144}$ (c) $\sqrt[5]{32}$
(d) $81^{-\frac{1}{2}}$ (e) $\sqrt{1001}$

We can solve the equation
$$x^2 - 8x - 11 = 0$$
graphically.

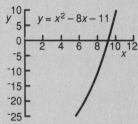
$y = x^2 - 8x - 11$

The above graph shows that one of the solutions is **approximately equal** to **9**.

We could, if we wished, use a method of **trial and improvement** to improve on this approximate solution.

We now develop a much more sophisticated trial and improvement type of method using a technique called **iteration**.

To do this we start by re-arranging the equation from
$$x^2 - 8x - 11 = 0$$
to
$$x^2 = 8x + 11$$
and then
$$x = \sqrt{8x + 11}$$

This now forms the basis of the **iterative process**. **The new value of x =**
$$\sqrt{8 \text{ times the old value of } x \text{ plus } 11}$$
or, in symbols
$$x_{n+1} = \sqrt{8x_n + 11}$$

We now start the process with our approximate value of x, taken in this case from the graph, of $x_1 = 9$. Then
$$x_2 = \sqrt{8x_1 + 11}$$
or
$$x_2 = \sqrt{8 \times 9 + 11}$$
$$x_2 = \sqrt{83}$$
$$x_2 = 9{\cdot}110\,433\,579$$

Then we use this to calculate the next value of x, that is x_3
$$x_3 = \sqrt{8x_2 + 11}$$
$$= 8 \times 9{\cdot}110\,433\,579 + 11 = 9{\cdot}158\,791\,876$$

Now we repeat the process to calculate x_4, x_5 and so on, until we obtain two successive values of x that are so close that we can ignore the difference. This will give a very good approximate solution.

1 The diagram shows part of the graph of
$$y = x^2 - 6x - 33$$

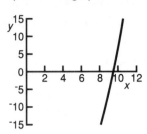

(a) Use the graph to give an approximate solution of the equation
$$x^2 - 6x - 33 = 0$$

(b) Show that the above equation can be solved using the iteration
$$x_{n+1} = \sqrt{6x_n + 33}$$

(c) Use this iteration three times to improve on your approximate solution obtained from the graph.

2 The equation $x^2 - 10x + 18 = 0$ has a solution in the region of $x = 7{\cdot}5$

(a) Re-arrange the equation into the form
$$x = \sqrt{10x - 18}$$

(b) Use the iteration
$$x_{n+1} = \sqrt{10x_n - 18}$$
to obtain the solution correct to four decimal places.

3 The diagram shows the graphs of
$$y = x^3 \text{ and}$$
$$y = 3x^2 - 7x + 11$$

$y = x^3 - 7x + 1$

$y = x^3$

It also shows that the two graphs intersect when x is approximately equal to 2, that is, $x = 2$ is an approximate solution to the equation
$$x^3 = 3x^2 - 7x + 11$$

(a) Show that the above equation can be re-arranged into
$$x = \sqrt{3x^` - 7 + \frac{11}{x}}$$

(b) Use the iteration
$$x_{n+1} = \sqrt{3x_n - 7 + \frac{11}{x_n}}$$
three times to improve the approximate solution solution of $x = 2$.

Iterations that do not work

We saw on the previous page that the equation
$$x^2 - 8x - 11 = 0$$
has a solution in the region of $x = 9$,
and by using the re-arrangement
$$x = \sqrt{8x + 11} \quad \text{and iteration} \quad x_{n+1} = \sqrt{8x_n + 11}$$
we improved the approximate solution to about
$$x = 9.16$$
The re-arrangement from $x^2 - 8x - 11 = 0$ to
$$x = \sqrt{8x + 11}$$
is not the only one we could have made.
For instance, we could have moved in the direction
$$x^2 - 8x - 11 = 0 \quad \text{or} \quad x^2 = 8x + 11$$
$$x = \frac{8x + 11}{x} \quad \text{or} \quad x = 8 + \frac{11}{x}$$
This re-arrangement would give the iteration
$$x_{n+1} = 8 + \frac{11}{x_n}$$
Starting with $x_1 = 9$, the approximate solution from the graph, we get
$$x_2 = 8 + \frac{11}{9} \qquad \text{so} \quad x_2 = 9.222\,222\,222$$
then
$$x_3 = 8 + \frac{11}{9.222\,222\,2222} \quad \text{so} \quad x_3 = 9.192\,771$$
and taking this one step further, check, that
$$x_4 = 9.196\,592$$
So again this process moves in on the correct solution.
But we could also re-arrange $x^2 - 8x - 11 = 0$ to
$$8x = x^2 - 11 \quad \text{or} \quad x = \frac{x^2 - 11}{8} \quad \text{suggesting the iteration}$$
$$x_{n+1} = \frac{x_n{}^2 - 11}{8} \quad \text{which we again start with } x_1 = 9$$
giving
$$x_2 = \frac{81 - 11}{8} = 8.75 \quad \text{and} \quad x_3 = \frac{8.75^2 - 11}{8} = 8.195\,3125$$
$$x_4 = \frac{8.195\,312\,5^2 - 11}{8} = 7.020\,393\,372$$
This sequence of results does not appear to be tending towards the correct solution. Sequences which tend towards the correct solution are said to **converge**. The ones that do otherwise are said to **diverge**.

You do not need to know any of the theory about convergent and divergent sequences, it is beyond the syllabus but you do need to know that the different possibilities can happen and recognise them.

4 It is known that the equation
$$x^2 - 6x - 2 = 0$$
has a solution in the vicinity of $x = 6$.

(a) Show that this equation can be re-arranged into any of the three equations:

   (i) $x = \sqrt{6x + 2}$ (ii) $x = 6 + \frac{2}{x}$ (iii) $x = \frac{x^2 - 2}{6}$

(b) Use each of these to form the basis of an iterative process.

(c) Check each process for convergence.

(d) Use one of the processes to obtain the solution of the equation
$$x^2 - 6x - 2 = 0$$
which is in the vicinity of $x = 6$, correct to two decimal places.

5 (a) By examining the graphs of
$$y = x^3 \text{ and } y = 10x + 1$$
or otherwise, show that the equation
$$x^3 - 10x - 1 = 0$$
has a solution in the vicinity of $x = 3.5$

(b) Show that the equation $x^3 - 10x - 1 = 0$ can be re-arranged to:

   (i) $x = \sqrt{10 + \frac{1}{x}}$

   (ii) $x = \frac{x^3 - 1}{10}$

   (iii) $x = \frac{10}{x} + \frac{1}{x^2}$

(c) Use each equation from (b) to set up an iterative process.

(d) Check whether or not the iterative process converges.

(e) Use a convergent iteration to obtain the solution, in the vicinity of $x = 3.5$, of the equation
$$x^3 - 10x - 1 = 0$$

6 (a) Check by any means that the equation
$$x^4 - x - 17 = 0$$
has a solution in the vicinity of $x = 2$

(b) Re-arrange the equation into three different forms.

(c) Use each form to set up an iterative process.

(d) Use a convergent process to find the solution, in the vicinity of $x = 2$, to the equation
$$x^4 - x - 17 = 0$$

Swings and roundabouts

This flow diagram will generate a sequence of numbers:

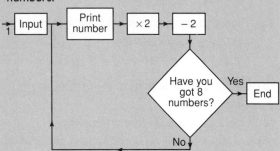

Starting with an input of 1 the flow diagram generates this sequence of numbers:

$1, 0, \bar{2}, \bar{6}, \bar{14}, \bar{30}, \bar{62}, \bar{126}$

The sequence is generated by using the first answer to generate the second and the second to generate the third and so on on a continuous loop. This process is called an **iterative process**.

This diagram shows a simple iterative process.

Each output becomes the input for the next calculation.

```
   ┌──────────────┐
   │    Input     │
   └──────────────┘
          ↓
   ┌──────────────┐   Loop
   │ Calculation  │
   └──────────────┘
          ↓
   ┌──────────────┐
   │    Output    │
   └──────────────┘
```

Iterative process have been known for thousands of years. However since the introduction of computers their use has grown and they have now become a very important process used in many different areas.

The first output is called U_1, the second U_2, the third U_3 and so on.

Note the use of subscript and U_{n+2} means the (U_{n+2})th term and *not* $Un + 2$.

Using this subscript notation the sequence generated is written:

$$U_1 = \text{start} \quad = 1$$
$$U_2 = 2U_1 - 2 = 0$$
$$U_3 = 2U_2 - 2 = \bar{2}$$
$$U_4 = 2U_3 - 2 = \bar{6}$$
$$U_5 = 2U_4 - 2 = \bar{14}$$
$$U_6 = 2U_5 - 2 = \bar{30}$$
$$U_7 = 2U_6 - 2 = \bar{62}$$
$$U_8 = 2U_7 - 2 = \bar{126}$$

1 (a) Using the first flow diagram write down the values of U_9, U_{10}, U_{11} and U_{12}.

(b) Write down but do not work out the relationship between U_{100} and U_{99}.

2 Write down the relationship between:

(a) U_n and U_{n-1}

(b) U_{n+1} and U_n

The 'gap' between sucessive terms of the series generated is getting larger and larger. There is no apparent limit to which it appears to be heading. Each term is getting greater negative.

This type of sequence **diverges** and is called a **diverging sequence**.

Graphs to show the trend of sequences that diverge look like this:

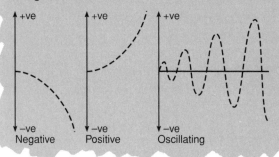

Negative   Positive   Oscillating

3 (a) Use the flow diagram to generate a sequence of numbers starting with a U_1 value of 4.

(b) Write down the main difference between the two sequences.

(c) What happens if you start with $U_1 = 2$?

This flow diagram also generates a sequence of numbers by an iterative process:

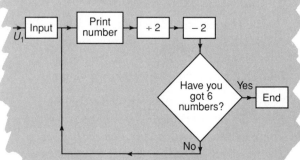

4 (a) Write down the output number generated by this flow diagram when the input number is 1.

(b) Copy and complete this number pattern giving the full calculator display:

U_1 = start = 1
U_2 = -2 = -1.5
U_3 = -2 = -2.75
U_4
U_5
U_6

5 (a) Work out the value of U_7, U_8, U_9 and U_{10}.

(b) Write down but do not work out the relationship between U_{50} and U_{49}.

6 Write down the relationship between:

(a) U_n and U_{n-1}

(b) U_{n+1} and U_n

7 Write down what you notice about the difference of successive terms of the sequence.

The sequence appears to be heading closer and closer to ¯4. When a sequence **converges** towards a number it is called a **converging sequence**. The number ¯4 is called the **limit of the sequence**.

8 The iteration formula $U_{n+1} = \dfrac{(U_n + 5)}{2}$ can be represented by this flow diagram:

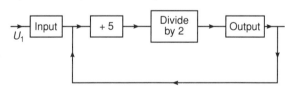

(a) Starting with an input value U_1 = 3, write down the values of U_2, U_3, U_4, U_5, U_6 and U_7.

(b) Is the sequence generated converging or diverging?

(c) If the sequence is converging suggest the limit of the sequence.

(d) Sketch a graph to show the trend of the sequence.

9 The iteration formula for a sequence is

$$U_{n+1} = \frac{U_n - 2}{0.5}$$

(a) Draw a flow diagram to show this formula.

(b) Calculate the first six terms with a starting value U_1 of 2.5.

(c) Is the sequence generated converging or diverging?

(d) Sketch a graph to show the trend of the sequence.

10 (a) Write down the iteration formula represented by this flow diagram:

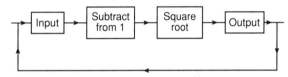

(a) Starting with a U_1 value of 0.5 calculate the value of U_1, U_2 and U_3.

(b) Continue calculating values of U_n as far as U_{12}.

(d) Is the sequence generated converging or diverging? Comment on the trend of the sequence.

(e) Sketch a graph to show the trend of the sequence.

11 A sequence is to be generated from the iteration formula $U_{n+1} = \dfrac{U_n + 3}{2}$

(a) Starting with a value of 7 generate a sequence of eight terms.

(b) Suggest a possible limit of this sequence.

(c) Now generate a second sequence starting with your suggested limit from part **(b)**.

(d) Can you explain why you get the sequence you did in part **(c)**?

12 An iteration formula is given as $U_{n+1} = 2(U_n)^2$. Investigate the type of sequences generated from a starting value of:

(a) $U_1 < 0.5$ **(b)** ¯$0.5 < U_1 < 0.5$

(c) $U_1 > 0.5$ **(d)** $U_1 = 0.5$

13 Use your answer to question 12 to solve the equation $x = 2x^2$.

Andrew is testing a new car on a test circuit. The distance D metres that the car travels in a time T seconds is recorded.

Time T (seconds)	2	3	4	5	6	7
Distance D (metres)	50	75	110	155	210	275

You need graph paper.

1 On graph paper draw these axes and a graph of D against T. Comment on the shape of the graph.

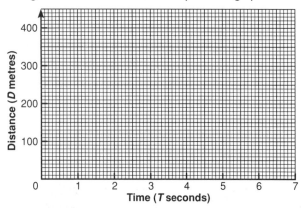

Andrew thought that the relationship between D and T might be of the form $D = mT^2 + c$.

This theory can be checked by relating the suspected law against the linear law $y = mx + c$.

$$D = m\,T^2 + c$$
$$y = m\,x + c$$

2 If Andrew is right what type of graph would you get if D is plotted against T^2?

3 (a) Copy and complete this table:

T^2	4	9				
D	50	75	110	155	210	275

   (b) Test Andrew's theory by drawing a graph of D against T^2. Comment on your findings.
   (c) Find the values of m and c.
   (d) Express the relationship between distance and time in the form $D = mT^2 + c$.
   (e) How far did the car travel in 4.8 seconds?

4 Two variables are connected by the law $t^2 = aS + d$. This table shows pairs of values of two variables.

S	12	33	61	98	142	194
t	4·2	7·75	10·7	13·8	16·7	19·5

Comparing this relationship with $y = mx + c$.

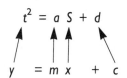

$$t^2 = a\,S + d$$
$$y = m\,x + c$$

   (a) Draw up a second table of results of t^2 against S.
   (b) By drawing a suitable graph confirm that the relationship $t^2 = aS + d$ and find the values of a and d.
   (c) Write down the formula connecting t and S.
   (d) Use the formula to find S when $t = 5$ and t when $S = 100$.

5 It is thought that two variables P and Q are connected by the relationship

$$P = m\sqrt{Q} + c$$

To confirm this theory the suspected law must be compared with $y = mx + c$.

   (a) Write down the two variables that must be plotted to confirm the relationship $P = m\sqrt{Q} + c$.
   (b) These values were obtained by experimental means:

Q	4	9	16	25	36	49
P	3·5	4·8	6·1	7·6	9·1	10·4

Copy and complete this second table of results:

$\sqrt{Q}$	2	3	4	5		
P	3·5	4·8			9·1	10·4

   (c) Draw a graph of P against $\sqrt{Q}$ and find the values of m and c.
   (d) Write down the relationship connecting P and Q.
   (e) Find the value of P when $Q = 18$.
   (f) Find the value of Q when $P = 8$.

6 Owen Davis is an investment adviser. He sells investment policies to his clients. During one period the value of the investments sold and the commission charged were:

Value of policy ÷ 1000	£1·1	£2·4	£3·6	£4·2	£5·5
Commission charged	£34	£72	£170	£252	£530

Roy, a client of Owen Davis suspects that value of the investment and the commission charged are connected by a law of the form

$C = aP^3 + b$

where C = commission charged
P = value of policy ÷ 1000
a and b are constants

(a) Construct a table giving values of P^3 and C.

(b) By drawing a suitable graph confirm that the relationship is $C = aP^3 + b$ and find the values of a and b.

(c) Write down the relationship between the commission charged and the value of the policy.

(d) Find the value of a policy when a commission of £200 is charged.

(e) What commission will be charged on an investment of £5200?

7 Two variables are connected by an equation of the form $A = \frac{m}{S} + c$

S	1·0	2·5	3·0	3·5	4·0	5·0
A	10·5	4·5	3·8	3·3	3·0	2·5

(a) By writing the equation $A = m\left(\frac{1}{S}\right) + c$ show how it can be compared with $y = mx + c$.

(b) By drawing a suitable graph find the values of m and c.

Challenge

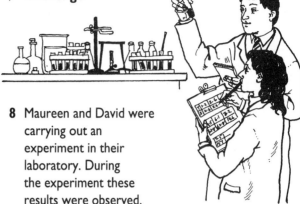

8 Maureen and David were carrying out an experiment in their laboratory. During the experiment these results were observed.

T	1·2	2·6	3·9	4·5	6·1	7·2	7·5
S	2·6	22·6	48·6	62·8	108	146	157

After much thought Maureen suspected that the law connecting T and S might be of the form

$S = mT^2 + 3mT + c$

(a) Show that $S = m(T^2 + 3T) + c$

(b) By completing the square show that $S = m(T + 1·5)^2 + k$ where $k = c - 2·25m$

(c) Show how this equation can be compared with the linear equation $y = mx + c$.

(d) On graph paper make a copy of these axes:

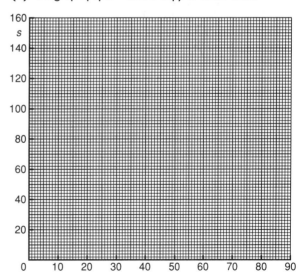

(e) By plotting S against a second variable show that Maureen's conjecture is true.

(f) Use your graph to find the values of m and k.

(g) Express the law in the form
(i) $S = m(T + 1·5)^2 + k$
(ii) $S = mT^2 + 3mT + c$

A train travels for 4 hours at a constant speed of 50 km/h. This travel graph shows its progress.

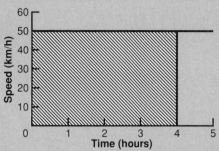

The shaded area under the graph shows the distance travelled by the train.

The area under the graph = 50 km/h × 4 hours
Distanced by the train = 200 kilometres

Distance travelled = Area under a speed-time graph

You need graph paper.

I This is a graph of a car leaving a set of traffic lights.

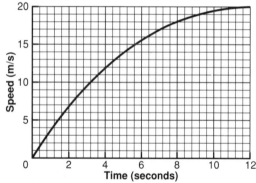

(a) What is the speed of the car after 8 seconds?
(b) Use the trapezium rule to find the distance travelled by the car in 12 seconds.

2 The car travels for 2 minutes at a constant speed of 20 m/s before coming to a second set of traffic lights which are on red. The speed of the car as it slows down is given by $20 - 0.2t^2$.
(a) Find how long it takes the car to come to a stop.
(b) Draw a speed-time graph to show the speed of the car as it slows down from 20 m/s until it comes to a stop.
(c) Use the trapezium rule to find the distance travelled during the slowing down stage.

3 The speed of a train leaving a station is shown in this table:

Time (seconds)	0	2	4	5	6	8
Speed (m/s)	0	2	12	20	30	56

(a) Draw a speed-time graph to show this information.
(b) Find the acceleration after 3 seconds.
(c) Use the trapezium rule to find the distance travelled by the train during the first 8 seconds.

4 This graph shows how the rate of flow of water from a shower head varied during a period of 2 minutes.

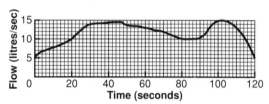

Use the trapezium rule to find the volume of water that flowed from the shower head during the two minute period.

5 This sketch shows the speed/time of a 100 metre runner for the first 4 seconds.

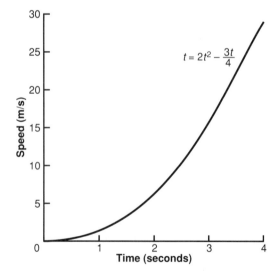

$t = 2t^2 - \dfrac{3t}{4}$

Calculate the distance covered by the runner.

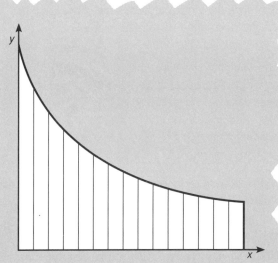

The smaller the width of the trapezia the more accurate the approximation is to the true area.

Unfortunately this requires tedious and time consuming calculations. But since the calculations are all similar the numerical work can be undertaken by a computer.

This computer program calculates the area under the curve $y = 2 + 0.5x^2$ using the trapezium rule.

```
10   INPUT"LOWER VALUE OF X "LX
20   INPUT"UPPER VALUE OF X "UX
30   INPUT"WIDTH OF TRAPEZIUM" W
40   FOR X = LX TO UX-W STEP W
50   Y1=2 + 0.5*X*X
60   Y2=2 + 0.5*(X+W)*(X+W)
70   A = W*((Y1+Y2)/2)80   AT=AT + A
80   AT=AT + A
90   NEXT
100  PRINT"APPROXIMATE AREA = " AT
```

6 (a) Use this program to find the area under the curve of $y = 2 + 0.5x^2$ between $x = 0$ and $x = 6$ for trapeziums widths of:
   (i) 0·5 **(ii)** 0·2 **(iii)** 0·1
(b) Compare your answers with those you obtained for question **4** of *Spring the trap*, page 48.

7 This circle has a radius of 1 unit. Write down correct to 5 decimal places the area of the circle.

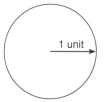

1 unit

This diagram shows a quarter of a circle drawn on a coordinate diagram. The equation of the curve is $y = \sqrt{1 - x^2}$

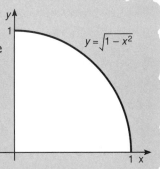

$y = \sqrt{1 - x^2}$

To use the upper bound/lower bound computer program on page 48 and the Trapezium Rule program to find the area of the complete circle change lines 50 and 60 on both programs:

```
50 Y1 =SQR(1-X*X)
60 Y2 =SQR(1-(X+W)*(X+W))
```

and line 100 on the Trapezium program to

```
100 "APPROXIMATE AREA " 4*AT
```

and line 120 on the Upper bound/lower bound program to

```
120 "APPROXIMATE AREA " 4*(UT + UL)/2
```

8 Find the maximum width of the rectangle or trapezium necessary to calculate the area of the circle correct to 5 decimal places using:
   (a) the upper/lower bound program
   (b) the trapezium rule program.
   (c) Compare and comment on the two methods.

9 The following results were found when investigating the motion of a particle moving from rest.

Time t (seconds)	0	1	2	3	4	5	6
Speed v (m/s)	0	3		15			48

(a) Find a possible rule connecting t and v.
(b) Use the rule to complete the table.
(c) Find the acceleration at:
   (i) 2 seconds **(ii)** 3·5 seconds
(d) Find the distance travelled in the first 6 seconds.
(e) Find the distance travelled between $t = 2$ and $t = 5$.

Let's get out of the joint

Tygers are promoting a new drink called Ion Blue. Carol's job is to design the size of tin can for the new drink.

For ease of manufacture the can must be in the shape of a cylinder.

The volume of a cylinder is proportional to its height.
$$V \propto h$$

The volume of the cylinder is also proportional to its diameter squared.
$$V \propto d^2$$

This means that volume is proportional to the height and the diameter squared.
$$V \propto hd^2$$

When a variable is proportional to two or more other variables it is called **joint variation**.

I What is the effect on the volume of a can if:
  (a) the height trebles but the diameter remains constant
  (b) the diameter halves but the height remains constant?

What would be the effect on the volume if the height trebles and the diameter is halved at the same time?

Old volume $V \propto hd^2$ New volume $V_n \propto h_n d_n^2$

New height $h_n = 3h$ $V_n \propto 3h\, d_n^2$

New diameter $d_n = \dfrac{d}{2}$ $V_n \propto 3h\left(\dfrac{d}{2}\right)^2$

$$V_n \propto 3h\left(\dfrac{d^2}{4}\right)$$

$$V_n \propto \dfrac{3}{4}\, hd^2$$

But $(hd^2) \propto$ old volume

The new volume is three quarters the old volume.

If the height trebles and the diameter halves the volume goes down by a factor of 0·75.

2 Calculate the effect on the volume of the can if the height halves and the diameter trebles.

The volume V of a balloon is directly proportional to its temperature t and inversely proportional to the pressure P inside it.

3 Write down a proportional statement connecting the volume V to the other two variables.

The pressure inside the balloon decreases from 800 millibars to 600 millibars and at the same time the temperature rises from 50°C to 75°C.

4 (a) Write down the factor by which the pressure decreases.
  (b) Write down the factor by which the temperature increases.
  (c) What is the effect of these two changes on the volume?
  (d) What is the new volume if the old volume was 480 m^3?

The heat W watts produced by an electric fire is directly proportional to the square of the voltage V volts and inversely proportional to the length of the element l cm.

5 Write down a proportional statement connecting W watts and the other two variables.

6 What is the effect on the heat output if:
  (a) the voltage only drops by 10%
  (b) the length of the element is increased by 10%
  (c) both changes take place simultaneously.

7 If the heat output W must remain constant, calculate the percentage change in the voltage if the length of the element is increased by 44%.

8 Given that $X \propto y\sqrt{Z}$ and $X = 12$ when $y = 40$ and $Z = 625$. Calculate X when y increases to 50 and Z decreases by 20%.

Mr Brookes wrote
this function on
the blackboard:

$$f(x) = x^2 - 1$$

The function $f(x)$ can be thought of as a flow
diagram.

x → [Square] → [− 1] → $x^2 - 1$
Input   Output

This means that every input value of x changes to an
output value of $x^2 - 1$.

An input of 5 gives an output of $5^2 - 1 = 24$

This is written as $f(4) = 24$.

1 When $f(x) = x^2 - 1$ find:
  (a) $f(4)$ (b) $f(-4)$
  (c) $f(0·5)$ (d) $f(-6)$

Given that $f(x) = x^2 - 1$ find the value of x when
$f(x) = 15$.

This means $15 = x^2 - 1$
             $x^2 = 16$
             $x = 4$ or $^-4$

2 When $f(x) = x^2 - 1$ find the values of x when:
  (a) $f(x) = 35$ (b) $f(x) = 99$
  (c) $f(x) = 5·25$

3 If $h(x) = x(x-1)$ find:
  (a) $h(^-3)$ (b) $h(1)$
  (c) the values of x when $h(x) = 2$.

4 Draw a flow diagram to represent these functions:
  (a) $f(x) = 6x - 2$
  (b) $g(x) = x^2 + 6$
  (c) $h(x) = x^2 + 6x$ (Hint: complete the square)
  (d) $j(x) = x^2 + 6x + 9$
  (e) $k(x) = x^2 + 6x - 9$

5 If $f(x) = x^2 - 8x + 14$ find:
  (a) $f(^-3)$
  (b) the values of x for which $f(x) = ^-2$

When functions are combined they are called
composite functions.

If $f(x) = x^2 + 1$ and $g(x) = 2x - 3$ then the
composite function $fg(x)$ can best be seen by
considering flow diagrams.

The flow diagram for $g(x)$ is:

→ [x 2] → [− 3] →

The flow diagram for $f(x)$ is:

→ [Square] → [+ 1] →

The flow diagram for $fg(x)$ is:

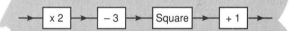

→ [x 2] → [− 3] → [Square] → [+ 1] →

Starting with input of x an output of $(2x- 3)^2 + 1$ is
obtained.

$$fg(x) = (2x - 3)^2 + 1$$
$$= 4x^2 - 12x + 9 + 1$$
$$= 4x^2 - 12x + 10$$

It is not always necessary to draw flow diagrams.

$$fg(x) = f(g(x))$$
$$= f(2x - 3)$$
$$= (2x - 3)^2 + 1$$
$$= 4x^2 - 12x + 10$$

> Note that $fg(x)$ means g operates on x first and
> f then operates on $g(x)$.

6 (a) Calculate $gf(x)$.
  (b) Compare your answer with $fg(x)$ and write
  down what you notice.

7 If $f(x) = 2x + 5$, $g(x) = 3x - 1$ and $h(x) = 5x$, find:
  (a) $fg(2)$ (b) $gf(2)$ (c) $fh(^-4)$
  (d) $hf(x)$ (e) $fg(x)$ (f) $gg(x)$

8 If $f(x) = x^2 + 4x + 4$ and $g(x) = 2x^2 - 1$ find:
  (a) $fg(x)$ (b) $gf(x)$ (c) $ff(x)$

The graphs of $y = f(x)$

If y is a function of x written $y = f(x)$ and $f(x) = x^2 + 2x$ then a sketch of $y = f(x)$ would look like this:

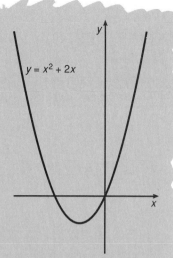

$y = x^2 + 2x$

But what would a graph of $y = -f(x)$ look like? What $y = -f(x)$ means is that each value of y changes to $-y$.

A sketch of $y = -f(x)$ looks like this:

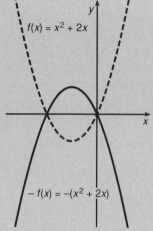

$f(x) = x^2 + 2x$

$-f(x) = -(x^2 + 2x)$

$y = -f(x)$ is a reflection in the x-axis of $y = f(x)$

1 This is a graph of $y = f(x)$ where $f(x) = 2x + 1$

    (a) Write down the equation of $y = -f(x)$

    (b) Sketch a graph of $y = f(-x)$

    (c) Write down the equation of $y = f(-x)$

    (d) Describe in terms of a transformation the relationship between $y = f(x)$ and $y = f(-x)$.

$y = 2x + 1$

2 y is a function of x and $f(x) = x^2 - 4x + 4$.

    (a) Write $x^2 - 4x + 4$ in its 'completing the square' form.

    (b) Make a sketch of $y = f(x)$.

    (c) On the same diagram sketch:

        (i) $y = -f(x)$ **(ii)** $y = f(-x)$

    (d) Write down the equations of the two functions $y = -f(x)$ and $y = f(-x)$.

This is a sketch of the function of $f(x) = x^2 - 6x$. In the form $(x + a)^2 + b$ the function is $(x - 3)^2 - 9$.

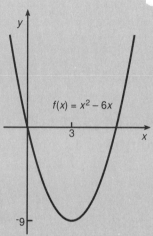

$f(x) = x^2 - 6x$

The graph of the function $y = f(x) + 2$ is a graph of $y = f(x)$ translated 2 units in the y direction.

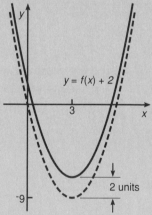

$y = f(x) + 2$

2 units

The equation of $y = f(x) + 2$ will be $y = (x^2 - 6x) + 2 = x^2 - 6x + 2$

3 **(a)** Sketch a graph of the function $y = f(x) - 3$.

    (b) Write down the equation of this function.

    (c) On the same diagram sketch the function $y = f(x) + 5$

    (d) Write down the equation of this second function.

4 y is a function of x and $f(x) = x^2 + 6x - 4$.

(a) Make sketch of this function.

(b) Write in completed square form:

   (i) $y = f(x)$

   (ii) $y = -f(x) + 1$

   (iii) $y = f(-x) - 3$

   (iv) $y = -f(x) - 7$

This is a sketch of the function $f(x) = x^2 - 6x$.

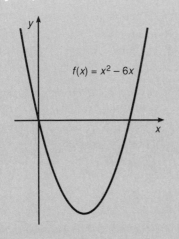

$f(x) = x^2 - 6x$

The function $y = f(x + 3)$ means that each value of x becomes $x + 3$. The function $y = f(x + 3)$ means $y = (x + 3)^2 - 6(x + 3)$

5 (a) Copy and complete this table:

x	0	1	2	3	4	5
$f(x)$						
$f(x + 3)$						

(b) On the same graph paper draw accurate graphs of $y = f(x)$ and $y = f(x + 3)$.

6 (a) Expand and simplify the expression $y = (x + 3)^2 - 6(x + 3)$.

(b) Write your simplified expression in the form $y = (x + a)^2 + b$ where a and b are integers.

(c) Describe in terms of a geometrical transformation the relationship between $y = f(x)$ and $y = f(x + 3)$.

7 (a) Describe in geometrical transformation terms how the function $f(x)$ can be transformed into the function $f(x - 1) + 2$.

(b) If $f(x) = x^2 - 6x$ sketch the function $f(x - 1) + 2$.

A **turning point** of a graph is where its gradient changes from positive to negative or negative to positive.

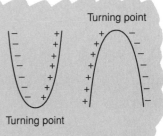

Graphs can have **maximum** turning points

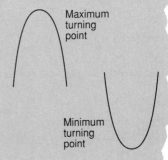

or **minimum** turning points.

This sketch of the function $y = f(x)$ where $f(x) = x^2 - 4x + 8$ has a minumum turning point at $(2, 4)$.

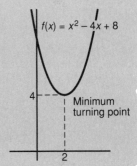

$f(x) = x^2 - 4x + 8$

Minimum turning point

8 Given the function $y = f(x)$ where $f(x)$ is equal to $x^2 - 4x + 8$, write down the coordinates of the turning point of each of these functions, stating if they are maxima or minima:

(a) $y = -f(x)$

(b) $y = -f(x + 2)$

(c) $y = f(x - 2)$

(d) $y = f(x) + 4$

(e) $y = -f(x) + 4$

(f) $y = f(x - 2) + 6$

(g) $y = -f(x - 2) - 6$

9 (a) By completing the square, or otherwise, write down in terms of geometrical transformations, the relationship between the functions $y = x^2 + 8x - 26$ and $y = x^2 + 2x - 21$.

(b) Given that $f(x) = x^2 + 8x - 26$ express $y = x^2 + 2x - 21$ in terms of $y = f(x)$.

If $y = f(x)$ then the graph of $y = -f(x)$ will be $y = f(x)$ reflected in the x-axis.

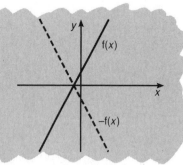

1 Write down the equation of the image of $y = 3x + 1$ reflected in the x-axis.

2 Copy and complete this mapping diagram:

$f(x) = 3x + 1$ $-f(x)$
(0, 1) $\longrightarrow$ (0, ¯1)
(1, 4) $\longrightarrow$
(2, 7)
(3, 10)
(4, 13)
(x, y)

If $y = f(x)$ the relationship between the coordinates of $f(x)$ with those of $-f(x)$ is:

$x \longrightarrow x$ $y \longrightarrow -y$

This relationship can be used to find the image equation of $-f(x)$.

If $y = f(x)$ and $f(x) = 4x^2 - 5$ then the equation of $-f(x)$ is $-y = 4x^2 - 5$
$y = -4x^2 + 5$

3 Use this relationship to find the image equation of $-f(x)$ when:

(a) $f(x) = 3x - 6$ **(b)** $f(x) = (x + 4)^2 - 1$
(c) $f(x) = \dfrac{12}{x}$ **(d)** $f(x) = 6 - x$

If $y = f(x)$ then the graph of $y = f(-x)$ will be $y = f(x)$ reflected in the y-axis.

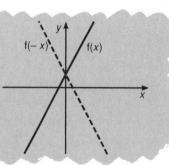

4 (a) Describe the relationship between the coordinates of $f(x)$ and $f(-x)$.
(b) Express the relationship in the form:

$x \longrightarrow ?$ $y \longrightarrow ?$

5 Write down the equation of the image of $y = 3x + 1$ after a reflection in the line $y = x$.

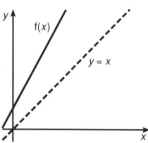

6 Copy and complete this mapping diagram:

$f(x) = 3x + 1$ Image
(0, 1) $\longrightarrow$ (1, 0)
(1, 4) $\longrightarrow$
(2, 7)
(3, 10)
(x, y)

7 (a) Describe the relationship between the coordinates of $f(x)$ and the image coordinates.
(b) Show this relationship in the form:

$x \longrightarrow ?$ $y \longrightarrow ?$

8 Use the relationship you have found to show algebraically that the image equation of $y = 3x + 1$ reflected in the line $y = x$ is $y = \dfrac{x - 1}{3}$

9 Find the equation of the image of $f(x)$ after a reflection in the line $y = x$ when:

(a) $f(x) = 6x - 1$ **(b)** $f(x) = x^2 + 4$
(c) $f(x) = 6 - x$ **(d)** $f(x) = \dfrac{12}{x}$
(e) $f(x) = (x + 2)^2$ **(f)** $f(x) = x^2 + 6x - 12$

There is a special relationship between $y = f(x)$ and its image function when reflected in the line $y = x$. They are the inverse or opposite of each other. That is one undoes the effect of the other.

10 (a) For each of the functions in question **9** find $f(4)$.
(b) Show that if the answer to $f(4)$ is 'fed in' to the image function you always get back to 4.
(c) Show that this is also true for $f(x)$ where x is a value of your own choice.

The inverse of a function is the function that reverses the action of the first function.

If $f(x) = 2x$ →　×2　→ the inverse will be

$g(x) = \dfrac{x}{2}$ →　÷2　→

If $f(x)$ is a function the inverse function is denoted $f^{-1}(x)$. **Note this does not mean** $\dfrac{1}{f(x)}$.

1 Write down the inverse of these functions:
  (a) $f(x) = 3x$ **(b)** $f(x) = 2x + 1$
  (c) $f(x) = \dfrac{x + 1}{3}$

Sometimes drawing flow diagrams helps to find inverse functions.

If $f(x) = \dfrac{2x - 4}{5}$ find $f^{-1}(x)$.

The flow diagram for $f(x)$ is:

x →　×2　→　−4　→　÷5　→

The reverse instructions are:

←　÷2　←　+4　←　×5　←　x

Which gives $f^{-1}(x) = \dfrac{5x + 4}{2}$

If $f(x)$ and $f^{-1}(x)$ are inverses of each other then one should undo or reverse the action of the other.

2 (a) For the function $f(x) = \dfrac{2x - 4}{5}$ find the value of $f(12)$.
  (b) Use your answer to part **(a)** to find the value of f^{-1} (your value).

3 Find the inverse functions $f^{-1}(x)$ of:
  (a) $\dfrac{3x + 1}{2}$ **(b)** $3 - x$ **(c)** $\dfrac{4 - 2x}{3}$

Here is another method of finding the inverse of a function as used in *Reflect on the problem*.

If $f(x) = \dfrac{2x - 4}{5}$ the inverse function $f^{-1}(x)$ can be found using this method.

Let $f(x) = y$ which means $y = \dfrac{2x - 4}{5}$

and $f^{-1}(x) = x$ defined as $x = \dfrac{2y - 4}{5}$

Rearrange the formula $x = \dfrac{2y - 4}{5}$

to make y the subject $y = \dfrac{5x + 4}{2}$

This method is particularly useful when it is difficult to construct a flow diagram.

4 Find the inverse function $f^{-1}(x)$ of:

  (a) $f(x) = 4x + 2$ **(b)** $f(x) = \dfrac{3 - x}{2}$

  (c) $f(x) = \dfrac{4}{x}$ **(d)** $f(x) = \dfrac{x + 1}{x - 1}$

  (e) $f(x) = \dfrac{4 + 2x}{x + 2}$ **(f)** $f(x) = \dfrac{3 - 2x}{4 + 3x}$

$f(x) = 3x + 5$, $g(x) = 2x - 3$ and $h(x) = \dfrac{1}{x}$

5 Find:
  (a) $fh(3)$ **(b)** $fgh(2)$ **(c)** $hhh(3)$
  (d) $f^{-1}(x)$ **(e)** $g^{-1}(x)$ **(f)** $h^{-1}(x)$
  (g) $hf^{-1}(x)$ **(h)** $(hf)^{-1}(x)$ **(i)** $(gh)^{-1}(x)$

6 Find:
  (a) $f^{-1}g^{-1}(4)$ and $f^{-1}g^{-1}(x)$
  (b) $(fg)^{-1}(4)$ and $(fg)^{-1}(x)$
  (c) $(gf)^{-1}(4)$ and $(gf)^{-1}(x)$
  (d) Write down what you notice.

7 Given that $f(x) = 3x + 1$ and $g(x) = x^2 + 4$ show that:
  (a) $f^{-1}g^{-1} = (gf)^{-1}$
  (b) $f^{-1}g^{-1} = (fg)^{-1}$
  (c) Find $gg^{-1}(x)$.

The School Council

Mrs Hallam is the Head of Year 11 at Russell High School.
She needs to choose two students from Year 11 to sit on the School Council.

Suppose, for a moment that there were only ten students in Year 11
and that their names were:
Andrew, Bridget, Claire, Derek, Eve, Fiona, Gaby, Henry, Ian, Joanne.
Then one such pairing could be:
Andrew and Bridget (which is the same as Bridget and Andrew)
whilst another different pairing could be:
Fiona and Joanne.

1   Show that if there are only ten students in Year 11 then Mrs Hallam has
    a total of 45 different choices of two people – or 45 different pairings.

2   How many different pairings would Mrs Hallam have if there were:
    (a) 6 students in Year 11   **(b)** 12 students in Year 11
    (c) 30 students in Year 11   **(d)** 50 students in Year 11?

3   Investigate the number of different pairings Mrs Hallam could choose
    for different numbers of students in Year 11. Illustrate your work with
    justified answers for the number of different pairings when there are:
    (a) 100 students in Year 11   **(b)** 150 students in Year 11
    (c) 200 students in Year 11   **(d)** n students in Year 11.

4   What is the least number of students there would be in Year 11 if
    Mrs Hallam was to be able to choose from at least 1000 different pairings?

5   On the last day of the summer holidays a new student signs on the school roll
    and by so doing increases the number of students in Year 11 from n to $n + 1$.
    How many possible extra pairings will this create for Mrs Hallam?

6   $P(n)$ is defined as the number of pairings from n students in Year 11.
    Obtain expressions for:
    (a) $P(n + 1) - P(n)$ **(b)** $P(n + 2) - P(n)$
    (c) $P(n + m) - P(n)$ **(d)** $P(2n) - P(n)$
    These expressions must be in terms of n (and m for **(c)**) and must be
    simplified as much as possible.

● **Remember**

This diagram shows a sector of a circle. The angle at the centre of the circle is written as θ.

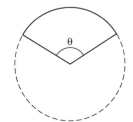

The arc length from A to B is given by

Arc length = $\dfrac{\pi r \theta}{180}$

The area of the sector is given by

Area of sector = $\dfrac{\pi r^2 \theta}{360}$

The area of this segment

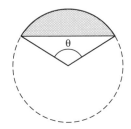

is given by

Area of segment = $\dfrac{\pi r^2 \theta}{360} - \dfrac{1}{2} r^2 \, \text{Sin} \, \theta$

The reasons for these formulae were given on page 113 of book A. Ask your teacher if you are not sure of them.

1

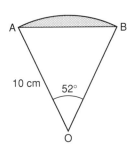

The diagram shows a sector of a circle of radius 10 cm. Calculate:

(a) the length of the arc from A to B

(b) the area of the sector OAB

(c) the area of the shaded segment.

2

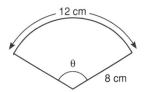

The arc in the above diagram has a length 12 cm. Calculate:

(a) the angle θ   **(b)** the area of the sector.

3

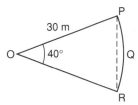

The diagram shows the landing area for a shot put tournament.

OPQR is a sector of a circle, centre O, of radius 30 metres.

(a) Calculate the length of the straight line PR.

(b) Calculate the length of the arc PQR.

(c) Calculate the area of the sector OPQR.

(d) Calculate the area of the segment PQR.

4 The diagram shows a church door.

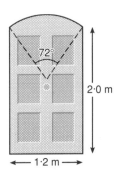

The door is in the shape of a rectangle ABCD with a segment of a circle.

Calculate the area of the door.

5 The top and base of a specially designed box of chocolates are in the shape of a sector of a circle, centre O, as shown below.

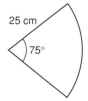

The height of the box is 4·5 cm. Calculate:

(a) the volume of the box

(b) the total surface area of the box.

Defining the trigonometric functions

You will recall that the three trigonometric ratios of Sine, Cosine and Tangent can be defined for a rotating arm of unit length by the diagram:

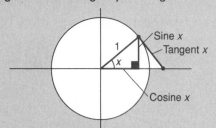

This will be equally true for angles of any size, not merely those which are less than 90°.

So the diagram below shows the values of the three ratios for an angle of 140°

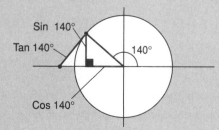

whilst this diagram shows them for the angle of 300°

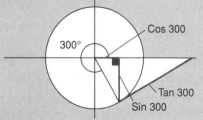

In a right-angled triangle, for an angle x, Sin x, Cos x and Tan x are specifically the ratios of the sides.

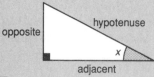

$$Sin\ x = \frac{opposite}{hypotenuse}$$

$$Cos\ x = \frac{adjacent}{hypotenuse}$$

$$Tan\ x = \frac{opposite}{adjacent}$$

For angles beyond 90°, it is more usual to talk about Sin x, Cos x, and Tan x as **functions of the angle x**.

Graphs of the trigonometric functions

The graph of Sin x
For ⁻360° to 360° the graph of Sin x is:

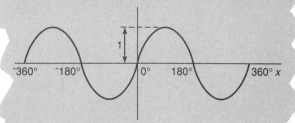

The graph of Cos x
For ⁻360° to 360° the graph of Cos x is:

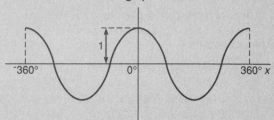

The graph of Tan x
For ⁻360° to 360° the graph of Tan x is:

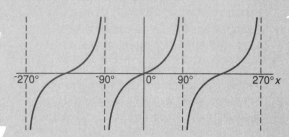

Note
The graph of Sin x is **periodic** in that it **repeats itself every 360°**.

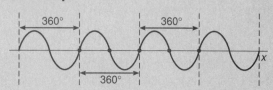

In this case we say that the **period** is 360°.
The graphs of Cos x and Tan x are also periodic.
Cos x has a period of 360°.
Tan x has a period of 180°.

1 (a) Copy and complete the table using intervals of $15°$ for x

$x°$	$2x°$	$\text{Sin } 2x$
0	0	0
15	30	0·5000
30		
.		
.		
.		
360	720	0

(b) Hence draw the graph of Sin x for values of x from $0°$ to $360°$.

(c) What is the period of the Sin $2x$ graph?

2 (a) Using your own values, draw the graph of Cos $2x$ for values of x from $^-360°$ to $360°$.

(b) What is the period of the Cos $2x$ graph?

3 (a) Using your own values, draw the graph of Tan $2x$ for values of x from $^-45°$ to $180°$.

(b) What is the period of the Tan $2x$ graph?

4 (a) Using your own values, draw each of the following graphs for values of x from $^-360°$ to $360°$:

(i) Sin $3x$ **(ii)** Cos $3x$ **(iii)** Tan $3x$

(b) State the period of each graph.

(c) State the maximum and minimum values of Sin $3x$, Cos $3x$ and Tan $3x$.

(d) State the values of x for which these maxima and minima occur.

5 (a) Sketch the graphs of:

(i) Sin $4x$ **(ii)** Cos $4x$ **(iii)** Tan $4x$
for values of x from $^-180°$ to $180°$.

(b) State the period of each graph.

(c) For each graph, state the maximum value, the minimum value and the value of x for which these occur.

6 (a) Draw the graph of 5Sin x for values of x from $^-360°$ to $360°$.

(b) Show that the graph has a maximum value of 5.

(c) Show that the graph has a minimum value of $^-5$.

(d) State the values of x for which the maxima and minima occur.

7 (a) For values of x from $^-360°$ to $360°$, draw the graph of 3Sin $2x$.

(b) Show that the graph has a maximum value of 3.

(c) Find the minimum value of 3Sin $2x$.

(d) State the values of x for which the maxima and minima occur.

8 (a) For values of x from $^-180°$ to $180°$, draw the graph of 2Cos $3x$.

(b) Find:
(i) the maximum value of 2Cos $3x$
(ii) the minimum value of 2Cos $3x$.

(c) State the values of x for which the maxima and minima occur.

9 The equation of a curve is $y = 5\text{Sin } 3x$

(a) Sketch the graph of the curve for values of x from $^-180°$ to $180°$.

(b) What are the maximum and minimum values of y?

(c) For what values of x do these maxima and minima occur?

10 (a) State the maximum value of 4Cos $5x$.

(b) State the minimum value of 4Cos $5x$.

(c) State the values of x for which these maxima and minima occur.

11 The equation of a curve is $y = n\text{Sin } mx$

(a) State the maximum value of y.

(b) State the minimum value of y.

(c) Write down, in terms of m, an expression for the values of x for which the maxima and minima occur.

(d) Show that the period of the graph of y against x is $\dfrac{360°}{m}$.

(e) Sketch the graph of y against x for values of x from $^-360°$ to $360°$.

12 (a) Draw the graph of Sin x + Cos x for values of x from $^-180°$ to $180°$.

(b) From your graph, estimate the maximum value of Sin x + Cos x

(c) From your graph, estimate the minimum value of Sin x + Cos x

(d) From your graph, estimate the values of x for which these maxima and minima occur.

Solving trigonometric equations

We can use our graphs of the trigonometric functions to find complete solutions to some trigonometric equations.

Worked example 1

(a) On the same axes draw the graphs of
$y = \frac{1}{2}$ and $y = \mathrm{Sin}\, x$
for values of x from $^{-}360°$ to $360°$.

(b) Use your calculator and graph to find all the solutions to the equation
$\mathrm{Sin}\, x = \frac{1}{2}$
In the range $^{-}360°$ to $360°$

Solution

(a) The two graphs are:

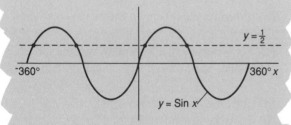

(b) These two graphs cross when
$\mathrm{Sin}\, x = \frac{1}{2}$
at the points indicated by the circles.
By calculator,
$\mathrm{Sin}\, x = \frac{1}{2}$ gives
$\quad x = 30°$
From the graph, the full set of solutions is
$x = 30°, 150°, ^{-}210°, ^{-}330°$

Worked example 2

Find all the solutions to the equation
$3\mathrm{Cos}\, x = 1$
Which lie in the range $^{-}180°$ to $180°$

Solution

From the calculator, the solution between $0°$ and $90°$ is:
$3\mathrm{Cos}\, x = 1$
$\mathrm{Cos}\, x = \frac{1}{3}$
$\mathrm{Cos}\, x = 0{\cdot}333\,333\,333$
$\quad x = 70{\cdot}53°$, correct to 2 decimal places.

Sketches of the graphs of $y = \mathrm{Cos}\, x$ and $y = \frac{1}{3}$ are as shown below:

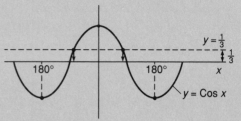

So the full set of solutions is
$x = 70{\cdot}53°$ and $x = ^{-}70{\cdot}53°$

13 (a) Draw the graphs of $y = \mathrm{Sin}\, x$ and $y = 0{\cdot}2$ for values of x from $^{-}360°$ to $360°$.

(b) Use your calculator and the graph to find all solutions to the equation
$\mathrm{Sin}\, x = 0{\cdot}2$
which lie in the range $^{-}360°$ to $360°$.

14 (a) Draw the graphs of $y = \mathrm{Tan}\, x$ and $y = 2$ for values of x from $0°$ to $360°$.

(b) Use your calculator and the graph to find all the solutions to the equation
$\mathrm{Tan}\, x = 2$
in the range $0°$ to $360°$.

15 (a) Draw the graphs of $y = \mathrm{Cos}\, x$ and $y = \frac{x}{90}$ on the same axes, for values of x from $0°$ to $90°$.

(b) Use your graph to show than an approximate solution to the equation
$\mathrm{Cos}\, x = \frac{x}{90}$
is $x = 50°$.

(c) Use your calculator and a trial and improvement method to improve on this solution.

16 (a) On the same axes, draw the graphs of
$y = 3\mathrm{Sin}\, x$ and $y = \frac{x}{60}$
for values of x from $^{-}360°$ to $360°$.

(b) Use your graphs to find all the approximate solutions to the equation
$\mathrm{Sin}\, x = \frac{x}{180}$
which lie in the range from $^{-}360°$ to $360°$.

17 Obtain all the solutions to the equation
$$4\text{Cos}\, x = 1$$
which lie in the range $^-180°$ to $360°$.

18 (a) On the same axes, draw the graphs of
$y = \text{Tan}\, x$ and $y = \text{Cos}\, x$
for values of x from $^-180°$ to $180°$.

(b) Use your graphs to find approximate solutions
to the equation $\text{Tan}\, x = \text{Cos}\, x$.

Advanced trigonometric equations
The following equations are of a standard that is
more advanced than you are likely to meet at
GCSE or Standard Grade levels.

---

19 (a) Show that, for any angle $x°$
$$\text{Tan}\, x = \frac{\text{Sin}\, x}{\text{Cos}\, x} \text{ and } (\text{Sin}\, x)^2 + (\text{Cos}\, x)^2 = 1$$

(b) By writing $\text{Sin}\, x = S$ and $\text{Cos}\, x = C$ show that:
$$C^2 = 1 - S^2$$

(c) Hence show that the equation
$\text{Tan}\, x = \text{Cos}\, x$
reduces to the quadratic equation
$$S^2 + S - 1 = 0$$

(d) Solve this quadratic equation and hence find all
the solutions to the equation
$\text{Tan}\, x = \text{Cos}\, x$
which lie in the range $^-360°$ to $360°$.

20 (a) Show that if $\text{Sin}\, x = 2\text{Cos}\, x$ then
$\text{Tan}\, x = 2$

(b) Hence obtain all the solutions to the equation
$\text{Sin}\, x = 2\text{Cos}\, x$
which lie in the range $0°$ to $360°$.

21 Obtain all the solutions of the equation
$$2(\text{Sin}\, x)^2 - \text{Sin}\, x - 1 = 0$$
which lie in the range $^-360°$ to $360°$.

22 (a) Given that $\text{Sin}\, x$ can be written as S and
$2\text{Tan}\, x = 3\text{Cos}\, x$
show that
$$3S^2 + 2S - 3 = 0$$

(b) Hence find all solutions of the equation that lie
in the range $0° < x < 360°$.

The equation Sin A = Sin B
The most trivial solution to this equation is when
$A = B$. Also, we can refer back to the definition of
$\text{Sin}\, x$ using the rotating arm of unit length:

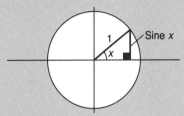

Then for two angles A and B, one situation when
$\text{Sin}\, A = \text{Sin}\, B$
will be

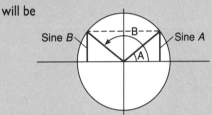

In this case, the two angles add up to $180°$.
So, when
Sin A = Sin B
then
$A + B = 180°$

Worked example 3
Solve the equation
$\text{Sin}\, 2x = \text{Sin}\, x$

Solution
Because $\text{Sin}\, 2x = \text{Sin}\, x$
then $2x + x = 180$
$$3x = 180$$
$$x = 60°$$

23 Find a solution to each of the following equations:

(a) $\text{Sin}\, 3x = \text{Sin}\, x$ (b) $\text{Sin}\, 5x = \text{Sin}\, x$
(c) $\text{Sin}\, 4x = \text{Sin}\, 2x$ (d) $\text{Sin}\, 5x = \text{Sin}\, 3x$

24 Show by considering the rotating arm that another
non-trivial solution to the equation
$\text{Sin}\, A = \text{Sin}\, B$
occurs when $B - A = 360°$.
Hence find two non-trivial solutions to the equation
$\text{Sin}\, x = \text{Sin}\, 5x$

The trigonometric ratios for a 45°, 45°, 90° triangle

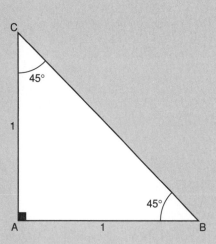

In the triangle ABC, AB = AC = 1 unit and the angles at B and C are both 45°.
So the angle at A is 90°.

By Pythagoras $BC^2 = AB^2 + AC^2$
so $\qquad BC^2 = 1^2 + 1^2$
$\qquad\qquad BC^2 = 2$ and $BC = \sqrt{2}$

Also
$\qquad Sin\ B = Sin\ 45°$

$$\frac{\text{opposite}}{\text{hypotenuse}} = \frac{AC}{BC} = \frac{1}{\sqrt{2}}$$

1 Use the same diagram to show that:

(a) $Cos\ 45° = \dfrac{1}{\sqrt{2}}$

(b) $Tan\ 45° = 1$

The 60°, 30°, 90° triangle

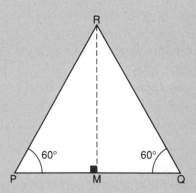

In the triangle PQR, PQ = PR = QR = 2 units.
The angles at P, Q and R will all be 60°.
M is the mid-point of PQ.
So PM = 1 unit and the angle PRM = 30°.

By Pythagoras, for the triangle PMR
$\qquad RM^2 = PR^2 - PM^2$
so $\ RM^2 = 2^2 - 1^2$
or $\ RM^2 = 4 - 1 = 3$
so $\ RM = \sqrt{3}$

For the triangle PMR

$Cos\ R = Cos\ 30°$
$\dfrac{RM}{PR} = \dfrac{\sqrt{3}}{2}$

2 Use the same diagram to show that:

(a) $Cos\ 60° = \dfrac{1}{2}$

(b) $Tan\ 30° = \dfrac{1}{\sqrt{3}}$

(c) $Sin\ 30° = \dfrac{1}{2}$

and to find, in a similar form:

(d) $Tan\ 60°$ \qquad (e) $Sin\ 60°$

Complementary angles

Two angles are complementary when they add up to 90°.

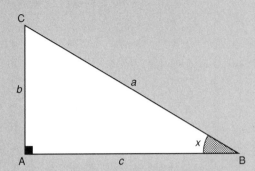

In the triangle ABC, $AB = c$, $AC = b$, $BC = a$.
The angle at B is x, so the angle at C is $(90 - x)$.

$\text{Sin } B = \text{Sin } x = \dfrac{b}{c}$ and also

$\text{Cos } C = \text{Cos }(90 - x) = \dfrac{b}{c}$

which leads to the conclusion

Sin x = Cos $(90 - x)$

For example
$\qquad$ Sin 40 = 0·642 787 61 by calculator
and Cos 50 = 0·642 787 61

3 Show that $\text{Cos } x = \text{Sin}(90 - x)$

4 Write down the acute angle whose:
(a) Cosine is equal to the Sine of 60°
(b) Sine is equal to the Cosine of 34°
(c) Sine is equal to its Cosine.

5 Show that $\text{Tan }(90 - x) = \dfrac{1}{\text{Tan } x}$

Sin²x + Cos²x = 1

The diagram shows Sine and Cosine defined in terms of the rotating arm OR with OR = 1
Sin x = RM
Cos x = OM

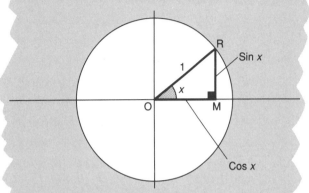

By Pythagoras $RM^2 + OM^2 = OR^2$
so $\qquad (\text{Sin } x)^2 + (\text{Cos } x)^2 = 1^2$

It is usual to write $(\text{Sin } x)^2$ as $\text{Sin}^2 x$ and $(\text{Cos } x)^2$ as $\text{Cos}^2 x$

so $\text{Sin}^2 x + \text{Cos}^2 x = 1$

Example

Calculate Cos x given that Sin x = 0·6

$\qquad \text{Sin}^2 x + \text{Cos}^2 x = 1$
so $\qquad 0·6^2 + \text{Cos}^2 x = 1$
or $\qquad 0·36 + \text{Cos}^2 x = 1$
$\qquad \text{Cos}^2 x = 1 - 0·36 = 0·64$
So $\qquad \text{Cos } x = 0·8$

6 Calculate:
(a) Sin x given that Cos x = 0·5
(b) Cos x given that Sin x = 0·8

When a large number of items are grouped together in a frequency table the standard deviation, s, can be calculated using the formulae

$$s = \frac{\Sigma f(x - \bar{x})^2}{\Sigma f}$$

Example:

This frequency distribution shows the number of eggs laid by chickens in one week.

Calculate the mean ($\bar{x}$) and standard deviation (s).

No. of eggs laid by a chicken in one week x	0	1	2	3	4	5	6
Frequency f	1	3	6	14	10	9	7

To calculate the mean ($\bar{x}$) and standard deviation (s).

* First calculate the mean by completing the table below:

x	f	fx
0	1	0
1	3	3
2	6	12
3	14	42
4	10	40
5	9	45
6	7	42
Totals	$\Sigma f = 50$	$\Sigma f = 184$

The mean $\bar{x} = \dfrac{\Sigma fx}{\Sigma f} = \dfrac{184}{50}$

$$\bar{x} = 3.68$$

* Then the standard deviation can be calculated by completing the following table:

x	f	$(x - \bar{x})$	$(x - \bar{x})^2$	$f(x - \bar{x})^2$
0	1	−3·68	13·54	13·54
1	3	−2·68	7·18	21·54
2	6	−1·68	2·82	16·92
3	14	− ·68	·46	6·44
4	10	·32	·10	1·0
5	9	1·32	1·74	15·6
6	7	2·32	5·38	37·6
Totals	50			112·64

So $\Sigma f = 50$ $\Sigma f(x - \bar{x})^2 = 112.64$

The standard deviation $s = \sqrt{\dfrac{\Sigma f(x - \bar{x})^2}{\Sigma f}}$

$$s = \sqrt{\frac{112.64}{50}}$$

$$s = \sqrt{2.253} = 1.50 \text{ to 2 dp}$$

* Another more frequently used method to calculate the standard deviation is written as:

$$s = \sqrt{\frac{\Sigma fx^2}{\Sigma f} - \left(\frac{\Sigma fx}{\Sigma f}\right)^2}$$

where $\dfrac{\Sigma fx}{\Sigma f}$ is the mean of the distribution.

To calculate $\bar{x}$ and s using this method draw up the following table:

x	f	fx	x^2	fx
0	1	1	0	0
1	3	3	1	3
2	6	12	4	24
3	14	42	9	126
4	10	40	16	160
5	9	45	25	225
6	7	42	36	252
Totals	$\Sigma f = 50$	$\Sigma fx = 184$		$\Sigma fx^2 = 790$

The standard deviation $s = \sqrt{\dfrac{790}{50} - \left(\dfrac{184}{50}\right)^2}$

$s = \sqrt{15.8 - 13.54}$

$s = \sqrt{2.26} = 1.50 \text{ to 2 dp}$

1 Calculate the mean and standard deviation for the following frequency distributions using either of the above methods.

(a)

No. of children in a family (x)	No. of families (f)
0	9
1	18
2	38
3	24
4	3
5	3
6	2
7	2
8	1
9	1

(b)

x	4	5	6	7	8	9	10
f	1	4	7	23	10	3	2

(c)

No. of pints of milk delivered (x)	No. of houses (f)
1	26
2	35
3	19
4	8
5	7
6	5
7	4
8	3
9	2
10	1

(d)

x	2·1	2·2	2·3	2·4	2·5	2·6	2·7
f	2	5	9	13	11	7	3

(e)

x	50	51	52	53	54	55	56
f	2	3	6	11	4	3	1

Group frequency distribution

It is often useful to calculate the standard deviation of **grouped frequency distributions** in order to compare distributions.

To calculate the standard deviation of a grouped frequency distribution the halfway mark or centre of each class interval must be used as the x-value.

In an examination at Irving Academy the data for 30 students were collected, grouped into class intervals with width 5 and the following table used to calculate an estimate of the standard deviation.

Mark	No. of students frequency (f)	Half-way mark (x)	fx	x^2	fx^2
1–5	1	3	3	9	9
6–10	3	8	24	64	192
11–15	4	13	52	169	676
16–20	8	18	144	324	2592
21–25	12	23	276	529	6348
26–30	2	28	56	784	1568
	$\Sigma f = 30$		$\Sigma fx = 555$		$\Sigma fx^2 = 11\,385$

The estimated standard deviation

$$s = \sqrt{\frac{\Sigma fx^2}{\Sigma f} - \left(\frac{\Sigma fx}{\Sigma f}\right)^2}$$

$$s = \sqrt{\frac{11\,385}{30} - \left(\frac{555}{30}\right)^2}$$

$$s = \sqrt{379 \cdot 5 - 342 \cdot 25}$$

$$s = \sqrt{37 \cdot 25}$$

$$s = 6 \cdot 10 \text{ to 2 dp}$$

2 The following grouped frequency distribution shows
the marks scored by 50 students in a test.

Mark (x)	1–10	11–20	21–30	31–40	41–50
Frequency (f)	1	4	16	24	5

Calculate estimates of the mean and standard
deviation.

3 The number of hours 100 people watched television
in a week is recorded in this grouped frequency
distribution.

Hours (x)	1–9	10–19	20–29	30–39	40–49
Frequency (f)	13	19	41	15	12

(a) Calculate an estimate of the mean.
(b) Calculate an estimate of the standard deviation.
(c) Illustrate the data with a suitable statistical
diagram.

4 The distance 50 people travel to work by car was
recorded in this frequency table.

Distance miles (x)	0–4	5–8	9–12	13–16	17–20
Frequency (f)	3	21	15	7	4

(a) Calculate an estimate of the mean.
(b) Calculate an estimate of the standard deviation.
(c) Illustrate your data with a suitable statistical
diagram.

The probability that the weather is to be fine tomorrow is estimated to be $\frac{1}{3}$. If it is fine, the probability I will catch the bus is $\frac{3}{4}$. If it is not fine, the probability I will catch the bus is $\frac{4}{5}$. Find the probability that I will catch the bus tomorrow.

In this type of problem the probabilities change depending on the changing situations. In a series of events, the probabilities change, depending on previous outcomes of events. Not all the probabilities are usually given in the problem, but can be found.

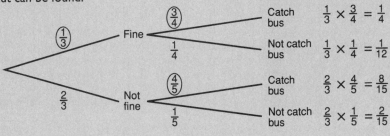

The probabilities which are circled in the tree diagram are the ones which are given in the problem. The remaining probabilities have then been added to complete the tree diagram.

$$P(\text{will catch the bus}) = \frac{1}{4} + \frac{8}{15} = \frac{15 + 32}{60} = \frac{47}{60}$$

1 The probability it is raining on any one day is $\frac{1}{4}$. If it is raining, the probability Mark will wear a coat is $\frac{3}{4}$. If it is not raining, the probability Mark will wear a coat is $\frac{1}{8}$. What is the probability Mark will wear his coat on any day?

2 Jill estimates the probability of her making a part correctly in her manufacturing job as $\frac{9}{10}$. If she fails to make a part correctly, and has a second attempt, the probability of her getting it right is $\frac{7}{10}$. Calculate the probability that Jill will:

(a) make the part correctly on the second attempt
(b) fail both attempts.

3 Roger has either coffee or tea with his lunch. There is a probability of $\frac{4}{5}$ that he has coffee on Monday. If he has coffee one day, then the probability of his having coffee on the next day is $\frac{2}{5}$. If he has tea one day, then the probability of his having tea on the next day is $\frac{1}{3}$. Find the probability that Roger has tea on:

(a) Tuesday   (b) Wednesday.

4 The probability that a girl wakes up late in the morning is $\frac{3}{5}$. When she wakes up late the probability that she arrives late for work is $\frac{7}{10}$. When she does not wake up late the probability that she arrives late for work is $\frac{3}{10}$. What is the probability of her arriving late for work on any day?

5 Sue likes to vary the way she goes to work. There is a probability of $\frac{1}{3}$ that on Monday she will go by train. If she travels by train one day, there is a probability of $\frac{2}{3}$ that she will go by car the next day. If she travels by car one day, there is a probability of $\frac{3}{4}$ that she will travel by train the next day. Find the probability that she travels by car on:

(a) Tuesday   (b) Wednesday.

6 Brian drives to work through two sets of traffic lights. The probability he will have to stop at the first set of lights is $\frac{3}{4}$. If he has to stop at the first set of lights, the probability he will have to stop at the second set is $\frac{5}{6}$, and only $\frac{2}{5}$ if he passes straight through the first set. Find the probability that Brian:

(a) has to stop at both sets of lights
(b) has to stop for at least one set of lights.

7 Shamsa can have up to three attempts at a test. The probability that she will pass on each attempt is $\frac{7}{10}$, $\frac{7}{9}$, and $\frac{7}{8}$ respectively. Find the probability that she will:

(a) pass on the second attempt
(b) fail on all three occasions?

This is very time consuming!

Sometimes calculating means and standard deviations can be time consuming and laborious and **coding** the values of x can be helpful. This is the case when x values are large and squaring would result in large values.

- To calculate the mean and standard deviation for the following frequency distribution where the values of x are very large.

x	40	45	50	55	60	65	70	75	80
f	1	4	9	16	25	13	7	3	2

- Choose a **suitable coding**. In this example a suitable coding would be subtract 60 and divide by 5.

Giving values of X of ⁻4, ⁻3, ⁻2, ⁻1, 0, 1, 2, 3, 4

i.e. $X = \dfrac{x - 60}{5}$

- Apply this coding and complete the following table.

x	Coded X	f	fX	X²	fX²
40	⁻4	1	⁻4	16	16
45	⁻3	4	⁻12	9	36
50	⁻2	9	⁻18	4	36
55	⁻1	16	⁻16	1	16
60	0	25	0	0	0
65	1	13	13	1	13
70	2	7	14	4	28
75	3	3	9	9	27
80	4	2	8	16	32
Totals		$\Sigma f = 80$	$\Sigma fX = $ ⁻6		$\Sigma fX^2 = $ 204

Mean $\bar{X} = \dfrac{\Sigma fX}{\Sigma f} = \dfrac{^-6}{80}$

$\qquad = {}^-0{\cdot}075$

Uncoding, multiply by 5 (inverse of divide by 5) and add 60

True mean $\bar{x} = 5 \times {}^-0{\cdot}075 + 60$

$\qquad\qquad = 59{\cdot}63$ to 2dp

Standard deviation

$S = \sqrt{\dfrac{\Sigma fX^2}{\Sigma f} - \left(\dfrac{\Sigma fX}{\Sigma f}\right)^2}$

$\quad = \sqrt{\dfrac{204}{80} - (-0{\cdot}075)^2}$

$\quad = \sqrt{2{\cdot}55 - (0{\cdot}0056)} = \sqrt{2{\cdot}544}$

$\quad = 1{\cdot}60$ to 2dp

Uncoding, **multiply by 5 only**

True s = 5 × 1·60

$\quad$ s = 8.00 to 2dp

Note When uncoding to find the true standard deviation you only need to divide as adding or subtracting does not affect the standard deviation.

1 Calculate the mean and standard deviation for the following frequency distributions using coding to help in the calculations.

(a)

x	35	36	37	38	39	40	41
f	1	9	16	23	14	5	2

(Hint: you only need to subtract 38 here.)

(b)

x	100	110	120	130	140	150	160
f	2	3	5	9	21	9	1

(c)

x	99·1	99·2	99·3	99·4	99·5	99·6
f	8	12	11	13	20	16

2 Calculate the mean and standard deviation for the following grouped frequency distributions using coding to help in the calculations.

(a)

x	f
0–9	4
10–19	7
20–29	12
30–39	24
40–49	15
50–59	8
60–69	3
70–79	2

(b)

x	f
0–4	3
5–8	8
9–12	11
13–16	25
17–20	14
21–24	9
25–30	5

Throughout all these calculations you may use an electronic calculator to help you with your calculations. However, it is always advisable to show your working, especially in external examinations.

If it is clear that *only* the *answer* is required or you wish to check your calculation then an electronic calculator with statistical functions will carry out the calculations.

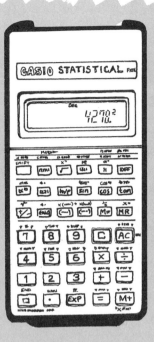

If you wished to calculate the mean and standard deviation of 4, 5, 7, 9, 10 on a statistical calculator

• Set the calculator in statistical mode.

• Enter the data by pressing
4 DATA 5 DATA 7 DATA 9 DATA 10 DATA

• Press $\bar{x}$ key to get the mean

• Press s key to get the standard deviation.

Electronic statistical calculators can also be used to find the mean and standard deviation of grouped frequency distribution.

If you wished to find the mean and standard deviation of:

x	2	3	4	5	6	7
f	1	3	5	7	4	2

then

• Set the calculator in statistical mode.

• Enter the data by pressing
2 × 1 DATA 3 × 3 DATA 4 × 5 DATA
5 × 7 DATA 6 × 4 DATA 7 × 2 DATA

• Press $\bar{x}$ key to get the mean.

• Press s key to get the standard deviation.

It all adds up

Esther was asked to investigate this arithmetic sequence of numbers:

3, 7, 11, 15, 19, 23, 27, 31, 35, 39

1 Write down:
  (a) the common difference
  (b) the total when the first term and last term are added together
  (c) the total when the 2nd term and the 2nd last term are added
  (d) Continue to add pairs of numbers and write down what you notice.

If all the terms of a sequence are added together the expression is called a **series**. This is a arithmetic series:

3 + 7 + 11 + 15 + 19 + 23 + 27 + 31 + 35 + 39

There are several ways of adding a series together. One method is to use a calculator and add the series term by term. However this can be very time consuming especially if the series contains a large number of terms.

You may have noticed that if you add the nth term and the nth last term you always get the same answer.

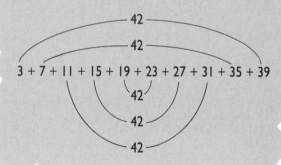

2 How many:
  (a) numbers are there in the series
  (b) sets of 42 are there?
  (c) What is the sum of this series?

Here is another arithmetic series:

1 + 4 + 7 + 10 + 13 + 16 + ... + 28 + 31 + 34

3 Find:
  (a) how many terms the series contains
  (b) the total when the first term and last term are added
  (c) the total when the nth term and the nth last term are added
  (d) how many 'pairs' with this total there are in the series
  (e) the sum of the series.

4 Write down in words or symbols a rule for finding the sum of an arithmetic series.

5 Find the sum of these arithmetic series:
  (a) 1 + 3 + 5 + ... + 81 + 83
  (b) 2 + 7 + 12 + ... + 82 + 87
  (c) − 9 − 6 − 3 − ... + 49 + 52
  (d) 20 + 13 + 6 + ... − 57

6 An arithmetic series has a 3rd term of 7 and a 8th term of 17. If the sum of the sequence is 624 find:
  (a) the commom difference
  (b) the first term
  (c) the number of terms in the sequence
  (d) the sum of the first 20 terms.

7 Find the sum of:
  (a) the odd numbers between 50 and 150
  (b) the even numbers between 49 and 199.

8 The first term of an arithmetic series is 5. The 7th term is twice the 3rd term.

Find:
  (a) the common difference
  (b) the sum of the first 20 terms
  (c) the number of terms required to give a total of 825.

Look carefully at these two series.
$x + 6 + 9 + 10 + 25 + 50$
$6 + 9 + 10 + 25 + 50 + y$

1 Write in as simplified form as possible the result if:
(a) both series are added
(b) the series are subtracted.

2 (a) Write down the result when these two series are subtracted:
$a + 2 + 4 + 8 + \ldots + 4096$
$2 + 4 + 8 + \ldots + 4096 + b$
(b) Write down the result when these two series are subtracted:
$a + b + c + d + e + f + g$
$b + c + d + e + f + g + h$
(c) Write down in your own words what happens when two series of this type are subtracted.

The result of subtracting two series of this type can be used to sum a geometric series without having to add it term by term.

Let S be the sum of this geometric series:
$S = 2 + 6 + 18 + 54 + \ldots + 1458$

3 Copy and complete this series when S is multiplied by 3. That is:
$3S = 6 + 18 + \ldots$

4 Write down the answer to $3S - S$:
(a) in terms of S
(b) as a numerical value.

5 (a) Write down an equation involving S.
(b) Solve the equation to find the value of S.
(c) Check that the value of S is the sum of the geometric sequence by adding it term by term.

Gerald has been asked to sum this geometric series S. That is:
$S = 5 + 10 + 20 + 40 + \ldots + 1280$

6 (a) Work out the common ratio, r.
(b) Write term by term the series (common ratio) $\times$ S. Call this series rS.
(c) Work out the value of $rS - S$.
(d) Write down an equation involving S and solve it to find the sum of the series.
(e) Check your answer by adding the series term by term.

7 The sum S of a geometric series is given as
$1 + 5 + 25 + 125 + \ldots + 15\,625$
(a) Work out the common ratio, r.
(b) Write term by term the series (common ratio) $\times$ S. Call this series rS.
(c) Work out and simplify an equation involving $rS - S$.
(d) Solve the equation to find the sum of the series.

8 The sum S of this geometric series is given as
$S = a + ar + ar^2 + ar^3 + ar^4 + \ldots$
(a) Write down in terms of a and r, the nth term.
(b) Write down term by term the series (common ratio) $\times$ S as far as the (n+1)th term.
(c) Write in terms of a and r an expression $rS - S$.
(d) Show that the expression simplifies to
$$S = \frac{a(r^n - 1)}{r - 1}$$

9 The first term of a geometric series is 5, the second 20 and the last term is 5120. Find:
(a) the common ratio
(b) the sum of its terms.

10 The 2nd term of a geometric series is 5 and the 5th term is 40. Find the sum of the first 10 terms.

Consider this iteration formula. If it generates a converging sequence then as *n* increases the value of U_{n+1} and U_n must get closer and closer. In the end they become so close that they can be considered the same and replaced by a single letter.

$$U_{n+1} = \frac{2}{U_n - 1}$$

$$x = \frac{2}{x - 1}$$

This means that the limit of the sequence will be the solution to the equation:

$$x = \frac{2}{x - 1}$$

The re-arrangement of a equation in order to obtain an iterative formula is very important. One arrangement leads to one solution, another to the second solution and the third gives a diverging sequence.

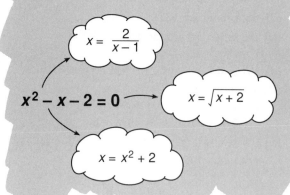

$$x = \frac{2}{x - 1}$$

$$x^2 - x - 2 = 0$$

$$x = \sqrt{x + 2}$$

$$x = x^2 + 2$$

1 (a) Start with a U_1 value of $^-1\cdot5$, calculate U_1, U_2, U_3 and U_4.

(b) Continue to calculate sucessive values of U_n until you can determine the limit of the sequence.

(c) Check that the limit you obtained is a solution to the equation.

2 (a) Show that $x = 2$ is also a solution to the equation $x = \dfrac{2}{x - 1}$

(b) Starting with a value of $U_n = 2\cdot5$ calculate U_2, U_3, U_4, U_5, U_6, U_7 and U_8.

(c) Continue calculating values of U_n until you can determine the limit.

(d) Write down what you notice about this limit.

3 (a) Show that the equation $x = \dfrac{2}{x - 1}$ can be re-arranged to give $x^2 - x - 2 = 0$

(b) Show that the equation $x^2 - x - 2 = 0$ can be re-arranged to $x = \sqrt{x + 2}$

(c) Starting with the U_1 value of $2\cdot5$ calculate successive values of U_n until you can suggest the limit of the sequence.

(d) Write down what you notice this time.

4 (a) Show that a further re-arrangement of $x^2 - x - 2 = 0$ is $x = x^2 - 2$.

(b) Starting with a value of $U_1 = 3$ calculate U_2, U_3 U_4 and U_5.

(c) What type of sequence is being generated this time?

5 (a) Show that the equation $x^2 + x - 7 = 0$ can be re-arranged to $x = \sqrt{7 - x}$

(b) Write down the corresponding iteration formula.

(c) Use the iteration formula to generate a sequence.

(d) Find the limit of the sequence correct to 3 decimal places.

(e) Check that the limit is an approximate solution to the equation.

6 The equation $x^2 + x - 7 = 0$ has another solution.

(a) Find a second re-arrangement of the formula to write down another iterative formula.

(b) Use the iterative formula to generate a converging sequence whose limit is the solution to the equation.

(c) Comment on your result.

7 It is known that the equation $x^3 - x - 1 = 0$ has a solution at about $x = 1\cdot3$.

(a) Show that the equation can be re-arranged to give:
(i) $x = \dfrac{1}{x^2 - 1}$ **(ii)** $x = (1 + x)^{\frac{1}{3}}$

(b) Write down two iteration formulae.

(c) One iteration formula will lead to a solution to the equation. Investigate which formula generates a converging sequence and find the solution correct to 3 decimal places.

The manager of the local cinema decides to set prices as a way of attracting customers.

She decides that on one specific night the prices are to be:

Adults   £10
Pensioners £1
Children   50p

The cinema has exactly 100 seats.

1 The manager wishes to know if it is possible to fill all 100 seats in the cinema and take exactly £100.

   Examine this situation.

2 It is the manager's belief that no matter what level the special prices are set at, it is always possible to fill the 100 seats and take exactly £100.

   Vary the special prices for adults, pensioners and children.

   Hence comment, as generally as possible, on the manager's belief.

Logging on

In calculations involving compound interest equations of this type had to be solved.
This was easy if either A, P or r were the unknown.

$$A = P(1 + r)^n$$

When A, P and r are known the only way to find the value of n was by trial and improvement.

$$250 = 165(1 + 0.6)^n$$

There is, however, a more direct way of solving these types of equations.

To solve the equation

$$100 = 10^{n-1}$$

rewrite the equation in terms of powers of 10.

$$10^2 = 10^{n-1}$$

Equating powers of 10 gives

$$2 = n - 1$$

and solving for n:

$$n = 3$$

1 By equating each side of the equation solve:
   (a) $10^3 = 10^{2n}$ (b) $10^2 = 10^{n+3}$
   (c) $10^{-4} = 10^{2n+4}$ (d) $10^{-3} = 10^{2n+6}$
   (e) $10^{2n+1} = 10^{3n-1}$ (f) $10^{4n-5} = 10^8$

2 Write each of these numbers as powers of 10:
   (a) 10 000   (b) 100 000   (c) 1000
   (d) 0.01   (e) 0.000 001   (f) 0.0001

3 By writing as a power of 10 solve this equation
   $1000 = 10^{2n-1}$

4 Solve each of these equations by first rewriting them in terms of powers of 10:
   (a) $100 000 = 10^{3n-4}$
   (b) $1000 = 10^{\frac{n}{2}}$
   (c) $0.0001 = 10^{n-6}$
   (d) $0.01 = 10^{-4n+1}$
   (e) $10 000 = 100^n$
   (f) $0.0001 = 1000^{5n-1}$
   (g) $10^{n^2} = 10 000$

As long as it is possible to write these types of equation in terms of powers of 10 then it is possible to solve them using this method.

$$100 = 10^2$$

Now consider this equation: $25 = 6^{n+1}$

It looks difficult to re-write in terms of powers of 10.

However, this is where your calculator comes to the rescue.

Most scientific calculators have a key marked: **log**

Enter **2** **5** and press **log** to get **1.39794**

This gives the power to which 10 must be raised to equal 25. In other words

$$25 = 10^{1.397\,94}$$

(Check this by using your x^y function on your calculator.)

Enter **6** and press **log** to get **0.778 15 12**

This gives the power to which 10 must be raised to equal 6. In other words

$$6 = 10^{0.778\,1512}$$

(Again, check this using the x^y function.)

Using this information the equation $25 = 6^{n+1}$ can be re-written, to 2 decimal places, in terms of powers of 10 as:

$$10^{1.40} = 10^{0.78(n+1)}$$

which means

$$1.40 = 0.78(n + 1)$$
$$1.40 = 0.78n + 0.78$$
$$0.78n = 0.62$$
$$n = \frac{0.62}{0.78} = 0.79 \text{ to 2 decimal places}$$

Gail invests £100 in National Saving Certificates. This investment pays 8·5% compound interest. After a certain length of time Gail's money has grown to £340. Find the length of time the money was invested.

$$A = P(1 + \frac{r}{100})^n$$

$$340 = 100(1 + \frac{8·5}{100})^n$$

$$340 = 100(1 + 0·085)^n$$

$$340 = 100(1·085)^n$$

$$3·4 = 1·085^n$$

Using the log function to express this equation in terms of powers of 10:

$$10^{0·5315} = 10^{0·0354n}$$

Equating powers of 10:

$$0·5315 = 0·0354n$$

$$n = \frac{0·5315}{0·0354}$$

$$n = 15·014 \text{ years}$$

Gail had invested her money for 15 years to the nearest year.

5 At the same time as Gail invested her £100 Mark invested £900 with an insurance company. This company paid a compound interest rate of 9%. Find, to the nearest year, how long it took Mark's money to increase in value to £2130.

6 Frank Knox robbed a bank and got away with £10 000. Being shrewd he invested the money in a savings account that paid an annual interest rate of 11%. However, the police soon caught Frank and he was put on trial. Passing sentence the Judge said, 'You will go to prison for as long as it would have taken the £10 000 to increase in value to £31 500.' How long was Frank in prison?

7 Davinder and Jupal start work together on the same day. They are each paid a salary of £12 000 per year. However, they have different contracts of employment. Davinder receives £1000 increase every year. Jupal receives an annual increase of 6·5%. Find:

(a) Davinder's salary after 5 years
(b) Jupal's salary after 5 years
(c) how long it will take for Jupal's salary to exceed £20 000.

A machinery firm buys a new lathe for £36 000 and estimates that the machine depreciates at an annual rate of 25%. Find its value after 4 years.

Since the lathe depreciates the formulae becomes

$$A = P(1 - \frac{r}{100})^n$$

The value after 4 years $= £36 000 (1 - 0·25)^4$
$$= £36 000 \times 0·3164$$
$$= £11 390$$

After 4 years the value of the lathe has fallen to £11 390.

8 Find:

(a) the value of the lathe after 6 years
(b) the time taken for the lathe to fall to 10% of its original value.

9 Find the time taken for the lathe to fall to:

(a) 5% of its original value
(b) 1% of its original value.
(c) When, in theory, will the lathe have zero value?

10 A second lathe also costing £36 000 depreciates at a fixed rate of 10%. Find:

(a) the value of the second lathe after 4 years
(b) after how many years the second lathe will have zero value.
(c) Find, by any method, the two times when the lathes have the same value.

Suppose we have to solve this quadratic equation.

$$x^2 + 4x - 32 = 0$$

We have found ways of solving these equations but here is another method. It is called solving by **transformation**.

$$x^2 + 4x - 32 = 0 \quad \text{or} \quad x(x + 4) = 32$$

Let $\qquad y = x + 2 \quad$ so $\quad x = y - 2$
and $\qquad x + 4 = y + 2$

This is the transformation. The equation

$$x(x + 4) = 32 \text{ becomes}$$

$$(y - 2)(y + 2) = 32$$

The left-hand size is the difference of two squares:

$$y^2 - 4 = 32$$
$$y^2 = 36$$
$$y = 6 \text{ or } ^-6$$

$$x = 6 - 2 \text{ or } x = ^-6 - 2$$
$$x = 4 \text{ or } ^-8$$

1 Solve the equation $x^2 + 2x - 24 = 0$ by:

  (a) factorising

  (b) re-arranging the equation to $x(x + 2) = 24$ and making the transformation $y = x + 1$.

This equation will not factorise and therefore cannot be solved using factors:
$$x^2 - 6x - 4 = 0$$
so $\quad x(x - 6) = 4$

The transformation to use is $y = x - 3$
If $y = x - 3 \quad$ then $x = y + 3$
and $\qquad\qquad x - 6 = y - 3$

The equation $x(x - 6) = 4$ is transformed

$$(y + 3)(y - 3) = 4$$
$$y^2 - 9 = 4$$
$$y^2 = 13$$
$$y = 3{\cdot}605 \text{ or } ^-3{\cdot}605$$

but $x = y + 3 \quad$ so $x = 3{\cdot}605 + 3 = 6{\cdot}605$ or
$$x = {}^-3{\cdot}605 + 3 = {}^-0{\cdot}605$$

Finally to solve the equation $2x^2 + 4x - 6 = 0$
$$2x^2 + 4x - 6 = 0$$
$$x(2x + 4) = 6$$

Multiplying by 2
$$2x(2x + 4) = 12$$

Use the transformation $y = 2x + 2$ so
$$2x = y - 2 \text{ and}$$
$$2x + 4 = y + 2$$

Therefore $(y - 2)(y + 2) = 12$
$$y^2 - 4 = 12$$
$$y^2 = 16$$
$$y = 4 \text{ or } ^-4$$

but $2x = y + 2$ so
$$2x = 4 + 2 \text{ or } ^-4 + 2$$
$$2x = 6 \text{ or } ^-2$$
$$x = 3 \text{ or } ^-1$$

The difficulty with this method is to work out the correct transformation to use.

2 Look back at the examples to see if you can spot how to make the transformation. (Hint: they all use the difference of two squares.)

3 Solve these equations by transformations:

  (a) $x^2 + 6x + 8 = 0 \qquad$ use $y = x + 3$
  (b) $x^2 - 4x - 10 = 0 \qquad$ use $y = x - 2$
  (c) $x^2 + 8x - 24 = 0 \qquad$ use $y = x + 4$
  (d) $2x^2 + 6x - 10 = 0 \qquad$ use $y = 2x + 3$
  (e) $3x^2 - 16x + 5 = 0$
  (f) $2x^2 + 5x - 2 = 0$
  (g) $4x^2 - 7x + 1 = 0$
  (h) $3x^2 - 11x + 10 = 0$

4 Explain what happens if you try to solve the equation $x^2 + 4x + 6 = 0$.

The Bank of Narvarna decide to pay an incredible interest rate of 100% per annum.

The shorter the time interval between the interest payments the greater in value your investment becomes. Suppose the bank paid the interest not merely annually or six monthly or monthly or even daily but every instant of every day. Would you become incredibly rich after one year's investment of just £1?

1 If you invest £1 at the beginning of the year and the interest is paid at the end of the year how much is your investment worth at the end of the year?

The Bank maintains the 100% interest rate per annum but decides to pay the compound interest on a six-monthly basis.

2 (a) How much interest would your investment receive after the first 6 months?
  (b) What is the total value of your investment after one year?

3 (a) Copy and complete this table giving the full calculator display:

Time interval of interest payments	Value of the £1 after one year
Annually	£2.00
6 monthly	
4 monthly	
3 monthly	
Monthly	
Weekly	
Daily	

(b) If the interest was paid every instant of every day suggest a value to which your £1 would have grown.
(c) Justify your answer to part **(b)**.

Much ado about a circle

Theorem 1

The angle at the centre is twice the angle at the circumference.

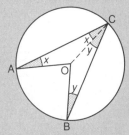

The diagram above shows a circle, centre O.
AB is a chord of the circle.
C is a point on the circumference of the circle.

The theorem basically states that the angle AÔB will always be twice the angle AĈB.

Proof

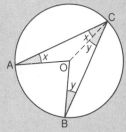

OA = OC (both equal the radius of the circle)
Hence the triangle OÂC is isosceles and the angles OÂC and OĈA are equal. They are labelled x.
The angle AÔC is then $180 - 2x$, angles in a triangle add to $180°$.
In a similar fashion the triangle OBC is isosceles, and in terms of the symbols of the diagram the angle BÔC = $180 - 2y$.
The angle AÔB = $360 - (AÔC + BÔC)$, because the angles around a point are $360°$.
So the angle AÔB $= 360 - AÔC - BÔC$
$= 360 - (180 - 2x) - (180 - 2y)$
$= 360 - 180 + 2x - 180 + 2y$
$= 360 - 360 + 2x + 2y$
$= 2x + 2y$
$= 2(x + y)$

But, from the diagram $x + y =$ the angle AĈB
Hence angle AÔB = twice the angle AĈB
The angle at the centre is twice the angle at the circumference.

Theorem 2

Angles in the same segment are equal.

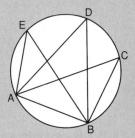

In the diagram above AB is a chord of the circle.
C, D and E are three points on the circumference of the circle.

The theorem basically states that the angles AĈB, AD̂B and AÊD are all equal.

1 Before looking at the proof of this theorem, do **Worksheet 3**.

Proof

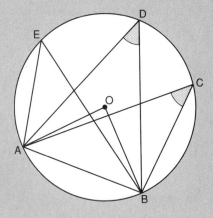

O is the centre of the circle.
Because the angle at the centre is twice the angle at the circumference, then
AÔB = $2 \times$ AĈB and AÔC = $2 \times$ AD̂B and AÔC = $2 \times$ AÊB
So AĈB, AD̂B and AÊB are all equal to $\frac{1}{2}$ of AÔB
In consequence AĈB = AD̂B = AÊB
and the positions of C, D and E are irrelevant.
So, for all points on the circumference the angles at the circumference, as far as chord AB are concerned, will be equal.

Theorem 3

The angle in a semi-circle is a right-angle.

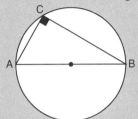

The theorem, basically states that when AB is a diameter then the angle $A\hat{C}B$ is 90°.

2 Before looking at this proof do **Worksheet 4**.

Proof

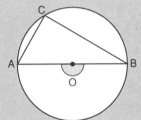

O is the centre of the circle.
$A\hat{O}B$ is a diameter of that circle.
C is a general point on the circumference of the circle.
The angle $A\hat{O}B = 180°$, because AB is a straight line.
But the angle $A\hat{O}B$ is twice the angle $A\hat{C}B$. This is because $A\hat{O}B$ is the angle at the centre and $A\hat{C}B$ is the angle at the circumference.

Theorem 4

Opposite angles in a cyclic quadrilateral add up to 180°.

ABCD is a cyclic quadrilateral, that is, the four points A, B, C and D lie on a circle.
The theorem states basically that the angles at A and C add up to 180°, as do the angles at B and D.

3 Before looking at the proof of this theorem, do **Worksheet 5**.

Proof

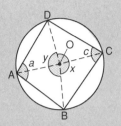

A, B, C and D lie on the circumference of a circle, centre O.
Angle $D\hat{O}B = 2 \times$ Angle $D\hat{C}B$, since the angle at the centre is twice the angle at the circumference.
Also the reflex angle $D\hat{O}B = 2 \times$ Angle $D\hat{A}B$, for the same reason.
So in the symbols of the diagram:
$x = 2a$ and $y = 2c$
So $x + y = 2a + 2c$
or $x + y = 2(a + c)$
But $x + y = 360°$, because they are the angles around a point,
so $2(a + c) = 360°$
and $a + c = 180°$
Also the sum of the angles in any quadrilateral is 360°. In consequence the sum of the angles $A\hat{D}C$ and $A\hat{B}C$ must also be 180°.
There is a corollary, or extension to this theorem which states that:
If the opposite angles of a quadrilateral add up to 180° then the vertices of that quadrilateral must lie on a circle.

Example

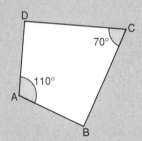

The sum of the angles $D\hat{A}B$ and $D\hat{C}B = 180°$
Likewise the sum of the angles $A\hat{B}C$ and $A\hat{D}C = 180°$
So the points A, B, C and D lie on a circle.

4 **Do Worksheet 6**.

Theorem 5

The angle between a tangent and radius is a right-angle.

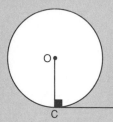

The line TC is a tangent to the circle, touching the circle at C. O is the centre of the circle, thus making OC a radius.
The theorem basically states that the angle TĈO is 90°.

5 Use compasses to draw a circle. Draw a tangent to the circle. Use a protractor to convince yourself that the angle between the tangent and radius to the point of contact with the tangent is 90°.

Theorem 6

The alternate segment theorem

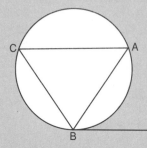

AB is a chord of the circle. TB is a tangent to the circle. C is a point on the circle, it must lie on the segment of the circle which is **alternate** to the segment between AB and the tangent.
The theorem basically states that the angle AB̂T is equal to the angle AĈB.

Proof

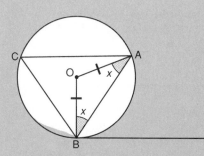

Draw the radius OB and the radius OA. Then OB = OA. In consequence the triangle BOA is isosceles and so the angles AB̂O and BÂO are equal. They have been labelled x. The angle BÔA = 180 − 2x, angles in a triangle.
But angle BĈA = ½ the angle BÔA, because of the angle at the circumference property.
Hence the angle BĈA = ½(180 − 2x) = 90 − x
Also the angle TB̂O = 90°, angle between a radius and tangent.
So, since angle AB̂O = x, then angle AB̂T = 90 − x.
So the angles AB̂T and AĈB are both equal to 90 − x. Hence angle AB̂T = angle AĈB.

6 Stating clearly your reason, find each of the angles marked with a letter.

(a)

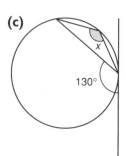

(b)

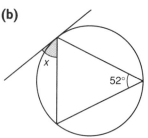

(c)

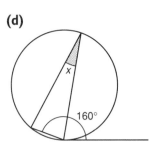

(d)

Theorem 7

The intersecting chords theorem

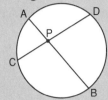

AB and CD are two chords of a circle which meet at a point P.
This theorem basically states that
$$PA \times PB = PC \times PD$$

Proof

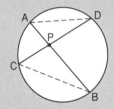

Join B to C and A to D.
Angle $A\hat{D}C$ = Angle $A\hat{B}C$, angles in the same segment
Angle $B\hat{A}D$ = Angle $B\hat{C}D$, angles in the same segment again.
Angle $A\hat{P}D$ = Angle $B\hat{P}C$, vertically opposite.
Hence the two triangles APD and CPB are similar, and so
$$\frac{PA}{PD} = \frac{PC}{PB}$$

so, cross-multiplication gives
$$PA \times PB = PC \times PD$$

This theorem is also true when the two chords meet at a point P which lies outside the circle.

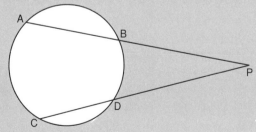

Again $PA \times PB = PC \times PD$

7 By considering the similarity of the triangles PAD and PCB, prove the last result.

Special case of the theorem

There is a special, or limiting case of the theorem when C and D get closer together, making PC and/or PD a tangent to the circle.

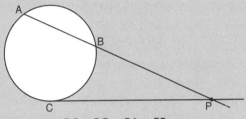

In this case $PC \times PC = PA \times PB$ or
$$PC^2 = PA \times PB$$

8 Use the other circle theorems to show that angle $B\hat{A}C$ = angle $P\hat{C}B$ and hence that the triangles BCP and CAP are similar.
Hence establish the result $PC^2 = PA \times PB$

9 For each of the diagrams below, calculate the lengths marked with a letter. All lengths are in centimetres.

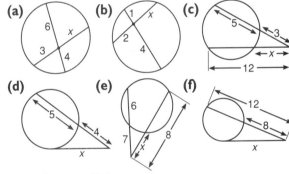

10 In the diagram, AB is a chord of a circle with AB = 5 cm. The chord AB extended, meets the tangent at C at a point P. BP = x cm and CP = 6 cm.
(a) Show that x satisfies the equation
$$x^2 + 5x - 36 = 0$$
(b) Solve this equation.

11 AB and CD are two chords of a circle which, when extended meet at a point P outside the circle.
AB = 4 cm, CD = 7 cm, DP = 3 cm and AP = x cm.
(a) Show that $x^2 - 4x - 30 = 0$
(b) Solve this equation.

Transformation geometry 1

The aim of this chapter is to provide you with an opportunity to recall the basic geometric transformations.

These transformations will be illustrated using a triangle for convenience. The shape we start with is called the **object**. The shape after the transformation is called the **image**.

All of the transformations are in the two-dimensional plane. Whilst the transformations are illustrated with a single shape you should keep in mind that **the transformation actually transforms all of the points in the plane, or the whole plane**.

Reflections in a mirror line

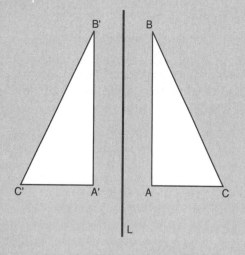

The object triangle ABC is transformed to the image A'B'C' by a reflection in the line L.

The key feature of such a reflection is that the perpendicular distance from each object point to the line is equal to the perpendicular distance from each image point to the line.
Or AL = A'L, BL = B'L etc

The points lying on the actual mirror line are transformed into themselves. These points are called the **invariants** of the transformation.

> For reflections you should **always** state the correct mirror line.

1 A triangle PQR has its vertices at the points P, Q and R where P is (2, 1), Q is (5, 1) and R is (5, 3).
   (a) Draw the triangle PQR.
   (b) Draw the image P'Q'R' of PQR after a reflection in the y-axis.
   (c) Draw the second image P"Q"R" after a reflection of P'Q'R' in the line y = x.

2 A triangle ABC has vertices A, B and C at the points ($^-$1, 3), (2, 6) and (3, 4) respectively. The triangle is reflected in a line L to form the image A'B'C'. The coordinates of B' and C' are (10, 6) and (9, 4) respectively.
   (a) Find the coordinates of A'.
   (b) Obtain the equation of the line L.

Translations

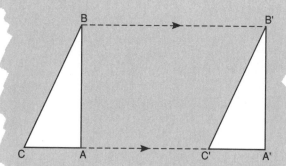

In this translation the object triangle ABC is just moved a certain distance to give the image triangle A'B'C'.

A translation through any non-zero distance has **no invariant points**.

A translation which moves all points 2 places to the right and 3 places upwards is usually written in **vector form** as $\begin{pmatrix} 2 \\ 3 \end{pmatrix}$

The transformation $\begin{pmatrix} ^-4 \\ 5 \end{pmatrix}$ means 4 places to the left and 5 up.

Whilst $\begin{pmatrix} 7 \\ ^-3 \end{pmatrix}$ means 7 places to the right and 3 down.

Sometimes a translation may be defined in vector form as:

$$T: \begin{pmatrix} x \\ y \end{pmatrix} \rightarrow \begin{pmatrix} x \\ y \end{pmatrix} + \begin{pmatrix} 3 \\ 4 \end{pmatrix}$$

This is simply a way of saying that each general point is moved **3** places to the right and **4** places up.

> For translations you should **always** make clear the direction of the translation.

3 The diagram shows a triangle PQR and its image P'Q'R' under a translation.

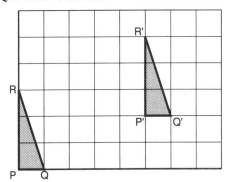

Write the translation in vector form.

4 A translation **T** is defined by

$$T: \begin{pmatrix} x \\ y \end{pmatrix} \rightarrow \begin{pmatrix} x \\ y \end{pmatrix} + \begin{pmatrix} {}^-5 \\ 2 \end{pmatrix}$$

(a) Write down the images, under this translation of the points:
   (i) $(7, 3)$ **(ii)** $(4, 0)$ **(iii)** $(0, {}^-3)$ **(iv)** $({}^-2, {}^-8)$
(b) Obtain the coordinates of the points which have images:
   (i) $(0, 0)$ **(ii)** $(1, 3)$ **(iii)** $({}^-3, {}^-1)$ **(iv)** (a, b)

5 A translation **T** is defined by

$$T: \begin{pmatrix} x \\ y \end{pmatrix} \rightarrow \begin{pmatrix} x \\ y \end{pmatrix} - \begin{pmatrix} 3 \\ 4 \end{pmatrix}$$

Under this translation the image of a point P is a point Q.

(a) Draw a sketch showing the translation from P to Q.
(b) Calculate the distance from P to Q.
(c) Calculate the acute angle between PQ and the x-axis.

Enlargements

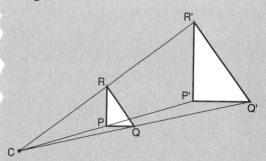

The diagram shows the triangle PQR and its image P'Q'R' which in this case is an enlargement, scale factor 2, centre the point C.
The scale factor 2 means that
CP' = 2CP, CQ' = 2CQ and CR' = 2CR
Also the lengths of the respective sides are in the ratio 2 : 1, so
P'Q' = 2PQ, P'R' = 2PR, Q'R' = 2QR

One further consequence of the scale factor being 2 is that
Area P'Q'R' = 4 × Area PQR = 2^2 × Area PQR

> This is a specific case of the general statement:
> For an enlargement of scale factor k
> Area of the image $= k^2 \times$ Area of the object

Enlargements can also be fractional.

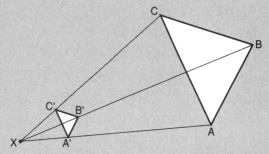

The diagram above shows a triangle ABC which has been *enlarged* by a scale factor of $\frac{1}{4}$, centre X.
It has actually been reduced, so that
XA' $= \frac{1}{4}$ XA, etc., and
Area A'B'C' $= \left(\frac{1}{4}\right)^2 \times$ Area ABC

Enlargements can also be negative.

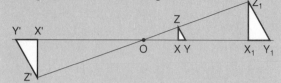

In the above diagram the object triangle XYZ has been enlarged by a scale factor ¯3, centre O to form X'Y'Z' (Note $X_1Y_1Z_1$ has been shown as an intermediate step to illustrate how the negative enlargement is formed – do the positive enlargement and then reverse the direction).

Again in this negative enlargement case
OX' = 3OX, OY' = 3OY, OZ' = 3OZ and
X'Y = 3XY, X'Z' = 3XZ, Y'Z' = 3YZ and
Area X'Y'Z' = $(¯3)^2 \times$ Area XYZ

Whenever you define or quote an enlargement you should **always** state both the **scale factor** and the **centre**. The centre is the only invariant point unless the scale factor is 1. Then all points are invariants.

You need squared paper.

6 (a) Plot the points A, B and C with coordinates (3, 3), (6, 3) and (6, 9) respectively.

(b) Find the images of the triangle ABC after enlargements, all of centre the origin, but with scale factors of:

  (i) 3   **(ii)** $\frac{1}{3}$ **(iii)** –2

  (iv) $¯\frac{1}{2}$ **(v)** $1\frac{1}{2}$ **(vi)** $¯1\frac{1}{3}$

(c) Calculate the area of ABC.

(d) Calculate the area of each image triangle.

7 The triangle XYZ is an enlargement of the triangle PQR.

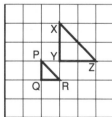

(a) State the scale factor of the enlargement.

(b) State the coordinates of the centre of the enlargement.

8 You need tracing paper.
The hexagon H_2 is an enlargement of the hexagon H_1.

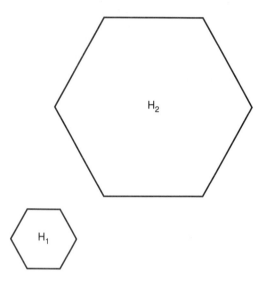

(a) Copy the two hexagons onto paper.

(b) Showing your working clearly, mark with a C the centre of enlargement.

(c) Calculate the scale factor of the enlargement.

(d) Given that the area of H_1 is s square units, write down an expression for the area of H_2.

9 An enlargement transforms a square of area 5 units into a square of area 80 square units.
Calculate the two possible scale factors of the enlargement.

10 $S_1, S_2, S_3, \ldots, S_n, S_{n+1}, \ldots$
is a sequence of squares, where for each value of n, S_{n+1} is an enlargement, scale factor $1\cdot1$, of S_n. The length of a side of S_1, is 1 unit.

(a) Calculate the length of a side of:
  (i) S_3 **(ii)** S_5 **(iii)** S_{10}

(b) Calculate the areas of each of the squares in **(a)**.

(c) Write down an expression for the length of a side of S_n.

(d) Write down an expression for the area of
  (i) S_n **(ii)** S_{n+1} **(iii)** S_{n+p}

(e) Calculate the area of $S_1 + S_2 + S_3 + \ldots S_{10}$

(f) Undertake some independent work on **Geometric Series** and hence find an expression for the total area of
$S_1 + S_2 + S_3 + \ldots + S_n$

Rotations

In the diagram above the triangle ABC has been rotated through 90° in the clockwise direction about the point O to give the triangle A'B'C'.

> A rotation **always** has
> an **angle of rotation** – which was 90° in the above case,
> a **direction** – which was clockwise in the above case, and
> a **centre of rotation** – which was the point O in the above case.
> These should **always** be clearly stated.

For all rotations the centre of the rotation is the only invariant point, unless the angle of rotation is 0°, 360°, 720° etc. in which case all points are invariant points.

11 The vertices A, B, C of a triangle are at the points with coordinates (2, 1), (5, 1) and (5, 7) respectively. The triangle is rotated above the origin, in a clockwise direction through an angle of 90° to give the image A'B'C'.
Find the coordinates of A', B' and C'.

12 **(a)** Repeat question 11, but make the centre of the rotation the point with coordinates:

   (i) (1, 1) **(ii)** (2, 1) **(iii)** (5, 1) **(iv)** (1, ⁻3)

   (b) Repeat question 11 twice more but make the centre of rotation any two points of your own choosing.

   (c) The triangle in question 11 is rotated about the point with general coordinates (a, b), through 90° in a clockwise direction. Find general expressions for the vertices of the image triangle.

13 The point P with coordinates (x, y) has an image P' under a clockwise rotation through 90° about the point (a, b). Find general expressions, in terms of x, y, a and b for the coordinates of P'.

14 The whole (x, y) plane is transformed by an anticlockwise rotation through an angle θ° about the origin. Find, in terms of θ, expressions for the coordinates of the image of the (1, 0).

15 The (x, y) plane is rotated in a clockwise direction about the origin through an angle of 30°. Show that the image of the point (0, 1) under this transformation is $(\frac{1}{2}, \frac{\sqrt{3}}{2})$.

Miscellaneous questions

16 Write down the image of the point (p, q) after a reflection in:
   (a) the line $x = a$ **(b)** the line $y = b$
   (c) the line $y = x$ **(d)** the line $y = -x$

17 The image of the point (p, q) after a reflection in a line L is (p, r).
   (a) State with a reason, whether the line L is horizontal, vertical or neither of these.
   (b) Obtain the equation of the line L.

18 A general shape S is enlarged by a scale factor of k to give a shape S': The area of S' is $n \times$ the area of S. Write down a formula connecting k and n which starts as:
   (a) $k =$ **(b)** $n =$

19 A square ABCD has its vertices at the points (1, 1), (3, 1), (3, 3) and (1, 3) respectively.
   Using this square as a guide, or otherwise, comment on the similarities and differences between each of the following transformations:
   (i) a reflection in the line $y = -x$
   (ii) a transformation through the vector $\begin{pmatrix} ^-4 \\ ^-4 \end{pmatrix}$
   (iii) an enlargement, centre the origin of scale factor ⁻1
   (iv) a rotation about the origin through 180°.

20 Under a given rotation about the origin, the image of the point (5, 0) is the point (4, 3). Describe fully the rotation.

Symmetry groups

The diagram shows an equilateral triangle ABC, with centre O.

It can be subjected to 6 transformations which leave its vertices in the same places in space as the original (although the positions of the letters will change).

These six transformations are:

a reflection in the
line through AO

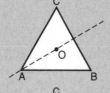 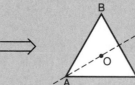

a reflection in the
line through BO

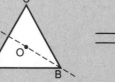 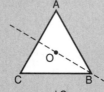

a reflection in the
line through CO.

 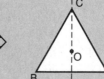

Each of these lines are fixed in space rather than fixed on the triangle.

A 120° clockwise
rotation about O

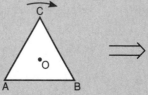

A 240° clockwise
rotation about O

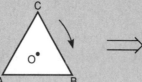

A 360° (or 0°)
rotation about O.

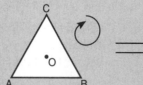

Mathematically this fact is written as:
There are 6 elements in the symmetry group of an equilateral triangle.

The work that follows provides a menu of questions which could be used as the basis for a coursework submission. You are advised to discuss with your teacher the relative difficulties and potential attainment levels associated with each of the questions. Some are unquestionably much easier than others, some are very difficult and good answers could lead to the very highest levels of attainment. It would be unrealistic to think of trying to answer all of these questions in the usual time available.

1 Show clearly that there are 4 elements in the symmetry group of a rectangle.

2 How many elements are there in the symmetry group of a square? Justify your response.

3 Investigate the number of elements in the symmetry group of a regular polygon.

For the equilateral triangle we could write:
the reflection in the line through AO as F_1
the reflection in the line through BO as F_2
the reflection in the line through CO as F_3
the rotation through 120° as R_1
the rotation through 240° as R_2, and
the rotation through 360° as R_3.

4 **(a)** Show that F_3 followed by F_1 is equivalent to the single transformation R_2.

  (b) Obtain, with justification, the single transformation equivalent to each pair of combined transformations. Communicate your results in as efficient manner as possible.

A table of all of the results to question **4** is known as a **group operation table**.

5 Obtain the group operation table for:
  (a) the square   **(b)** the regular pentagon
  (c) any other regular polygon.

6 Investigate the group operation tables for the equilateral triangle, square, regular pentagon and at least one other regular polygon as fully as possible.

7 Obtain, with justification, the number of elements in the symmetry group of each of the following two- and three-dimensional shapes:
  (a) an isosceles triangle   **(b)** an ellipse
  (c) a circle   **(d)** a parallelogram
  (e) a regular tetrahedron **(f)** a cube
  (g) a cuboid
  (h) any other 3D shape of your choosing.

Sets of two- and three-dimensional shapes can be classified as equivalent when they have the same number of elements in their symmetry groups.

8 Classify sets of two- and three-dimensional shapes according to the above criteria.

In your report on this work you are advised to:
- **make and record any observations**
- **explain your methods, working and findings**
- **state and test any conjectures**
- **offer forms of symbolic communication**
- **form and explain any generalisations**
- **offer any proofs of your results.**

More on circles

In *Much ado about a circle* you were introduced to the circle theorems. This chapter is devoted to a set of miscellaneous problems related to those theorems.

1 Stating clearly your reasons, find each of the angles marked with a letter.

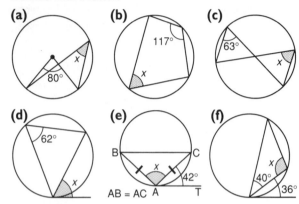

(a) **(b)** **(c)**

(d) **(e)** **(f)**

$AB = AC$

2 AB is a diameter of a circle. C is a point on the circumference of that circle such that AC = 5 cm and BC = 12 cm. Calculate the length of the radius of the circle.

3

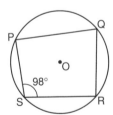

In the diagram, PQ is a diameter of a circle centre O. C is a point on the circumference of the circle. Angle QÔC = 106°.
Find, giving your reasons, the size of:
(a) the angle OQ̂C   **(b)** the angle OP̂C.

4

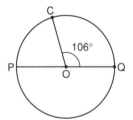

PQRS is a cyclic quadrilateral. O is the centre of the circle. Angle PŜR = 98°.
Calculate, stating clearly your reason, the size of the angle PQ̂R.

5

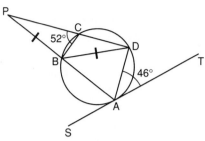

ABCD is a cyclic quadrilateral. The line SAT is the tangent at A to the circle. The lines AB and CD when extended meet at the point P and PB = BD.

The angle DÂT = 46° and the angle PĈB = 52°.

Stating your reasons clearly, calculate the sizes of the angles:
(a) AB̂D   **(b)** DÂB   **(c)** PD̂B   **(d)** PB̂D

6

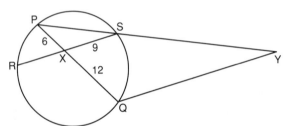

PQ and RS are two chords of a circle which meet at a point X inside the circle.

XP = 6 cm, XS = 9 cm and XQ = 12 cm.
(a) Calculate the length of XR.

The chord PS is extended to a point Y. The line YQ is parallel to RS.
(b) Prove that PS = $\frac{1}{3}$PY

7

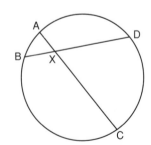

AC and BD are two chords of a circle which meet at the point marked X.
AC = 8 cm, BD = 7 cm,
XB = 2 cm and XA = x cm.
(a) Show that $x^2 - 8x + 10 = 0$
(b) Solve this equation.

On route to winning the 1994 World Cup, Brazil beat Holland in the quarter-final by a score of 3 goals to 2.

The sequence of scoring was as follows:
1 – 0 Brazil
2 – 0 Brazil
2 – 1 Holland
2 – 2 Holland
3 – 2 Brazil
This sequence of scores could be written as:
Brazil, Brazil, Holland, Holland, Brazil
and it is just one of the **sequences leading to a final score of 3 – 2**.

1 Write down at least three other sequences leading to a final score of 3 – 2.

2 Show that there are a total of 10 sequences leading to a final score of 3 – 2.

3 How many different sequences are there leading to a final score of:
   (a) 2 – 3   **(b)** 3 – 0   **(c)** 4 – 1   **(d)** 4 – 2   **(e)** 3 – 3
   (f) any two other final scores of your own choosing?

4 Investigate the number of different sequences leading to any final score of the form:
   (a) $n - 0$ **(b)** $n - 1$ **(c)** $n - 2$ **(d)** $n - m$

5 Try to find a general expression for the number of sequences leading to a final score of $n - m$.

In your report you are advised to:
● **make and record any observations**
● **explain your methods and working**
● **state and test any conjectures**
● **offer forms of symbolic communication**
● **form and explain any generalisations**
● **offer any proofs of your results.**

All of the theory behind this chapter has been done before. The problems are deemed to be more difficult because they are set in a three-dimensional context.

Example

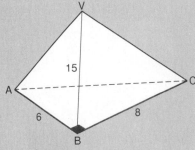

ABCV is a tetrahedron with the vertex V being vertically above the point B.
The base, ABC, is a triangle, right-angled at B. AB = 6 cm, BC = 8 cm and BV = 15 cm.

(a) Calculate the distances:
    (i) AC   **(ii)** VA   **(iii)** VC

(b) Calculate the angles:
    (i) B$\hat{A}$V   **(ii)** B$\hat{V}$C   **(iii)** A$\hat{V}$C

(c) Calculate the volume of the tetrahedron ABCV.

(d) Calculate the surface area of the tetrahedron ABVC.

M is a point on AC such that the angle V$\hat{M}$C = 90°.

(e) Calculate the distances:
    (i) VM   **(ii)** AM

Solution

(a) (i) Triangle ABC is right-angled at B
$$\text{so } AC^2 = AB^2 + BC^2$$
$$= 36 + 64$$
$$= 100$$
$$AC = 10 \text{ cm}$$

(ii) Triangle VBA is right-angled at B
$$\text{so } VA^2 = VB^2 + AB^2$$
$$= 225 + 36$$
$$= 261$$
$$VA = 16 \cdot 16 \text{ cm correct to two decimal places.}$$

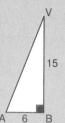

(iii) Triangle VBC is right-angled at B
$$\text{so } VC^2 = VB^2 + BC^2$$
$$= 225 + 64$$
$$= 289$$
$$VC = 17 \text{ cm}$$

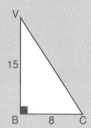

(b) (i) For angle BÂV

$$\text{Tan } B\hat{A}V = \frac{15}{6} = 2\cdot5$$

BÂV = 68·2° correct to 1 dp

(ii) For angle BV̂C

$$\text{Tan } B\hat{V}C = \frac{8}{15} = 0\cdot5333$$

BV̂C = 28·1° again to 1 dp.

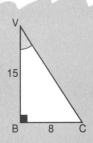

(iii) For angle AV̂C,

by the cosine rule $\cos A\hat{V}C = \dfrac{16\cdot16^2 + 17^2 - 10^2}{2 \times 16\cdot16 \times 17}$

$$= 0\cdot81928$$

So AV̂C = 35·0°, correct to 1 dp

(c) Volume of tetrahedron $= \dfrac{\text{Area of base} \times \text{vertical height}}{3} = \dfrac{\frac{1}{2} \times 6 \times 8 \times 15}{3} = 120$ cubic cm or cm³

(d) The surface area = area of ABC + area of ABV + area of BVC + area of AVC.
Looking at the diagrams, the areas are:

$$ABC = \frac{1}{2} \times 6 \times 8 = 24 \quad ABV = \frac{1}{2} \times 6 \times 15 = 45 \quad BVC = \frac{1}{2} \times 8 \times 15 = 60$$

and for the area of AVC we have:

using $\frac{1}{2} ab\sin C$ area of AVC $= \frac{1}{2} \times 16\cdot16 \times 17 \times \sin35 = 78\cdot8$ to 1 dp

So the surface area $= 24 + 45 + 60 + 78\cdot8 = 207\cdot8$ cm², to 1 dp

(e) (i)

Area of AVC $= \frac{1}{2} AC \times VM$

So $78\cdot8 = 5 \times VM$

VM = 15·76 cm

(ii)

$$AM^2 = AV^2 - VM^2$$
$$= 16\cdot16^2 - 15\cdot76^2 = 12\cdot768$$

AM $= 3\cdot57$ cm, correct to 2 dp

1 VABCD is a square-based pyramid.

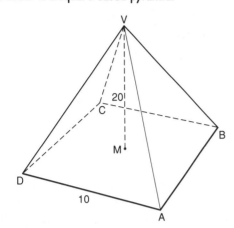

The vertex V is vertically above the centre, M, of the base ABCD.

AB = 10 cm and VM = 20 cm.

(a) Calculate the distances:

   (i) AC **(ii)** VA

(b) Calculate the angles:

   (i) VÂM **(ii)** BV̂C

(c) Calculate the volume of VABCD.

(d) Calculate the surface area of VABCD.

P is the mid-point of BC.

(e) Calculate the angle VP̂M.

2 A vertical radio mast, BD, stands on horizontal ground and is held in place by two tight wires, as shown below.

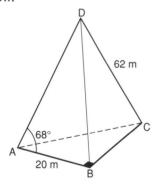

The angle AB̂C = 90°.

The angle DÂB = 68°.

The distance AB = 20 m and the length of DC = 62 m.

(a) Calculate the height of the radio mast BD.

(b) Calculate the length of AD.

(c) Calculate the distance BC.

(d) Calculate the angle DĈB.

3

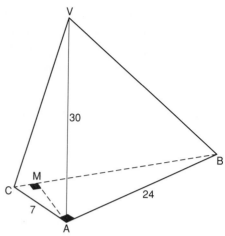

The above diagram represents a pyramid ABCV. The horizontal base, ABC, is a triangle, right-angled at A.

AB = 24 cm and AC = 7 cm.

The vertex V is vertically above A with VA = 30 cm.

The point M lies on BC with angle AM̂C = 90°.

(a) Show the BC = 25 cm.

(b) Calculate the lengths:

   (i) VB **(ii)** VC

(c) Calculate the volume of ABCV.

(d) Calculate the length AM.

(e) Calculate the angle VM̂A.

4 In the diagram below ABCDEF is a wedge. The horizontal base ABFE is a rectangle.

The vertical face ACDE is also a rectangle.

Angle CÂB = Angle DÊF = 90°

CA = 5 cm   AB = 12 cm

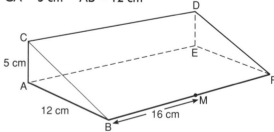

(a) Calculate CB.

The volume of the wedge is 750 cm².

(b) Calculate CD.

(c) Calculate the angles:

   (i) DF̂E **(ii)** CB̂D **(iii)** DB̂E

A point M lies on BF such that BM = 16 cm.

(d) Calculate:

   (i) the distance DM **(ii)** the angle DM̂E.

The work in this chapter extends the previous work on trigonometry, in particular that of the chapter titled *Trigonometry 5*.
You will need to make use of basic trigonometry, the area of a triangle formula, the sine rule and the cosine rule.

1

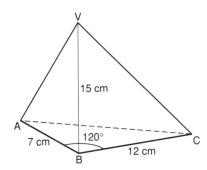

VABC is a tetrahedron. The vertex V is 15 cm vertically above the vertex B.
The triangular base ABC lies in the horizontal plane.

AB = 7 cm, BC = 12 cm and the angle $A\hat{B}C = 120°$.

(a) Use the cosine rule to calculate the length AC.

(b) Calculate the lengths:

    (i) VA   **(ii)** VC

(c) Calculate the angles:

    (i) $B\hat{V}A$ **(ii)** $B\hat{V}C$ **(iii)** $A\hat{V}C$

2

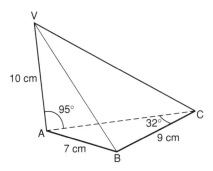

VABC is a tetrahedron.

AB = 7 cm, BC = 9 cm and the angle $A\hat{C}B = 32°$.
The angle $B\hat{A}C$ is acute.

(a) Show that, to the nearest degree,
the angle $B\hat{A}C = 43°$.

Using this value for the angle $B\hat{A}C$:

(b) show that, to one decimal place, AC = 12·8 cm.
The angle $V\hat{A}C = 95°$ and VA = 10 cm.

(c) Calculate the length of VC.

3

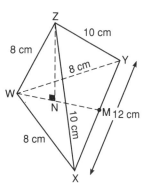

WXYZ is a tetrahedron with a horizontal, triangular base WXY. WZ = WX = 8 cm and XY = 12 cm.
The vertex Z is above the plane of the triangle WXY.
ZX = ZY = 10 cm. M is the midpoint of XY. N is the foot of the perpendicular from Z to the plane of WXY.

(a) Show that ZM = 8 cm.

(b) Show that:

    (i) WM = 2 $\sqrt{7}$ cm   **(ii)** WN = $\sqrt{7}$ cm

(c) Show that ZN = $\sqrt{57}$ cm

(d) Calculate, to the nearest degree, the size of the angles:

    (i) $X\hat{W}Y$ **(ii)** $Z\hat{W}N$ **(iii)** $W\hat{Z}Y$

4

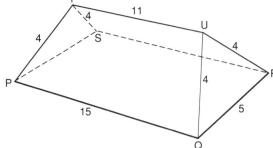

The above diagram represents a tent which has been erected. The horizontal base is a rectangle PQRS.
The top edge TU is also horizontal.

In metres, the lengths of the edges are as follows:
PT = ST = QU = RU = 4   PQ = SR = 15
TU = 11   PS = QR = 5

(a) Giving your answer to the nearest degree,
calculate the size of the angle $T\hat{P}S$.

M is the midpoint of PS.

(b) Calculate the distance TM.

(c) Calculate the height of the edge TU above the horizontal base PQRS.

(d) Calculate the angle $T\hat{U}Q$.

Conditional probability

In this book you have been reminded of the range and diversity of the problems concerning probability, and you have been shown the various methods used to solve probability problems.

What you now need to do is to put this experience into practice; identify the type of problem, and the appropriate procedure needed to solve the problem.

What is the probability of getting a 5 or a Head when tossing a dice or a coin simultaneously? In this type of problem we can use probability spaces or tabulation. All the possible outcomes are:

1&H	2&H	3&H	4&H	5&H	6&H
1&T	2&T	3&T	4&T	5&T	6&T

12 outcomes altogether.

7 outcomes which include a 5 or Head

So $P(5 \text{ or Head}) = \frac{7}{12}$

The probability of my getting the first two questions in a test correct is $\frac{3}{4}$ and $\frac{2}{3}$ respectively. Calculate:

(a) the probability I get them both right **(b)** the probability I get at least one question correct.

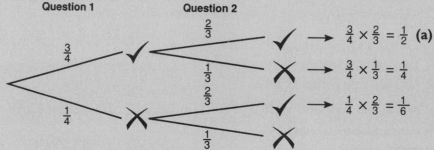

$\frac{3}{4} \times \frac{2}{3} = \frac{1}{2}$ (a)

$\frac{3}{4} \times \frac{1}{3} = \frac{1}{4}$

$\frac{1}{4} \times \frac{2}{3} = \frac{1}{6}$

(b) $P(\text{at least one correct}) = \frac{1}{2} + \frac{1}{4} + \frac{1}{6} = \frac{11}{12}$

To find the probability of two events happening:

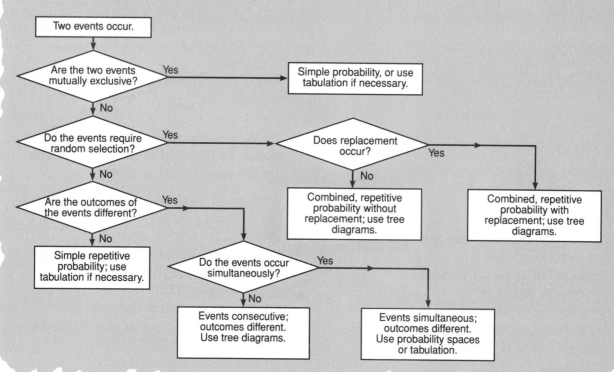

1 Two numbers are selected at random, without repetition, from the numbers 1–10. Find the probability that:

(a) both numbers are prime

(b) neither are powers of 2

(c) only one exactly is a power of two.

2

Two octagonal dice, each with the numbers 1–8, are thrown together. What is the probability that:

(a) both scores are equal

(b) scores are both odd numbers

(c) at least one score is more than 5

(d) the total of both scores is no more than 10?

3

The probability that a racing driver will win a race is $\frac{3}{10}$. Find the probability that the racing driver will:

(a) win two races in succession

(b) only win the fourth race

(c) win at least two races out of the four.

4 Simone has six red pens and four blue pens in a drawer. Two pens are each selected at random and replaced. What is the probability that they are of different colours?

5 A biased coin will turn up heads three times out of five. Find the probability that when tossed twice it shows:

(a) two heads

(b) two tails

(c) one head and one tail

(d) at least one head.

6

During the evening the probability that a man watches television is $\frac{4}{7}$. If he decides to watch television the probability that he will fall asleep is $\frac{4}{7}$. If he doesn't watch television the probability that he will fall asleep is $\frac{1}{7}$. Find the probability that he falls asleep.

7 Twelve people, seven females and five males, are seated in the front row of a television audience. One, and then another, are to be picked at random to help in a magic act. Of the two chosen, what is the probability that they will:

(a) both be male

(b) be of different sexes?

(c) If a third person is then chosen, what is the probability that there will be at least one female?

8

A box of chocolates contains seven hard-centred and nine soft-centred chocolates. Two chocolates are selected at random, and not replaced. What is the probability that:

(a) the two chocolates have different types of centre

(b) both chocolates are soft-centred?

9 A hand of cards contains ten cards: six are hearts, and four are clubs. Two cards are each drawn at random and replaced. Find the probability that:

(a) one card is a heart and one is a club

(b) the two cards belong to the same suit.

10 A pack of 52 playing cards contains 4 aces. Three cards are each removed and not replaced. What is the probability that they are all aces?

11 Two dice are tossed. What is the probability of getting a prime number on one dice and the number 1 on the other dice?

12

On her way to work Miss Jefferies drives through two Pelican crossings. The probability she has to stop at the first is $\frac{2}{5}$, at the second $\frac{2}{7}$. Find the probability that:

(a) she does not have to stop at all

(b) she stops at just one set of lights.

13 Three coins are tossed. Find the probability of getting:

(a) three tails

(b) at least one head.

14 The probability that my bus is late is $\frac{4}{9}$. If my bus is on time, then the probability of my catching a train which leaves on time is $\frac{5}{7}$. If my bus is late, then the probability of my catching a train which leaves on time is $\frac{2}{7}$. Calculate the probability:

(a) of both bus and train being late

(b) of either bus or train being late.

15

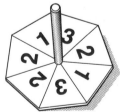

The spinner is spun, and a record kept of whether the score is even or odd. After three throws, find the probability that:

(a) all three scores are even

(b) there are at least two odd scores

(c) there are no even scores

(d) there is one odd score.

16 A dice game is played by Ann and Karen. A throw of 1 or 2 means the dice is passed to the other player. A throw of 3 or 4 gives an extra throw. A throw of 5 or 6 is a winning throw. Ann has the first throw. In the first three throws of the dice what is the probability that:

(a) Ann wins

(b) Karen wins?

17

There are 16 cans of coke on a shelf. Ten are ordinary coke, and six are diet coke. Two cans are each selected at random and removed. Find the probability that:

(a) both cans are diet coke

(b) there is one can of each type of coke.

18 A fairground game is set up so the probability of gaining scores is as follows:

Score	1	5	10	15	20
Probability	$\frac{1}{10}$	$\frac{1}{5}$	$\frac{2}{5}$	$\frac{1}{5}$	$\frac{1}{10}$

With two scores gained at random, find the probability of achieving total scores of:

(a) 16 **(b)** 20.

With three scores gained at random find the probability of achieving total scores of:

(c) 16 **(d)** 20.

19

A box contains four red cards, three green cards, and two blue cards. Three cards are each chosen at random, and replaced. Find the probability that:

(a) the three cards are red

(b) there are at least two red cards

(c) there are at least two green cards.

20 Repeat question **19** for the situation where each of the three cards are removed at random one at a time, and *not* replaced.

Example 1
Find the maximum value of $x + 2y$ given that:
$0 \leqslant x \leqslant 3, 0 \leqslant y \leqslant 2$

Solution
Firstly shade the feasible region for x and y:

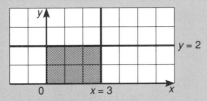

Now write $x + 2y = n$, so we need to find the maximum value of n.

But $x + 2y = n$ will give a straight line graph for each value of n. These are called a **family** of straight lines.

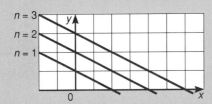

Now combine the graph of the feasible region with those of the family of straight lines.

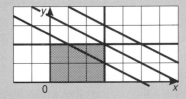

From these combined graphs it is clear than n will be greatest when
$x = 3$ and $y = 2$

and in this case
$x + 2y = 3 + 2(2) = 3 + 4 = 7$

1 Find the maximum value of $3x + 4y$ in each of the cases:
   (a) $0 \leqslant x \leqslant 5, 0 \leqslant y \leqslant 3$
   (b) $0 \leqslant x \leqslant 4, 0 \leqslant y \leqslant 5$
   (c) $1 \leqslant x \leqslant 4, 2 \leqslant y \leqslant 7$

2 Find the minimum value of $3x + 4y$ in each of the cases in question **1**.

Example 2
Find the maximum value of $2x + 3y$ when
$x > 0, 0 < y < 3, y > x$

In this case the feasible region is:

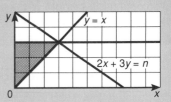

and it is the point P, with coordinates (3, 3) at which the straight line $2x + 3y$ reaches its maximum possible value for points within that region.

So the maximum value of $2x + 3y$ is
$2(3) + 3(3) = 6 + 9 = 15$

3 Find the maximum value of $4x + 3y$ when
   $0 < x < 6, y \leqslant 2x, y > 0$

4 A feasible region is defined by
   $x > 0, y > 0, x + 3y \geqslant 15, 3x + 2y \geqslant 30, 4x + y \geqslant 20$
   (a) Draw the feasible region.
   (b) Find the minimum value of $2x + 3y$ within this region.
   (c) Find the maximum value of $x^2 + y^2$ within this region.

5 Audley High School are staging their annual concert. The number of people in the audience must satisfy the following conditions.
   (i) The maximum size of the audience is 300.
   (ii) The number of children in the audience cannot exceed 240.
   (iii) There must be at least three times as many children as adults in the audience.

   On one particular evening there are c children and a adults in the audience.
   (a) Write down all the inequalities that c and a must satisfy.
   (b) Draw the feasible region for these inequalities.
   Tickets cost £3 for each child and £5 for each adult.
   (c) Write down an algebraic expression in terms of c and a for the amount of money received on that particular evening.
   (d) Work out the maximum possible income from ticket sales on any particular evening.

● **Remember**

It is often either impossible or too expensive to survey everything or everybody in a population. To overcome this a **sample** of the population is taken. The sample should represent the whole population as accurately as possible and so needs to be carefully chosen.

A **random sample** involves each member of the population having an **equal chance of being chosen**. This can be achieved adequately using dice, names on paper drawn from a box or, for a large population, random number tables or the RAN function on a calculator or computer.

1 Select a random sample of 10 people in your class or school. Record how many sisters and/or brothers they each have. Calculate the mean and variance of your data. Compare your answers with others. What conclusions can you draw about the whole class or school?

2 Describe in detail how you would select a random sample of 30 people from a population of 813 using:

(a) random number tables

(b) the RAN function on a calculator or computer.

Where a population is not too large and it can be listed then a **systematic random sample** can be taken by randomly selecting an integer n and then sampling every nth entry in the list. The starting point should be randomly selected in the first n entries in the list. This technique is also used to test products being produced continuously. It would not make sense to test every item from a production line especially if the test involved changing the items in any way.

3 A company is intending to share out local telephone calls to its sales staff. It wants to allocate a roughly equal number of calls to each person by allocating them groups of the first two digits. Describe how you could use a systematic random sampling process to find the proportions of the local telephone numbers sharing the first two digits to avoid considering all the numbers in the directory.

4 A drug company wants to ensure that its syringes deliver the dose stated on them with appropriate accuracy. Its 10 ml syringes must deliver a mean of 10 ml with a standard deviation of less than 0·4 ml and always within 1 ml of 10. The company buys a new machine that makes and fills syringes. Tests on the first 60 syringes produced in a trial run revealed the following data:

Test No.	1st ten	2nd ten	3rd ten	4th ten	5th ten	6th ten
1	⁻1	⁻1	⁻6	0	0	⁺2
2	0	⁺3	⁻2	⁺2	⁻1	⁺5
3	⁻3	⁻4	⁺3	⁻3	0	⁻4
4	⁺4	⁺2	⁺5	⁺5	⁺1	⁻1
5	⁺1	⁻4	⁻3	⁻4	⁺1	⁺3
6	⁺1	⁻6	⁺5	⁺2	⁻4	⁺2
7	⁻5	0	⁻9	⁻6	⁻3	⁺4
8	⁺3	⁻3	⁺7	⁻4	⁺6	⁻6
9	⁻2	⁺2	0	⁺2	⁻3	⁻3
10	0	⁺1	⁻2	⁺8	⁻4	⁺5

Figures in this table are multiples of 0·1 ml below (−) and above (+) 10 ml.

(a) Carry out a systematic random sample of every fourth test for each of the four starting points. Calculate the mean and standard deviation of each sample, compare to the results required by the company and comment upon any trends which might arise.

(b) Calculate the mean and standard deviation of the whole set of 60 tests.

(c) Compare and contrast the results from your samples with the results from the whole set and comment specifically on whether systematically sampling every fourth syringe has provided secure information about the whole set.

(d) Does using a larger number than four in the sampling give a secure picture of the whole data set? Try some other possibilities which are also factors of 60.

A further variation on the theme of random sampling is the **stratified random sample**. In this case the population will have a spread across an attribute such as age or species. The population will possibly be distributed unevenly across the spread of ages or species. So that a sample which closely mirrors the whole population can be taken, it is chosen so that the proportion sampled from each category in the distribution matches the proportion in the whole population. This assumes that the proportions in the whole population are known. For example,

In a school there are different numbers of pupils in each year.

Year	7	8	9	10	11	12	13
Pupils	43	57	62	52	44	23	17
Sample	4	6	6	5	4	2	2

To survey these using a 10% stratified random sample you would probably round off the number of pupils in each year to the nearest 10 and then randomly select those as usual. The information gleaned from the pupils in the sample is then pooled before analysis.

5 Describe how you could survey your local park to estimate the mean girth of the trees from a stratified random sample of approximately 100 trees of mixed species. Include in your description aspects of where you would measure them and how you could select a random sample within each stratum. If you can get permission, carry out your survey.

6 An hypothesis is that people who live in avenues own more cars per family than in any other type of address. Ask you teacher to supply a list of all the children in your school and whether they live in avenues, roads, streets, etc. Decide upon a stratified sample to be questioned and carry out a survey to investigate the hypothesis. Describe the full process and your results in detail.

You might have found that people will not give you information in a survey and this is not unusual. To overcome this effect surveyors of opinions decide upon how many people need to give answers to fill the proportion from each stratum of a random sample. Agents are then told to approach people within each category until they receive answers from the required number, or in technical terms the **quota**. This technique is called **quota sampling**.

The danger is that the people approached do not form a random sample within each category. The agent will only have responses from a group of people who will have the time and inclination to answer questionnaires. So busy people might not contribute in proportion to quota sampling.

7 Write down the subjects of five surveys that might be effected greatly by the limitations of quota sampling and its potential respondents. Are they any ways that the problems could be overcome?

8 Plan, carry out and write a report on a survey of opinion in your school based upon an hypothesis about school meals. The survey should involve quota sampling from the school population taking into account the following:
(a) strata of the population
(b) questionnaire design
(c) ordering preferences.

Analyse the data gained and prepare charts about the relative popularity of meals and perhaps aspects of timing, paying and queueing. Prepare a presentation to the rest of your class or parents and governors. Rehearse your presentation and be prepared to justify mathematically all your assumptions and processes.

Histograms and distributions

Histograms can take several shapes.

Normal distribution

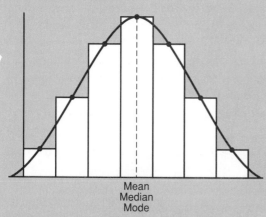

Mean
Median
Mode

This histogram is symmetrical about the centre. If we draw a curve through the midpoints of the bars which represents the same area we obtain a **frequency curve**.

This represents the **normal distribution and is a bell-shaped curve**.

It is symmetrical about the centre (at its maximum) and **50% of its area** lie on either side of the centre. The mean, median and mode are all at this maximum point.

The types of distributions which are normally distributed are:

- External examinations
- Weights of people
- Heights of people

In a normal distribution about:

- 68% of the area lies within one standard deviation of the mean.

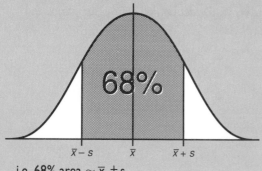

$$\bar{x} - s \qquad \bar{x} \qquad \bar{x} + s$$

i.e. 68% area $\simeq \bar{x} \pm s$

- 95% of the areas lies within $\pm$ two standard deviation of the mean.

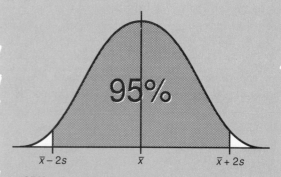

$$\bar{x} - 2s \qquad \bar{x} \qquad \bar{x} + 2s$$

i.e. 95% area $\simeq \bar{x} \pm 2s$

- 99·8% of the area lies within $\pm$ three point one standard deviations of the mean.

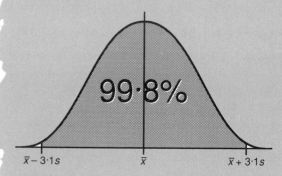

$$\bar{x} - 3 \cdot 1s \qquad \bar{x} \qquad \bar{x} + 3 \cdot 1s$$

i.e. 99·8% area $\simeq \bar{x} \pm 3 \cdot 1s$

This information allows you to **predict** parts of distributions which approximately **fit the normal distribution**.

In an external examination the mean mark is 55% with a standard deviation of 12%.

$\therefore$ 68% area $\simeq \bar{x} \pm s$

$\therefore$ 68% area $\simeq 55 \pm 12$

$\therefore$ 68% of candidates obtained 43% to 67%.

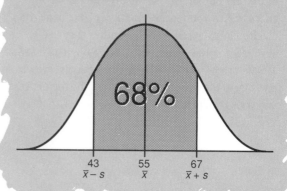

$$\begin{array}{ccc} 43 & 55 & 67 \\ \bar{x} - s & \bar{x} & \bar{x} + s \end{array}$$

95% area $\simeq \bar{x} \pm 2s$
95% area $\simeq 55 \pm 24$
95% of candidates obtained 31% to 79%.

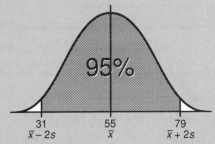

99·8% area $\simeq \bar{x} \pm 3\cdot 1s$
99·8% area $\simeq 55 \pm 37\cdot 2$
99·8% of candidates obtained 17·8% to 92·2%.

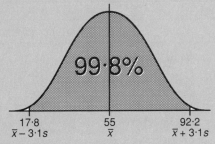

The pass mark is set at 55%.

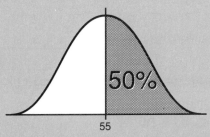

As this is the mean and 50% of the candidates lie either side of the mean.
50% of the candidates pass.

Suppose the pass mark was set at 43%.

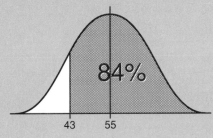

As this is one standard deviation below the mean 84% of the candidates would pass as 16% of candidates would be less than 43%.

In these questions assume the distributions are normal.

1 Bags of flour have a mean weight of 1 kg with a standard deviation of 0·016 kg.

   (a) What percentage of bags weigh less than 1 kg?

   (b) What percentage of bags weigh less than 0·984 kg?

   (c) What percentage of bags lie between 0·968 kg and 1·032 kg?

   (d) How many bags out of 1000 would you expect to weight less than 0·968 kg?

2 In a geography examination the mean mark is 61% and the standard deviation 12.

   What should the pass mark be if:

   (a) 50% must pass

   (b) 68% must pass

   (c) 95% must pass

   (d) 98·8% must pass?

3 Over a long period of time Jessica calculates her journey to work as a mean of 40 minutes and a standard deviation of 8 minutes.

   She wants to be 99·9% certain of arriving at work on time.

   How long should she allow for her journey to work?

4 A factory produces components with mean length 51 mm and standard deviation 2·5 mm.

   The factory produces 5000 in one day.

   The factory must reject components if the length exceeds 56 mm.

   How many components must the factory reject?

Negative skew distribution

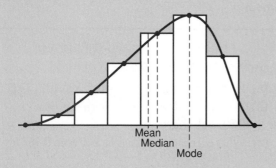

Mean
Median
Mode

The distribution is skewed to the right (negatively).

The **mode** is the maximum point.

The **median** is the value that divides the area equally.

The mean is slightly to the left of the median. An external examination which is too easy would be negatively skewed.

Positive skew distribution

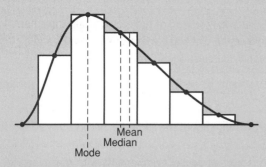

Mean
Median
Mode

Here the frequency curve is drawn through the histogram and it can be clearly seen that the distribution is skewed to the left (positively).
The **mode** is the maximum point.
The **median** is the value that divides the area equally.
The mean is slightly to the right of the median. An external examination which is too hard would be positively skewed.

For the following distributions draw the frequency distribution curve and describe the type of distribution. Calculate the mean and standard deviation. Show these on the graph.

5

Mark	No. of candidates
10–19	2
20–29	4
30–39	7
40–49	14
50–59	20
60–69	8
70–79	3

6

Mark	No. of candidates
0–10	15
11–20	31
21–30	56
31–40	45
41–50	24
51–60	15
61–70	7
71–80	5
81–90	1

7

Weight (x)	Number (f)
$30 < x \leqslant 40$	1
$40 < x \leqslant 50$	3
$50 < x \leqslant 60$	8
$60 < x \leqslant 70$	16
$70 < x \leqslant 80$	24
$80 < x \leqslant 90$	15
$90 < x \leqslant 100$	7
$100 < x \leqslant 110$	4
$110 < x \leqslant 120$	2

8

Age (x)	Frequency (f)
$20 \leqslant x < 30$	57
$30 \leqslant x < 40$	71
$40 \leqslant x < 50$	42
$50 \leqslant x < 60$	16
$60 \leqslant x < 70$	9
$70 \leqslant x < 80$	3

Given the right conditions of food, moisture and warmth some bacteria can divide into two every 10 minutes. This is known as binary fission and is particularly important in the food industry in order to avoid food poisoning.

This diagram shows the growth by division of one bacterium.

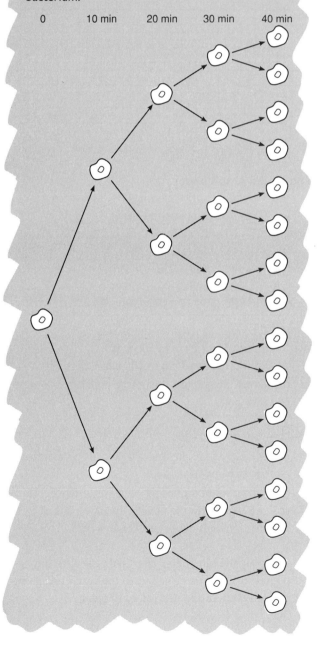

1 How many bacteria will this single one have become after multiplying for:
 (a) 60 minutes
 (b) 120 minutes?

2 Copy and complete this table:

Time in minutes	0	10	20	30	40	50	60
Number of bacteria	2^0	2^1		2^3			

3 (a) Use the table of results to help you write down a formula for the number of bacteria after n minutes.
 (b) How many bacteria will be present after 150 minutes.

4 For her 18th birthday party Avril orders a buffet meal. The caterers prepare and lay the buffet some time before Avril and her friends are to eat it.

 (a) If the buffet is left in good bacteria breeding conditions, how long will it take for one bacteria to multiply to become over 1 000 000?
 (b) How many bacteria will there be if the buffet is left for 5 hours? Give your answer to 1 significant figure.

If the conditions are really bad the bacteria find it even easier to breed. For example they can split into two every single minute.

5 Write down a formula to find the number of bacteria that splits into two every minute.

6 How many bacteria will there be after:
 (a) 5 minutes
 (b) 10 minutes
 (c) 1 hour?

That's the way it grows

A well-known trick question is:
'A lily growing in a pond doubles in size every 4 days. After 16 days it has covered half the pond. How long does it take to cover the full pond?'

How long do you think it takes?

This graph shows the growth of the lily.

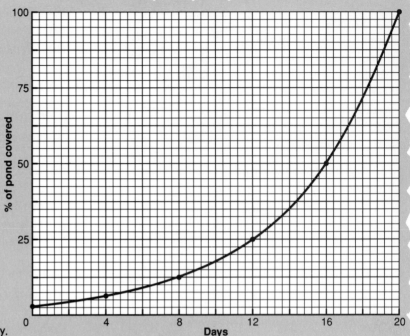

1 From the graph, find the percentage of the pond covered:

   (a) after 10 days
   (b) after 13 days
   (c) between the 4th and 12th days
   (d) between the 8th and 16th day.

2 How long did it take for the lily to cover 60% of the pond?

A quantity multiplied by the same number each time period is said to grow **exponentially**. The bacteria and the lily are examples of exponential growth.

Abbeytown, Brasston and Cudlip are three villages in the Midlands. In 1700 the populations of each of the three villages was 120 inhabitants.

Abbeytown had an exponential growth rate of 1·4 every 50 years.

Brasston had a uniform growth rate of 100 inhabitants every 50 years.
Cudlip had a constant number of inhabitants for the next 100 years and then an exponential growth rate of 1·8 every 50 years.

You need graph paper.

3 (a) Copy and complete this table:

Date	1700	1750	1800	1850	1900	1950	2000
A	120	168	235				
B	120	220					
C	120		120	216			

   (b) On graph paper draw these axes:
       across: Date 2 cm to 50 years
       up: Population 2 cm to 100 inhabitants
   (c) Draw the graphs of the three populations on the same axes.

4 Use your graph to find:
   (a) the year when all three villages had approximately the same population
   (b) the population of all three towns in 1825
   (c) the increase in the number of inhabitants of all three villages between 1725 and 1975.

5 Assuming the same rates of growth, calculate the population of all three villages in the year 2100, giving your answers to the nearest 10 villagers.

Tom started by smoking 100 cigarettes a week. He knows cigarettes are harmful. To help him stop smoking he decided to reduce the number of cigarettes to $\frac{3}{4}$ (or 0·75 or 75%) each week. This is an example of an **exponential decay** with a multiplier of 0·75.

You need graph paper.

1 (a) Copy this table which shows how the number of cigarettes Tom smoked reduced each week.

Week	1	2	3	4	5	6
Number	100	75	56	42	31	23

(b) Plot these points with weeks on the horizontal axis and draw a smooth exponential decay curve through them.

The manufacturer of Atakodox, an anti-bacteria solution, claims that when sprayed onto cleaning surfaces the number of bacteria decreases by 75% every second.

2 On a cleaning surface there are 20 000 bacteria. The surface is then sprayed with Atakodox anti-bacteria solution. Calculate how many bacteria are left after 1 second.

3 (a) Copy and complete this table:

Time in seconds	0	1	2	3	4
Number of bacteria	20 000				

(b) On graph paper draw a graph to show this exponential decay.

4 Use your graph to find the number of bacteria still present after:

(a) 1·5 seconds

(b) 2·5 seconds

(c) 3·5 seconds.

5 How long does it take the bacteria to fall to half its original number?

The manufacturer of a de-humidifier claims that it will extract 60% of the moisture in the air every 2 hours.

6 The living room of a house has a new concrete floor laid. The builder hires a de-humidifier to remove the excess moisture from the air. The amount of moisture in the air is 4 litres and reduces to 2·4 litres after two hours.

(a) Copy and complete this table

Time after switch on (hours)	0	2	4	6	8	10
Amount of moisture removed (litres)	4	2·4				

(b) Draw a graph to show the information in your table.

(c) Use your graph to find:

    (i) the time for the amount of moisture to fall to 50% of its original value

    (ii) the amount of water left in the air after 5 hours.

7 In 1800 a village had 200 inhabitants. During the next 150 years the village had an exponential growth of 1·5 every 50 years. However, from 1950 onwards the population declined at an exponential decay of 0·8 every 20 years.

(a) Copy and complete:

Year	Population of village
1800	200
1850	300
1900	
1950	
1970	
1990	
2010	

(b) Draw a graph to show the information in your completed table.

(c) Use your graph to find the year(s) when the population of the village was 500.

(d) If the decline rate remains 0·8 every 20 years, estimate the year when the village will have the same population as 1800.

The roots of all evil

Today's problem:
solve the equation
$x^2 + 7x + 12 = 0$

Jessica has been asked to solve the equation $x^2 + 7x + 12 = 0$.

She decides to factorise the equation in order to help her solve it.

This is the method she uses:
$x^2 + 7x + 12 = 0$
$(x + 3)(x + 4) = 0$
$x = {}^-3$ or $x = {}^-4$

1 Factorise each of the equations and then solve them:
(a) $x^2 + 6x + 8 = 0$
(b) $x^2 + 8x + 15 = 0$
(c) $x^2 + 5x + 6 = 0$

The solutions to the equation $x^2 + 7x + 12 = 0$ were $x = {}^-3$ or $x = {}^-4$.
If the two solutions to the equation are called α and β respectively then
$\alpha\beta = {}^-3 \times {}^-4 = 12$ (the number coefficient)
and
$\alpha + \beta = {}^-3 + {}^-4 = {}^-7$ (–the x-term coefficient)

2 Write down the value of $\alpha + \beta$ and $\alpha\beta$ for each of these quadratic equations:
(a) $x^2 + 6x + 12 = 0$
(b) $x^2 - 5x + 7 = 0$
(c) $x^2 + 12x - 15 = 0$
(d) $x^2 - 4x - 9 = 0$
(e) $x^2 + 1 \cdot 5x = 0$
(f) $x^2 - 9 = 0$

Given that the equation $x^2 + bx + c = 0$ has two solutions α and β (called the roots of the equation) these two general statements can be made.

$\alpha + \beta = {}^-b$ and $\alpha\beta = c$

Find an equation whose roots are the squares of the roots of the equation $x^2 - 2x - 3 = 0$.

One way of finding the new equation is to solve the equation $x^2 - 2x - 3 = 0$ to find its roots

$x^2 - 2x - 3 = 0$
$(x + 1)(x - 3) = 0$

The roots of the equation are $x = {}^-1$, $x = 3$.

To find the equation whose roots are the squares of these numbers, the $^-1$ and 3 must be squared

$({}^-1^2) = 1$ and $3^2 = 9$
giving $(x - 1)(x - 9) = 0$

The new equation is $x^2 - 10x + 9 = 0$

3 Find an equation whose roots are the square of the roots of:
(a) $x^2 + 6x + 8 = 0$
(b) $x^2 - 2x - 8 = 0$

This method of finding an equation whose roots are the squares of another equation will work provided that the equation easily factorises. If it doesn't easily factorise an alternative method is needed.

The original problem
Find an equation whose roots are the square of the roots of equation $x^2 - 2x - 3 = 0$.

Let the roots of $x^2 - 2x - 3 = 0$ be α and β.

Then $\alpha + \beta = 2$ and $\alpha\beta = {}^-3$

To find the new equation we need to know

(i) $\alpha^2 + \beta^2$ and (the squares of the original roots)

(ii) $\alpha^2\beta^2$

(i) $\alpha^2 + \beta^2 = (\alpha + \beta)^2 - 2\alpha\beta$ Explain why.
$\alpha^2 + \beta^2 = ({}^-1 + 3)^2 - 2({}^-1 \times 3)$
$\alpha^2 + \beta^2 = ({}^-2)^2 - 2({}^-3)$
$\alpha^2 + \beta^2 = 4 + 6$
$\alpha^2 + \beta^2 = 10$

(ii) $\alpha^2\beta^2 = (\alpha\beta)^2$. Explain why.

$\alpha^2\beta^2 = (^-1 \times 3)^2$

$\alpha^2\beta^2 = (^-3)^2$

$\alpha^2\beta^2 = 9$

If $\alpha^2 + \beta^2 = 10$ and $\alpha^2\beta^2 = 9$ the equation must be $x^2 - 10x + 9 = 0$ (as before).

4 Use this method to check the equation $x^2 + 6x + 8 = 0$ given in question **3**.

5 An equation is given as $x^2 - 3x - 7 = 0$

(a) Copy and complete:
$\alpha + \beta =$ and $\alpha\beta =$

(b) Work out the value of:
$2\alpha + 2\beta$ (Hint: factorise)

(c) Work out the value of
$2\alpha\, 2\beta$

(d) Use your answer to find an equation whose roots are twice as big as the roots of $x^2 - 3x - 7 = 0$.

6 Find an equation whose roots are three times those of $x^2 - 2x - 3 = 0$ by:

(a) factorising

(b) using the relationships $\alpha + \beta = 2$ and $\alpha\beta = -3$

7 Find an equation whose roots are each one more than those of $x^2 - 3x - 7 = 0$.

8 An equation is given as $x^2 - 2x - 4 = 0$.

(a) Copy and complete these statements
$\alpha + \beta =$ and $\alpha\beta =$

(b) Find the value of
$\frac{1}{\alpha} + \frac{1}{\beta}$ (Hint: think fractions)

(c) Find the value of:
$\frac{1}{\alpha} \times \frac{1}{\beta}$

(d) Use your answer to parts **(b)** and **(c)** to find an equation whose roots are the reciprocals of the roots of $x^2 - 2x - 4 = 0$.

In the equations we have looked at so far the coefficient (number in front) of x^2 has been one.

Consider this equation $ax^2 + bx + c = 0$

dividing each term by a $x^2 + \frac{bx}{a} + \frac{c}{a} = 0$

If the equation has roots α and β,
then $(x - \alpha)(x - \beta) = 0$

9 Write down in terms of a, b and c an expression for $\alpha + \beta$ and $\alpha\beta$.

10 Write down the value of $\alpha + \beta$ and $\alpha\beta$ for each of these equations:

(a) $2x^2 + 4x - 6 = 0$

(b) $3x^2 - 9x + 15 = 0$

(c) $6x^2 - 3x - 6 = 0$

(d) $4x^2 + 8 = 0$

(e) $9x^2 - 16 = 0$

11 An equation is given as $4x^2 - 8x + 2 = 0$
Find the value of:

(a) $\alpha + \beta$ **(b)** $(\alpha + \beta)^2$

(c) $\frac{1}{\alpha} + \frac{1}{\beta}$ **(d)** $\alpha^2 + \beta^2$

(e) $\alpha^3\beta^3$

12 The roots of the equation $2x^2 + 3x - 2$ are α and β.
Find an equation whose roots are:

(a) α^2, β^2 **(b)** α^2, β^2

Challenge

13 It is known that the roots of the equation $2x^2 + 3x - n = 0$ are both equal.

(a) Write down and simplify expressions for $\alpha + \beta$ and $\alpha\beta$.

(b) Use this information to find the value of n.

(c) Find an equation whose roots are the cubes of those of $2x^2 + 3x - n = 0$.

Let's bisect this equation

There are several methods of solving quadratic equations
- using graphs
- quadratic formula
- factorising
- completing the square
- transforming the equation
- iterative process

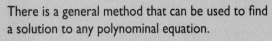

There is a general method that can be used to find a solution to any polynominal equation.

Consider the equation $x^2 = 28$

A solution interval is $5 < x < 6$

For the 1st approximation take the middle value of the solution interval (5.5). This value is tested to see how close it is to the correct solution.

$$\left.\begin{array}{c} 6 \\ 5 \end{array}\right\} \quad \text{1st approx } x = 5 \cdot 5 \quad 5 \cdot 5^2 = 30 \cdot 25 \quad \textbf{Too big}$$

The new solution interval is $5 < x < 5 \cdot 5$

For the 2nd approximation take the middle value of the new solution interval (5.25).

$$\left.\begin{array}{c} 5 \cdot 5 \\ 5 \end{array}\right\} \quad \text{2nd approx } x = 5 \cdot 25 \quad 5 \cdot 25^2 = 27 \cdot 5625 \quad \textbf{Too small}$$

The new solution interval is $5 \cdot 25 < x < 5 \cdot 5$
Middle value $= 5 \cdot 375$

$$\left.\begin{array}{c} 5 \cdot 5 \\ 5 \cdot 25 \end{array}\right\} \text{3rd approx } x = 5 \cdot 375 \quad 5 \cdot 375^2 = 28 \cdot 890\,62 \quad \textbf{Too big}$$

The new solution interval $5 \cdot 25 < x < 5 \cdot 375$

$$\left.\begin{array}{c} 5 \cdot 375 \\ 5 \cdot 25 \end{array}\right\} \text{4th approx } x = 5 \cdot 3125 \quad 5 \cdot 3125^2 = 28 \cdot 222\,656 \quad \textbf{Too big}$$

This process of halving or bisecting the previous solution interval is continued until the correct degree of approximation is obtained.

The whole process looks like this:

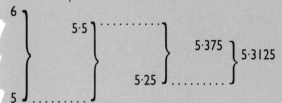

The results can be put into a table:

Interval	Middle value	Test	Comment
5 to 6	5·5	30·25	Too big
5 to 5·5	5·25	27·5625	Too small
5·25 to 5·5	5·375	28·8906	Too big
5·25 to 5·375	5·3125	28·2226	Too big
5·25 to 5·3125	5·281 25	27·8916	Too small
5·281 25 to 5·3125	5·296 875	28·0568	Too big

An approximate solution to the equation is $x = 5 \cdot 296\,875$ or $5 \cdot 297$ to 3 dp

Using a calculator the method of bisection can be used to solve any polynomial equation to a good degree of accuracy.

1 To solve the equation $x^2 - 2x - 7 = 0$

(a) Show that there is a solution in the interval $3 < x < 4$.

(b) Copy and complete this table.

Interval	x	$x^2 - 2x - 7$	Comment
3 to 4	3·5	⁻1·75	Too small
3·5 to 4	3·75	⁻0·4375	Too small
3·75 to 4	3·875	0·265 625	Too big
3·75 to 3·875	3·8125		
3·8125 to			

(c) Extend the table for two more solution intervals.

(d) Write down an approximate solution to the equation $x^2 - 2x - 7 = 0$.

(e) Compare your solution with the solution obtained by any other method you know to solve quadratic equations.

2 (a) Show that the equation $x^3 - 2x - 6 = 0$ has a solution in the interval $x = 2$ to $x = 3$.

(b) Solve the equation $x^3 - 2x - 6 = 0$ by copying and completing this table:

Interval	x	$x^3 - 2x - 6$	Comment
2 to 3	2·5	4·625	Too big

(c) Sketch the graph of $y = x^3 - 2x - 6 = 0$.

(d) How many different solutions does this equation have?

3 This is a graph of $y = x^3 - 2x^2 + 7$.

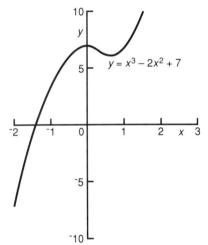

Use the graph:

(a) to find the solution interval

(b) to help you fully solve the equation $x^3 - 2x^2 + 7 = 0$.

This method of bisection is ideally suited for use with a computer.

This program will ask you for a range of x values which it scans in order to find the solution intervals.

It then uses the method of bisection to find the approximate solution within each interval.

This program will solve the equation $x^3 + 2x^2 - 2x - 1 = 0$

```
10CLS
20INPUT"INPUT RANGE OF VALUES OF X"LX,UX
30PRINTTAB(11)"INTERVAL"TAB(28)"Y1";TAB(38)"Y2"
40FOR I = LX TO UX
50X = I:GOSUB270:Y1=Y:X = I+1:GOSUB270:Y2=Y
70 IF Y2 >0 AND Y1 < 0 THEN110
80 IF Y2 <0 AND Y1 > 0 THEN110
90IF Y1 = 0 THENPRINT"SOLUTION X = "; X
100 GOTO120
110PRINTX-1,X,Y1,Y2
120 NEXT
130PRINT
140INPUT"LOWER VALUE OF SOLUTION INTERVAL " LV
150INPUT"UPPER VALUE OF SOLUTION INTERVAL "UV
160PRINTTAB(3);"X";TAB(30)"Y"
170X = LV:GOSUB270:Y1=Y:X =UV:GOSUB270:Y2=Y
190IF Y2<Y1 THEN A = LV:LV=UV:UV=A
200X=(LV+UV)/2
210GOSUB270
220PRINT;TAB(3)X;TAB(30)Y
230IF Y >0 THEN UV = X: GOTO250
240IF Y <0 THEN LV = X
250IF Y <0.01 AND Y-0.01 THEN 130
260GOTO200
270Y=X*X*X+2*X*X-2*X-1
280RETURN
```

4 Use the program to:

(a) find the number of solutions there are to the equation $x^3 + 2x^2 - 2x - 1 = 0$

(b) find the solution intervals where appropriate

(c) solve the equation.

To change the equation to be investigated rewrite line 270 of the program with the new equation.

5 Use the program to solve:

(a) $x^2 + 7x - 11 = 0$

(b) $2x^3 + 3x^2 - 5x - 6 = 0$

(c) $x^4 + x^3 - x^2 - 1 = 0$

(d) any other equations that you like.

Points in space

The diagram below shows a three-dimensional coordinate grid.

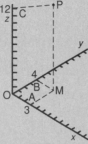

The point P is **3** units along the *x*-axis,
i.e. OA = **3** units
4 units along the *y*-axis,
i.e. OB = **4** units, and
12 units up the *z*-axis,
i.e. OC = **12** units.

So the coordinates of P are (3, 4, 12),
whilst the coordinates of A are (3, 0, 0),
and the coordinates of B are (0, 4, 0),
and the coordinates of C are (0, 0, 12)
and finally the coordinates of M are (3, 4, 0).

To calculate the distance OP
By Pythagoras $OM^2 = OA^2 + OB^2$
$= 9 + 16$
$= 25$
so OM = 5 units
Then, again by Pythagoras
$OP^2 = OM^2 + PM^2$
$= 25 + 144$
$= 169$
so OP = 13 units

Note $OP^2 = OA^2 + OB^2 + PM^2$ which is a quick way of finding the distance from the origin to a point in space.

The angle PÔM

OM = 5 units   PM = 12 units
So Tan $\hat{POM} = \frac{12}{5} = 2\cdot4$

So $\hat{POM} = 67\cdot38°$ to two decimal places

---

1 For the point, P, show that, correct to two decimal places the angles PÂM and PB̂M are 71·57° and 75·96° respectively.

2

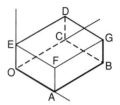

The diagram shows a cuboid OABCDEFG with its sides OA, OC and OE respectively lying along the *x*-, *y*- and *z*-axes of a three-dimensional coordinate frame, with origin at O.
OA = 4 units, OC = 5 units and OE = 2 units.

(a) Write down the coordinates of A, B, C, D, E, F and G.

(b) Calculate the distance:
    (i) OB   **(ii)** OG   **(iii)** CG

(c) Calculate the angles:
    (i) GÔB   **(ii)** EĜO   **(iii)** DĜC

3 Calculate the distance from the origin to the point (4, ‾3, 10).

To calculate the distance between any two points

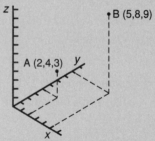

The coordinates of A are (2, 4, 3).
The coordinates of B are (5, 8, 9).
So to move from A to B we move

$5 - 2 = 3$ units in the *x* direction
$8 - 4 = 4$ units in the *y* direction, and
$9 - 3 = 6$ units in the *z* direction.

Then the distance from A to B is given by
$AB^2 = 3^2 + 4^2 + 6^2$
$= 9 + 16 + 36$
$= 61$
so AB = 7·81 units, correct to two decimal places.

4 The coordinates of three points A, B and C are (3, 5, 1), (5, 9, 7) and (¯2, 4, ¯8). Calculate the distance:

(a) AB   **(b)** AC   **(c)** BC

5 For the three points given in question **4**, above, find the coordinates of the midpoint of:

(a) AB   **(b)** BC   **(c)** AC

6

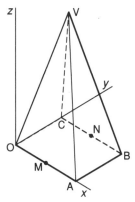

The diagram shows a rectangular-based pyramid OABCV. The rectangular base OABC lies on the x-y plane with OA and OC lying along the x- and y-axes respectively. O is the origin. The vertex V is 15 units vertically above the mid-point of OABC.
The coordinates of A are (8, 0, 0).
The coordinates of C are (0, 6, 0).
M is the mid-point of OA.
N is the mid-point of BC.

(a) Write down the coordinates of M.
(b) Write down the coordinates of B.
(c) Write down the coordinates of N.
(d) Find the coordinates of V.
(e) Find the coordinates of the mid-point of MV.
(f) Calculate the distance VO.
(g) Calculate the angle $C\hat{A}B$.
(h) Calculate the angle $V\hat{O}B$.
(i) Calculate the angle $V\hat{M}N$.
(j) Calculate the angle $B\hat{V}C$.
(k) Calculate the angle $M\hat{V}N$.
(l) Calculate the area of the triangle OVA.
(m) Calculate the volume of the pyramid OABCV.

7 Two points A and B have coordinates (1, 1, 1) and (7, 4, 10) respectively. A point P lies on the line AB and divides the line segment AB in the ratio 2:1. Find the possible coordinates of P.

8 Two points M and N have coordinates (2, 1, 4) and (10, 5, 8) respectively. A point K lies on the line from M to N and divides the line segment MN in the ratio 3:1. Find the possible coordinates of K.

9 A and B are two points in three-dimensional space which have general coordinates (x_1, y_1, z_1) and (x_2, y_2, z_2) respectively. A point K lies on the line from A to B and divides the line segment AB in the ratio k : 1 Obtain a general expression for the coordinates of k.

10

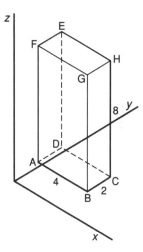

The cuboid shown is located on a set of three-dimensional axes.
The point A has coordinates (1, 1, 1).
AB is parallel to the x-axis.
AD is parallel to the y-axis.
AF is parallel to the z-axis.

The numbers on the diagram show distances in terms of the units of the coordinate system.

(a) Write down the coordinates of B, C, D, E, F, G and H.
(b) Calculate the length of BH.
(c) Calculate the length of a longest diagonal of the cuboid.
(d) Calculate the angle $H\hat{A}B$.
(e) Write down the coordinates of the midpoint of GH.
(f) Write down the coordinates of the midpoint of the top face EFGH.
(g) Write down the coordinates of the point P which divides the line segment AH in the ratio 3:1 and for which AP > PH.

On pages 119–22 you revised work on the basic transformations of reflections, translations, enlargements and rotations. The last two of the miscellaneous questions led you to taking a look at some simple combined transformations. Then on page 123 there was some work on symmetry groups, in which, again, there was an opportunity for you to look at the effects of combining some transformations. This chapter deals exclusively with the effects of combining transformations.

You may find it helpful to have a supply of tracing paper and some small mirrors.

As on page 123, a small triangle will often be used to illustrate the results.

The combination of two reflections

Case 1: In two parallel lines
L and M are two parallel lines. The triangle ABC has been drawn to the left of L.

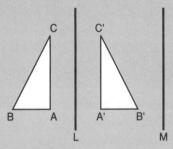

The image of ABC when it is reflected in L is A'B'C'.

Now, when A'B'C' is reflected in M it creates a second image A"B"C".

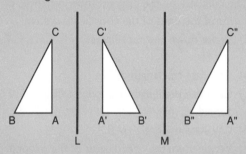

The single transformation from ABC to A"B"C" is a translation.
The distance from ABC to A"B"C is
double the distance between the two lines L and M.

1 **Do Worksheet 7.**

2 Two lines L and M have equations $x = 2$ and $x = 5$ respectively. The point P has coordinates (3, 4).
   (a) Write down the coordinates of P', the image of P in L.
   (b) Reflect P' in M to create the second image P".
   (c) Write down the coordinates of P".
   (d) Show that the single transformation from P to P" is a translation through a distance equal to twice the distance between the lines L and M.

Case 2: Two lines at an angle
In this case the two lines L and M are at an angle.

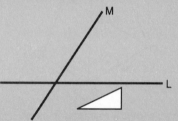

When the triangle PQR is reflected in L it creates an image P'Q'R'.

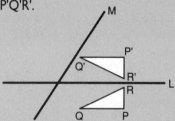

When P'Q'R' is reflected in M it creates a second image P"Q"R".

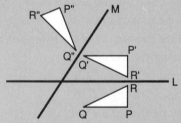

The single transformation from PQR to P"Q"R" is a **rotation**.
The centre of the rotation is the **point of intersection of L and M.**
The angle of rotation is **twice the angle between L and M.**
The direction of the rotation is the **direction from L to M.**

3 Do Worksheet 8.

4 (a) Mark the point P with coordinates (3, 4).
  (b) Reflect P, in the y-axis to give P'.
  (c) Reflect P' in the x-axis to give P".
  (d) Show that the single transformation from P to P"
  is a rotation through 180° about the origin.

5 (a) Draw the triangle ABC with vertices at (0, 3),
  (0, 5) and (1, 5).
  (b) Reflect ABC in the line y = x to give A'B'C'.
  (c) Reflect A'B'C' in the y-axis to give A"B"C".
  (d) Confirm that the single transformation from
  ABC to A"B"C" is a rotation, about the origin, in
  an anti-clockwise direction through twice the
  angle between the line y = x and the y-axis.

6 Find the single transformation equivalent to a
reflection in the line y = x followed by a reflection in
the line y = 3x.

Two translations
The combined effect of two translations is merely a
third translation. This is illustrated below.

The triangle PQR is translated 3 units across and
4 units up

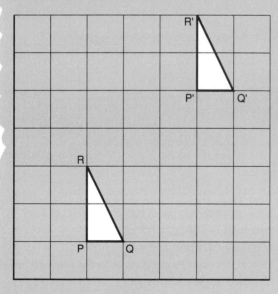

to create the image P'Q'R'.

P'Q'R' is now translated 5 units across and 2 units up
to create the second image P"Q"R".

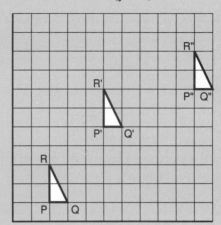

The transformation taking PQR to P"Q"R" is a
translation of
3 + 5 = 8 units across, and
4 + 2 = 6 units up.

In general terms if

T: $\begin{pmatrix} x \\ y \end{pmatrix} \rightarrow \begin{pmatrix} x \\ y \end{pmatrix} + \begin{pmatrix} a \\ b \end{pmatrix}$ and

S: $\begin{pmatrix} x \\ y \end{pmatrix} \rightarrow \begin{pmatrix} x \\ y \end{pmatrix} + \begin{pmatrix} c \\ d \end{pmatrix}$

Then the effect of combining **T** and **S** is to form
the single translation **U**, where

U: $\begin{pmatrix} x \\ y \end{pmatrix} \rightarrow \begin{pmatrix} x \\ y \end{pmatrix} + \begin{pmatrix} a + c \\ b + d \end{pmatrix}$

7 Two translations **T** and **S** are defined by

T: $\begin{pmatrix} x \\ y \end{pmatrix} \rightarrow \begin{pmatrix} x \\ y \end{pmatrix} + \begin{pmatrix} 5 \\ {}^-2 \end{pmatrix}$

S: $\begin{pmatrix} x \\ y \end{pmatrix} \rightarrow \begin{pmatrix} x \\ y \end{pmatrix} + \begin{pmatrix} {}^-3 \\ 1 \end{pmatrix}$

Write down, in vector form, the single translation
formed by combining **T** and **S**.

8 **T** and **S** are two translations.

T is defined by T: $\begin{pmatrix} x \\ y \end{pmatrix} \rightarrow \begin{pmatrix} x \\ y \end{pmatrix} + \begin{pmatrix} 5 \\ {}^-3 \end{pmatrix}$

The combined effect of T and S translates the point
(1, ⁻6) to the point (9, ⁻4).
Obtain, in vector form, the translation **S**.

Combining a reflection and a translation

The diagram shows a line L and a triangle ABC.

ABC is firstly reflected in L to give the image A'B'C'.

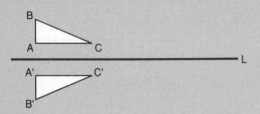

Now ABC is translated 5 units to the right and parallel to L to create the second image A"B"C".

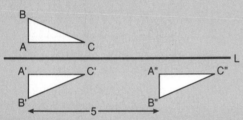

The effect of these two transformations is called a **glide reflection**.

This must be restricted to the case where the translation is parallel to the mirror line.

9   A glide reflection is formed by combining a reflection in the x-axis with a translation of 6 units to the left and parallel to the x-axis.

   (a) Under this glide reflection, write down the images of the points:
   (i) $(0, 1)$ **(ii)** $(1, 0)$ **(iii)** $(3, 5)$
   (iv) $(^-2, 7)$ **(v)** $(^-3, ^-2)$

   (b) The image, under this glide reflection, of a point P is the point Q, where the coordinates of Q are $(15, ^-23)$. Find the coordinates of P.

10 R_L is a reflection in a line L and T_L is a translation parallel to L. The combination of the two transformations R_L followed by T_L is written as $R_L * T_L$.

   (a) Show clearly that $R_L * T_L = T_L * R_L$.

   (b) Interpret $(R_L * T_L) * (R_L * T_L)$ and explain as fully as possible the single transformation equivalent to this expression.

   (c) Given that $(R_L * T_L) * (R_L * T_L)$ can be written as $(R_L * T_L)^2$ describe, as fully as possible $(R_L * T_L)^n$.

Two rotations

Case 1: Common centre of rotation.

In the diagram below the triangle PQR is rotated in an anti-clockwise direction through an angle A about the point O.

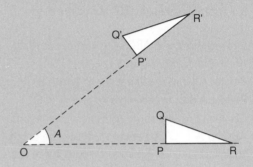

This gives the image P'Q'R'.

Now P'Q'R' is rotated in an anti-clockwise direction about the point O and through an angle of B.

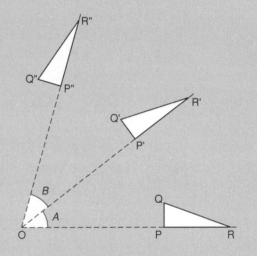

The combined effect of these rotations is an anti-clockwise rotation about O through an angle of $A + B$.

So, in general terms the combined effect of any two rotations about a common centre is **always** a **rotation** about the **common centre** through an angle equal to the **sum of the two angles** of rotation.

11 Do Worksheet 9.

12 (a) On squared or graph paper draw the triangle with vertices A, B and C at the points (1, 0), (3, 0) and (3, 2).

(b) Rotate ABC about the origin in an anti-clockwise direction through an angle of 90° to form the image A'B'C'.

(c) Now rotate A'B'C' about the origin in an anti-clockwise direction through an angle of 45° to create a second image A"B"C".

(d) Show that the single transformation from ABC to A"B"C" is a rotation about the origin through an angle of 135°.

13 A rotation about the origin in a clockwise direction through 90° is symbolised by **R**. Two successive applications of this rotation is written as $\mathbf{R}^2$ and three successive applications as $\mathbf{R}^3$.

(a) Give a geometric interpretation of:

(i) $\mathbf{R}^4$ **(ii)** $\mathbf{R}^5$ **(iii)** $\mathbf{R}^{\frac{1}{2}}$
(iv) $\mathbf{R}^{-1}$ **(v)** $\mathbf{R}^n$

(b) Given that a and b are positive integers and $\mathbf{R}^a = \mathbf{R}^b$ state the general connection between a and b.

Case 2: The centres of rotation are not common

This is not particularly easy. It will be illustrated by a simple case.

The triangle ABC is first to be rotated about the point (0, 2) in the clockwise direction through an angle of 90°.

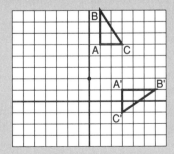

This gives the image A'B'C'.

Now A'B'C' is rotated about the point (2, 0) in the clockwise direction through an angle of 90°.

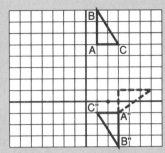

This gives the second image A"B"C".

The single transformation from ABC to A"B"C" is a rotation about the point (2, 2), through an angle of 180°.

> So the combined effect of these two rotations is a single rotation through the addition of the two original angles of rotation. This result holds in the general case. The main problem is finding the centre of the overall single rotation.

14 Do Worksheets 10 and 11.

15 (a) Draw two points P and Q which are 10 cm apart with Q to the right of P.
A shape, S is to be rotated in the anti-clockwise direction about P through an angle of 30° to form an image S'. S' is then rotated in the anti-clockwise direction about Q and through an angle of 60° to form a second image S".

(b) Show that the combined effect of these two rotations is a single rotation.

(c) State the direction and angle of that single rotation.

(d) Show how to find the centre of that single rotation.

16 AB is the line segment joining the two points A and B which have coordinates (4, 0) and 4, ⁻1) respectively. Under a rotation about the point (2, 0) in an anti-clockwise direction through 90°, AB is transformed to the image A'B'. Under a rotation about the point (⁻2, 0) in an anti-clockwise direction through 90°, A'B' is transformed to A"B". Describe fully the single transformation from AB to A"B".

Transformation geometry 3

A rotation and a translation

A triangle has been drawn with its vertices A, B and C at the points with coordinates (2, 0), (5, 0) and (0, 2) respectively.

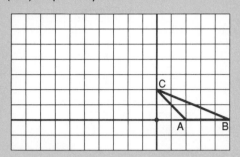

ABC is rotated about the origin in the anti-clockwise direction through 90° to create the image A'B'C'.

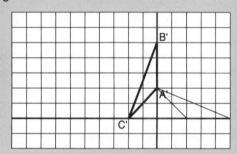

A'B'C' is then translated 8 units to the left to create the second image A"B"C". This is the combined effect of a rotation and translation.

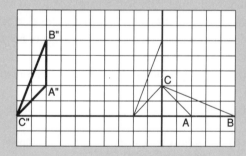

It should be clear that the combined effect of these two transformations is a rotation. The centre of this rotation is the point with coordinates (⁻4, ⁻4).

So the combined effect of a rotation about a point O through an angle θ is still a rotation through θ, but the centre of the rotation changes from O to some other point. The problem is finding the location of this point.

17 **Do Worksheet 12**

18 A triangle has its vertices P, Q and R at the points with coordinates (3, 0), (7, 0) and (7, 2) respectively.

(a) Draw the triangle PQR.
The image of PQR under a 90°, anti-clockwise rotation about the origin is P'Q'R'.
(b) Draw P'Q'R'.
The image of P'Q'R' under a translation 12 units to the right is P"Q"R".
(c) Draw P"Q"R".
(d) State clearly the single transformation which transforms PQR to P"Q"R".
(e) State clearly the single transformation which transforms P"Q"R" back to PQR.

19 A, B and C are the points with coordinates (5, 4), (5, 1) and (7, 1). The line segments AB and BC are drawn to form a letter L.

(a) Plot the points and draw the letter L.
The L-shape is rotated clockwise through an angle of 90° about the origin to form an image L'.
(b) Plot L'.
The image L is then translated by the translation **T**, defined by

$$\mathbf{T}: \begin{pmatrix} x \\ y \end{pmatrix} \to \begin{pmatrix} x \\ y \end{pmatrix} + \begin{pmatrix} 0 \\ 6 \end{pmatrix}$$

to form a second image L".
(c) Plot L".
(d) State clearly the single transformation which maps L onto L".

20 A square has its vertices A, B, C and D at the points with coordinates (7, 1), (9, 1), (9, 3) and (7, 3) respectively. The square ABCD is translated 10 units to the left to form an image A'B'C'D'. A'B'C'D' is then rotated 90° about the origin in a clockwise direction to form a second image A"B"C"D".

(a) On the same axes show the relative positions of ABCD, A'B'C'D' and A"B"C"D".
(b) State clearly the single transformation which maps ABCD onto A"B"C"D".

21 A shape S is rotated 90° anti-clockwise about (0, 2) to form S'. The S' is translated 12 units upwards to form S". State clearly the single transformation which maps S to S" directly.

In *The Quadratic Formula* the formula for solving quadratic equations was given as

$$x = \frac{-b \pm \sqrt{b^2 - 4ac}}{2a}$$

1 Use the formula to solve:
  (a) $x^2 + 6x - 1 = 0$
  (b) $2x^2 - 8x + 5 = 0$
  (c) $4x^2 + 5x - 8 = 0$

Although this formula is useful for solving equations it can also be used to give general information about quadratic functions.

2 (a) Using the quadratic formula try to solve each of these equations:
  (i) $x^2 + 4x + 3 = 0$
  (ii) $x^2 + 4x + 4 = 0$
  (iii) $x^2 + 4x + 5 = 0$

  (b) Try to match each of these diagrams to the equations in part **(a)** giving a reason for your matching.

(i)

(ii)
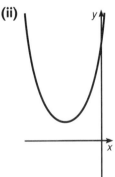

(iii)
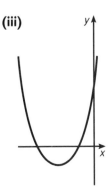

The reason the formula gave you the results that it did can be understood by considering this part of it:

$b^2 - 4ac$ This part is called the **discriminant**.

If $b^2 - 4ac$ is positive the equation will have two real roots.

If $b^2 - 4ac$ is zero the equation will have repeated or equal roots.

If $b^2 - 4ac$ is negative the equation will have no real roots.

To summarise:

The equation will have:

two distinct roots if	$b^2 > 4ac$
repeated (or equal) roots if	$b^2 = 4ac$
no real roots if	$b^2 < 4ac$

3 Write down, with reasons, whether these equations will have two distinct roots, repeated roots or no real roots. Do *not* solve the equations.
  (a) $x^2 - 6x + 10 = 0$ **(b)** $3x^2 + 4x - 3 = 0$
  (c) $2x^2 - 5x + 3 = 0$ **(d)** $4x^2 - 12x + 9 = 0$
  (e) $2x^2 - 10x + 12 \cdot 5 = 0$ **(f)** $3x^2 - 6x + 5 = 0$

4 An equation is given as $x^2 - 5x + c$.
  (a) Write down the value of $b^2 - 4ac$ if the equation has repeated roots.
  (b) Find the value of c in order that the equation does have repeated roots and solve the equation.

5 The equation $1 \cdot 25x^2 + bx + 20 = 0$ is known to have repeated roots.
  (a) Find two possible values of b.
  (b) For both values of b draw a sketch of $y = 1 \cdot 25x^2 + bx + 20 = 0$

▼ Challenge

6 (a) Prove that the equation
    $x^2 + bx + (b - 1) = 0$
    has real roots for all values of b.
  (b) Show that for one of the values of b the roots are repeated roots and find their value.

In some of the earlier chapters you have undertaken work on transformation geometry. This chapter develops that work into the use of a symbolic or algebraic method of representing many of the transformations using what are called **matrices**, or in the singular a **matrix**.

> It is important that you remember that matrices are only relevant for transformations for which the origin (0, 0) remains fixed. If the origin moves under the transformation then we cannot use matrices.

You may have met matrices before, but we shall start at the beginning again.

A reflection in the vertical axis
The whole plane is reflected in the y-axis, or the vertical axis.

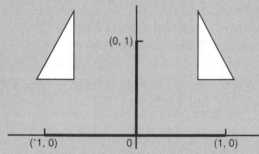

Under this transformation the origin does not move, so we can use matrices.

From the diagram it should be clear that the point (1, 0) is transformed to the point ($^-$1, 0).
We write this as:

$$\begin{pmatrix} 1 \\ 0 \end{pmatrix} \rightarrow \begin{pmatrix} ^-1 \\ 0 \end{pmatrix}$$

Similarly the point (0, 1) remains unmoved, or is transformed to itself, that is (0, 1) again.
We write this as:

$$\begin{pmatrix} 0 \\ 1 \end{pmatrix} \rightarrow \begin{pmatrix} 0 \\ 1 \end{pmatrix}$$

The matrix representing the transformation of a reflection in the y-axis is written as:

$$\begin{pmatrix} ^-1 & 0 \\ 0 & 1 \end{pmatrix}$$

It has two columns:
the first column is where (1, 0) goes to, i.e. ($^-$1, 0)
the second column is where (0, 1) goes to, i.e. (0, 1).
In other words, for all transformations under which the origin is invariant, the matrix representing the transformation is:

$$\begin{pmatrix} \text{the} & \text{the} \\ \text{image of} & \text{image of} \\ (1, 0) & (0, 1) \end{pmatrix}$$

Example 1
Find the matrix representing a rotation of 90° about the origin in an anti-clockwise direction.

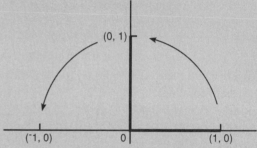

Under this transformation the image of (1, 0) is (0, 1)

so $\begin{pmatrix} 1 \\ 0 \end{pmatrix} \rightarrow \begin{pmatrix} 0 \\ 1 \end{pmatrix}$

the image of (0, 1) is ($^-$1, 0)

so $\begin{pmatrix} 0 \\ 1 \end{pmatrix} \rightarrow \begin{pmatrix} ^-1 \\ 0 \end{pmatrix}$

Hence the matrix is $\begin{pmatrix} 0 & ^-1 \\ 1 & 0 \end{pmatrix}$.

Example 2
Find the transformation represented by the matrix

$$\begin{pmatrix} 1 & 0 \\ 0 & ^-1 \end{pmatrix}$$

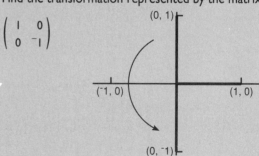

This matrix represents a transformation for which
the image of (1, 0) is (1, 0)
and the image of (0, 1) is (0, $^-$1).
So the transformation has to be a reflection in the x-axis.

1 Find the matrix representing:

  (a) a rotation through 180° about the origin

  (b) a reflection in the line $y = x$

  (c) an enlargement, centre the origin of scale factor 2

  (d) a rotation, about the origin through 90° in the clockwise direction

  (e) a reflection in the line $y = -x$

2 State clearly what is wrong with the following.
Under a reflection in the line $x = 2$
the image of (1, 0) is (3, 0) and the image of (0, 1) is (4, 1).
Hence the matrix representing this transformation is

$$\begin{pmatrix} 3 & 4 \\ 0 & 1 \end{pmatrix}.$$

Example
A triangle has it vertices A, B and C at the points with coordinates (3, 1), (5, 2) and (4, 3) respectively. Under the transformation represented by the matrix

$$M = \begin{pmatrix} 1 & 0 \\ 0 & -1 \end{pmatrix}$$

the image of the triangle ABC is the triangle A'B'C'. Find the coordinates of A', B' and C'.

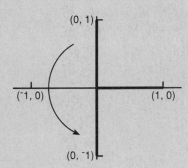

Under the matrix, the image of (1, 0) is (1, 0) and the image of (0, 1) is (0, ⁻1).

So the matrix represents a reflection in the x-axis.

Hence reflecting ABC in the x-axis we have:

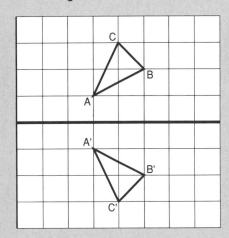

Consequently A' is (3, ⁻1), B' is (5, ⁻2) and C' is (4, ⁻3).

3 The vertices P, Q and R of a triangle are at the points (3, 0), (5, 0) and (5, 2) respectively. Under a transformation represented by the matrix

$$A = \begin{pmatrix} 0 & -1 \\ 1 & 0 \end{pmatrix}$$

the image of P, Q and R are P', Q' and R' respectively. Find the coordinates of P', Q' and R'.

4 Find the images A', B' and C' of the vertices of a triangle ABC where A = (2, 4), B = (3, ⁻1) and C = (⁻2, 5) when ABC is subjected to the transformation defined by the matrix

$$M = \begin{pmatrix} 3 & 0 \\ 0 & 3 \end{pmatrix}$$

5 A transformation is defined by the matrix A where

$$A = \begin{pmatrix} 0 & 1 \\ 1 & 0 \end{pmatrix}$$

  (a) State the transformation defined by A.

  (b) Find the image P'Q'R' of the triangle PQR, where P = (2, 3), Q = (5, 1) and R = (⁻1, 2), under this transformation.

The general rotation matrix

Suppose that the whole plane is rotated about the origin in the anti-clockwise direction through an angle θ.

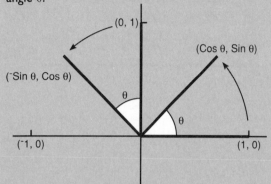

Under this transformation the images of $(1, 0)$ and $(0, 1)$ are

$(1, 0) \rightarrow (\text{Cos } \theta, \text{Sin } \theta)$

$(0, 1) \rightarrow (-\text{Sin } \theta, \text{Cos } \theta)$

or

$$\begin{pmatrix} 1 \\ 0 \end{pmatrix} \rightarrow \begin{pmatrix} \text{Cos } \theta \\ \text{Sin } \theta \end{pmatrix} \text{ and } \begin{pmatrix} 0 \\ 1 \end{pmatrix} \rightarrow \begin{pmatrix} -\text{Sin } \theta \\ \text{Cos } \theta \end{pmatrix}$$

So the matrix representing this general rotation is:

$$\mathbf{M} = \begin{pmatrix} \text{Cos } \theta & -\text{Sin } \theta \\ \text{Sin } \theta & \text{Cos } \theta \end{pmatrix}$$

---

6 Write down the matrix which represents a rotation about the origin:

(a) through $30°$ anti-clockwise

(b) through $75°$ anti-clockwise

(c) through $105°$ anti-clockwise.

Give the numerical values correct to 3 decimal places.

7 Show that the matrix representing a rotation about the origin through a general angle θ in the clockwise direction is:

$$\begin{pmatrix} \text{Cos } \theta & \text{Sin } \theta \\ -\text{Sin } \theta & \text{Cos } \theta \end{pmatrix}$$

8 Write down the matrix representing a clockwise rotation about the origin through an angle of:

(a) $60°$ (b) $30°$ (c) $75°$

Write all numbers correct to 3 decimal places.

9 Write down the matrices A and B which represent anti-clockwise rotations about the origin through angles of $45°$ and $90°$ respectively.

Comment, as much as you can, on the two results.

10 Use the above diagram to show that

$$\text{Sin } 45° = \text{Cos } 45° = \frac{1}{\sqrt{2}}$$

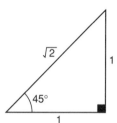

Hence write down the matrix representing a clockwise rotation about the origin through an angle of $45°$.

11

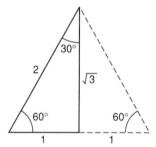

Use the above diagram to help establish the transformation represented by matrix:

$$\begin{pmatrix} \frac{1}{2} & \frac{-\sqrt{3}}{2} \\ \frac{\sqrt{3}}{2} & \frac{1}{2} \end{pmatrix}$$

12 Find the transformation represented by the matrix:

$$\begin{pmatrix} -0·6 & 0·8 \\ 0·8 & 0·6 \end{pmatrix}$$

13 Given that θ is acute and $\text{Tan } \theta = \frac{5}{12}$, obtain the matrix representing an anti-clockwise rotation about the origin through an angle θ.

14 Given that θ is acute and $\text{Sin } \theta = \frac{7}{25}$, obtain the matrix representing a clockwise rotation about the origin through an angle θ.

15 Given that θ lies between $0°$ and $180°$ and that Tan $\theta = {}^-2{\cdot}4$, find the matrix representing an anti-clockwise rotation about the origin through an angle of θ.

16 OABC is a square with vertices O, A, B and C at the origin, (5, 0), (5, 5) and (0, 5) respectively. A transformation represented by the matrix $\begin{pmatrix} 0{\cdot}8 & {}^-0{\cdot}6 \\ 0{\cdot}6 & 0{\cdot}8 \end{pmatrix}$ gives the square OA'B'C'.

Find the coordinates of A', B' and C'.

17 A transformation is represented by the matrix A where $A = \begin{pmatrix} 1 & 0 \\ 0 & {}^-1 \end{pmatrix}$

(a) Find the transformation represented by A.
(b) Write down the inverse matrix A^{-1} of A.
(c) What can you say about A and A^{-1}? Explain.

18 (a) Find the matrix P which represents a reflection in the line $y = x$.
(b) Write down the matrix P^{-1}.

19 The plane is transformed by a rotation about the origin through an angle of $30°$ in the anti-clockwise direction.
(a) Find the matrix, R, representing this transformation.
(b) Write down the matrix R^{-1}.

20 (a) Obtain the matrix E which represents an enlargement, centre the origin of scale factor 3.
(b) Obtain the matrix E^{-1}.

21 A transformation **T** is defined by **T**: $\begin{pmatrix} x \\ y \end{pmatrix} \rightarrow k \begin{pmatrix} x \\ y \end{pmatrix}$ where k is a constant.
(a) Find the matrix, M, representing **T**.
(b) Find the matrix M^{-1}.

Inverse matrices

The matrix $M = \begin{pmatrix} 0 & {}^-1 \\ 1 & 0 \end{pmatrix}$

represents a rotation about the origin in the anti-clockwise direction through an angle of $90°$.

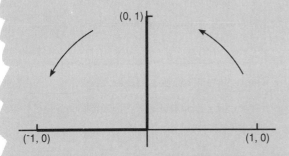

The transformation which undoes this original transformation, that is it takes us back to where we started is a rotation about the origin through $90°$ but this time in the clockwise direction.

This is called **the inverse** of the original transformation.

This inverse transformation has a matrix, which is written as M^{-1}.

$M^{-1} = \begin{pmatrix} 0 & 1 \\ {}^-1 & 0 \end{pmatrix}$

The identity matrix

This is a very special matrix

$\begin{pmatrix} 1 & 0 \\ 0 & 1 \end{pmatrix}$

because it is the one which leaves all points of the plane fixed. For this reason it is called the identity matrix and is often symbolised as **I**.

Matrix products

You were shown on page 149 that the overall effect of two reflections in lines that meet at an angle is a rotation about the point of intersection of the lines and through twice the angle between the lines.

In consequence, the overall effect of
a reflection in the x-axis followed by
a reflection in the y-axis is a
a rotation through 180° about the origin.

The matrices representing these two transformations are:

reflection in the x-axis $M = \begin{pmatrix} 1 & 0 \\ 0 & ^-1 \end{pmatrix}$

reflection in the y-axis $N = \begin{pmatrix} ^-1 & 0 \\ 0 & 1 \end{pmatrix}$

whilst the matrix representing their combined effect is:

rotation about the origin through 180° $R = \begin{pmatrix} ^-1 & 0 \\ 0 & ^-1 \end{pmatrix}$

This is written as **NM = R** and called **the matrix product of N and M**

> Note that NM means 'do M first and then do N'.

The reason for this appears on Worksheet 13.

22 Do Worksheet 13.

23 (a) Find the transformation represented by each of the matrices:

$$A = \begin{pmatrix} 0 & 1 \\ 1 & 0 \end{pmatrix} \quad B = \begin{pmatrix} ^-1 & 0 \\ 0 & 1 \end{pmatrix}$$

(b) Find the single transformation which is the combined effect of first doing A then doing B.

(c) Hence determine the matrix product BA.

24 (a) For the matrices in question **23** determine the single transformation which is the combined effect of first doing B then doing A.

(b) Determine the matrix product AB.

(c) Comment on similarities or differences between BA and AB.

25 (a) Find the matrices A and B which represent a rotation about the origin through 90° anti-clockwise and a reflection in the y-axis.

(b) Find the single transformation which is equal to the combined effect of doing A first then doing B.

(c) Hence obtain the matrix BA.

26 Do Worksheet 14.

27 (a) Describe fully the transformations represented by the matrices:

(i) $A = \begin{pmatrix} 1 & ^-0 \\ 0 & 1 \end{pmatrix}$ **(ii)** $B = \begin{pmatrix} ^-1 & 0 \\ 0 & 1 \end{pmatrix}$

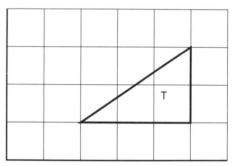

The triangle T has been drawn above.

S is the image of T under the transformation represented by AB.

(b) (i) Draw and label S on a grid.

(ii) Describe fully the single transformation which maps T onto S.

(c) Work out the matrix which represents the single transformation which maps S onto T.

28 A transformation is represented by the matrix

$$M = \begin{pmatrix} 0 & 1 \\ ^-1 & 0 \end{pmatrix}$$

(a) Describe fully the transformation represented by M.

A triangle T has vertices A, B and C at the points (2, 1), (5, 1) and (2, 3) respectively. T' is the image of T under M.

(b) Draw and label T and T'.

(c) Find the matrix M^{-1} which represents the transformation from T' back to T.

(d) Obtain the matrices:
(i) M^2 **(ii)** M^3 **(iii)** M^4

(e) Explain the connection between M^{-1} and M^3.

The diagram below shows a standard board for the game of Snakes and Ladders.

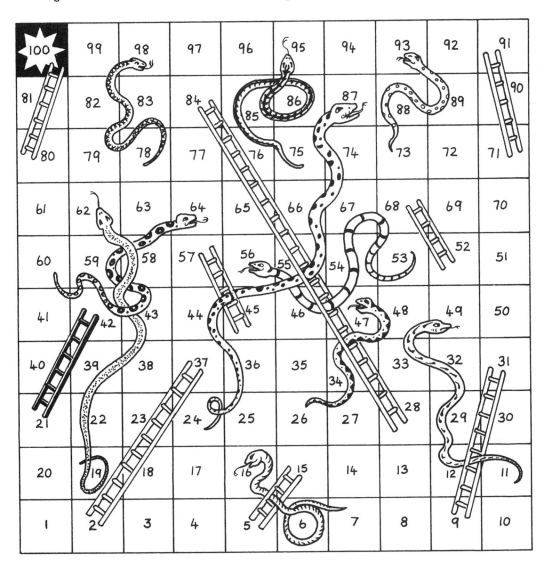

The game is played with a dice and counters.

Each player rolls the dice and moves his or her counter forward by a number of squares equal to the number shown on the dice.

If a player lands on a ladder then he or she climbs to the top of that ladder, that is they move their counter to the top of the ladder. If a player lands on a snake then their counter is moved to the bottom of the snake.
This game is now put to you as a problem solving exercise.

1 **(a)** Your task is to analyse the game and try to establish the sequence of scores which will move your counter from the start to the finish **in the least number of rolls of the dice**.
What you are doing here, is to more or less establish the critical path for the game of Snakes and Ladders.

(b) Change the rules so that you move *up* the snakes and *down* the ladders. Try to establish the critical path in this case.

(c) Create your own Snakes and Ladders board or a similar board game and again try to establish the critical path.

The critical path

Fatima and her family are planning a day out.

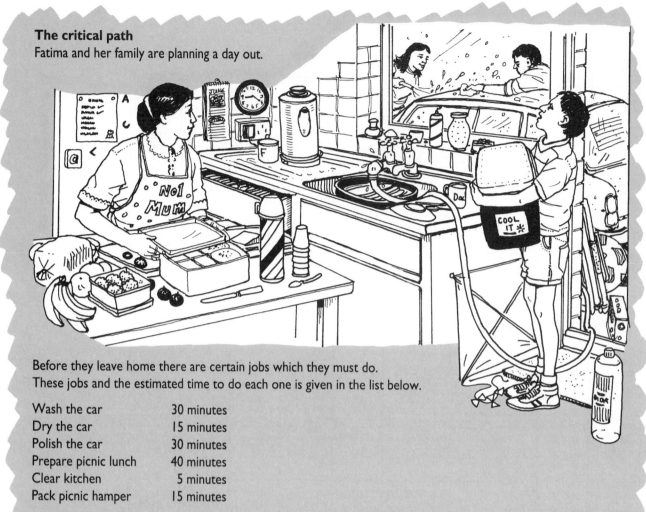

Before they leave home there are certain jobs which they must do.
These jobs and the estimated time to do each one is given in the list below.

Wash the car	30 minutes
Dry the car	15 minutes
Polish the car	30 minutes
Prepare picnic lunch	40 minutes
Clear kitchen	5 minutes
Pack picnic hamper	15 minutes

All of the family can help to do these jobs, some of which must be done before others.

They must wash the car before they can dry it and dry it before they can polish it.

They must also prepare the picnic before they can pack the hamper. They cannot clear the kitchen before they have prepared the picnic lunch.

They want to know what will be the least amount of time required to do all these jobs.

To work out this least time, the first thing to do is set up what is called a **precedence table**, which looks like this:

Job	Symbol	Time (mins)	Preceding job
Wash car	W	30	—
Dry car	D	15	W
Polish car	P	30	D
Prepare picnic lunch	L	40	—
Clear kitchen	C	5	L
Pack hamper	H	15	C

Now they can set these jobs out in a **directed network diagram** with each job labelled at one of the **nodes** and the time to do each job shown on the **arc** which follows it.

It is customary to use S for the start and F for the finish of the network.

The network will look like:

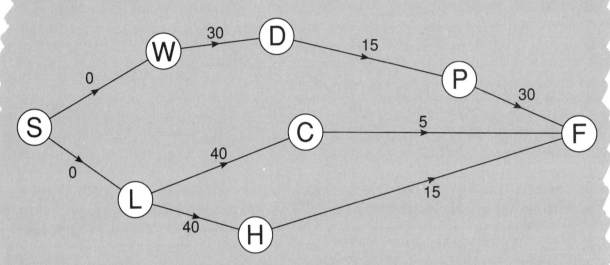

Note: As is customary, the arcs from S to the first jobs, W and L have been labelled with 0 to denote a zero time from the Start to these first jobs.

The routes through this network from S to F and the times for each route are:

S,L,H,F   0 + 40 + 15 = 55 mins   ⎫   You may find it best

S,L,C,F   0 + 40 + 5 = 45 mins   ⎬   to work back

S,W,D,P,F   0 + 30 + 15 + 30 = 75 mins   ⎭   from F.

This means that **75 minutes** is the **least amount of time** they need in order to be able to complete all of the jobs. And the route **S to W to D to P to F** is called **the critical path.**

2 Obtain the critical path for each of the networks below:

(a)

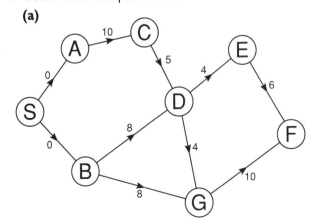

(b)

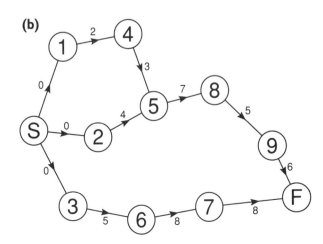

3 Obtain the critical path for the complex network shown below:

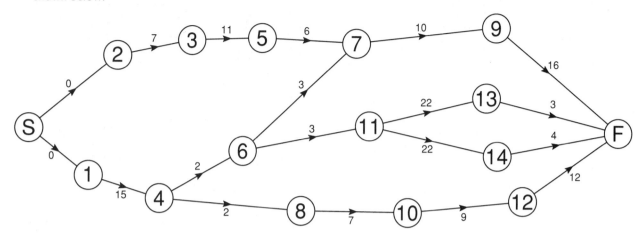

4 The precedence table for an administrative process is:

Task	Time in days	Preceding task(s)
A	3	—
B	3	—
C	2	—
D	2	B
E	1	C
F	2	C
G	4	E
H	2	A
I	2	D
J	3	F
K	2	H and B
L	3	J
M	1	L
N	2	K

(a) Draw the directed network diagram for this process.

(b) Obtain the critical path.

5 An industrial process consists of 14 stages. The precedence table for the network is given below:

Stage 1	Time in hours	Preceding stages
1	35	—
2	19	—
3	26	2
4	9	1
5	17	3
6	11	4
7	25	5 and 6
8	19	4
9	37	7
10	23	8
11	50	6
12	29	10
13	11	11
14	13	11

(a) Create the directed network diagram for this process.

(b) Use your diagram to determine:
   (i) the critical path
   (ii) the minimum time for the completion of the process.

Answers

Page 1 Keep up the standard 1

1 (a) 3·4 million   **(b)** 7·5 million
   (c) 2 million   **(d)** 8·95 million
   (e) 6·25 million   **(f)** 5·03 million

2 (a) 4·3 thousand   **(b)** 6·5 thousand
   (c) 9·8 thousand   **(d)** 1·9 thousand
   (e) 6·0 thousand   **(f)** 2·0 thousand

3 (a) 3.44×10^6 **(b)** 7.90×10^6
   (c) 2.74×10^6 **(d)** 9.44×10^6
   (e) 3.67×10^6 **(f)** 2.00×10^6

4 (a) 10^2 **(b)** 10^3 **(c)** 10^4 **(d)** 10^1
   (e) 10^6 **(f)** 10^0 **(g)** 10^5 **(h)** 10^{12}

5 (a) 8×10^2 **(b)** 8×10^6 **(c)** 8×10^8
   (d) 8×10^0 **(e)** 8×10^5 **(f)** 8×10^{12}

6

10^6	10^5	10^4	10^3	10^2	10^1	10^0	Standard form
		7	2	0	0	0	7.2×10^4
				6	4	0	6.4×10^2
8	5	0	0	0	0	0	8.5×10^6
			3	5	8	0	3.58×10^3
					9	2	9.2×10^1
						7	7.0×10^0

7 (a) 1.65×10 **(b)** 2.5×10 **(c)** 5.678×10^3
   (d) 6.45×10^3 **(e)** 6.8×10^5 **(f)** 8.69×10
   (g) 9.867×10^7 **(h)** 9.9×10^6

8 (a) 4300   **(b)** 68 000 000   **(c)** 543 000   **(d)** 346
   (e) 79·8   **(f)** 1·2

9 (a) 2.272×10^4 **(b)** 6.24×10^0 **(c)** 6.27×10^3
   (d) 1.557×10^2 **(e)** 7×10 **(f)** 2×10
   (g) 4.53×10 **(h)** 1.4332×10^3 **(i)** 1.1848×10^4
   (j) 1.758×10^2 **(k)** $3.404\,57 \times 10^4$ **(l)** $5.587\,54 \times 10^5$

Page 2 Keep up the standard 2

1

10^0	10^{-1}	10^{-2}	10^{-3}	10^{-4}	10^{-5}	Standard form
0	2	4	0	0	0	2.4×10^{-1}
0	0	5	7	0	0	5.7×10^{-2}
0	0	0	0	2	3	2.3×10^{-4}
0	0	0	8	5		8.5×10^{-3}
0	0	0	7			7×10^{-3}
0	5	7	8			5.78×10^{-1}
0	0	0	0	0	7	7×10^{-5}
0	0	2	5			2.5×10^{-2}

2 (a) 5.68×10^{-1} **(b)** 4.5×10^{-3} **(c)** 9.8×10^{-3}
   (d) 6.5×10^{-5} **(e)** 7.86×10^{-5} **(f)** 6.78×10^{-4}
   (g) 3.01×10^{-1} **(h)** 1×10^{-3} **(i)** 9.7×10^{-1}
   (j) 8.8×10^{-6}

3 (a) 0·034   **(b)** 0·88   **(c)** 0·000 079 5
   (d) 0·000 102 4   **(e)** 0·4011   **(f)** 0·000 009 87
   (g) 0·000 000 56   **(h)** 0·000 000 000 88

4 7.0×10^{-11}

5 (a) 7.68×10^{11} **(b)** 3.6×10^{-7} **(c)** 1.2336×10^{-2}
   (d) 1.96×10^2 **(e)** 6.36×10^{-8} **(f)** 2.8×10^{28}
   (g) 1×10^2 **(h)** 1.156×10^9 **(j)** 1.0648×10^{-5}

6 (a) 1.68×10^8 **(b)** 3.5×10^{-5} **(c)** 2.7×10^{-1}
   (d) 2.744×10 **(e)** 9·75   **(f)** 4.75×10^{-5}
   (g) 1.91×10^3 **(h)** 1.289×10^{-6}

7 3.1×10^7

8 (a) Jupiter
   (b) Mercury
   (c) Approximately 10^4 times bigger
   (d) 10

Pages 3 and 4 More interesting 1

1 £355

2

Year	Capital	Interest	Total
6th	£334·56	£334·56 × 0·06	£354.63
7th	£354·63	£354·63 × 0·06	£375.91
8th	£375·91	£375·91 × 0·06	£398.46
9th	£398·46	£398·46 × 0·06	£422.37
10th	£422·37	£422·37 × 0·06	£447.71

3 Compound interest £447·71
Simple interest £400·71
Difference £47·71

4

Year	Capital	Interest	Total
11th	£447·71	£447·71 × 0·06	£474.58
12th	£474·58	£474·58 × 0·06	£503.05

12 years

5 (a) £1083   **(b)** £1489·85   **(c)** £1892·46
6 (a) 9 years   **(b)** 12·0 years
7 Students' own answers
8 (a) £2250, 125% growth   **(b)** £1960, 96% growth   **(c)** 41·4%
9 (a) $3P = P + rP + r(P + rP)$
     $3P = P + rP + rP + r^2P$
     $3P = P + 2rP + r^2P$
     $3 = 1 + 2r + r^2$
     $3 = (1 + r)^2$
   (b) 73·2%
10 $2 = (1 + r)^2$
11 Students' own answers
12 $m = (1 + r)^2$
13 (a) 100%   **(b)** 144·9%   **(c)** $100\,(m - 1)\%$
14 (a) $mP = P + rP + r(P + rP) + r(P + rP + r(P + rP))$
     $= P + rP + rP + r^2P + rP + r^2P + r^2P + r^3P$
     $= P + 3rP + 3r^2P + r^3P$
   (b) $2P = (P + 3rP + 3r^2P + r^3P)$
     $2 = (1 + r)^3$
15 (a) $m = (1 + r)^3$ **(b)** 14·47%
16 $m = (1 + r)^n$
17 $500 = 250(1 + 0.06)^{12}$
18 9·4%
19 11·25% growth
20 6 years

Pages 5 and 6 Just a fraction

1 (a) $\dfrac{10}{8}$ **(b)** $\dfrac{19}{20}$ **(c)** $\dfrac{23}{20}$
   (d) $\dfrac{31}{35}$ **(e)** $\dfrac{59}{42}$ **(f)** $\dfrac{101}{72}$

2 (a) $\dfrac{1}{8}$ **(b)** $\dfrac{4}{12}$ **(c)** $\dfrac{5}{28}$

3 (a) $\dfrac{a + b}{ab}$ **(b)** $\dfrac{ad + cb}{cd}$ **(c)** $\dfrac{2a + a^2}{2a}$
   (d) $\dfrac{b - a}{ab}$ **(e)** $\dfrac{c - ab^2}{ac}$ **(f)** $\dfrac{3b^2 + 10a}{2ab^2}$

4 (a) $\dfrac{R_1 + R_2}{R_1 R_2}$ **(b)** 0·2
   (c) $R_e = \dfrac{R_1 R_2}{R^1 + R^2}$ **(d)** 0·266 …

5 (a) $\dfrac{1}{a} = \dfrac{1}{Kc} - \dfrac{1}{c} = \dfrac{c - Kc}{Kc^2} = \dfrac{c(1 - K)}{Kc^2} = \dfrac{1 - K}{Kc}$
   (b) $a = \dfrac{Kc}{1 - K}$ **(c)** −9·33 …

6 (a) $\dfrac{9x}{20}$ **(b)** $x = 10$

7 (a) $\dfrac{2x}{15}$ **(b)** $x = 15$

8 Students' own answers

164

9 (a) $\dfrac{3x+2}{x^2+x}$ **(b)** $\dfrac{3x-y}{xy+y^2}$ **(c)** $\dfrac{3x-6}{x^2+3x}$

(d) $\dfrac{5x-7}{x^2-2x-3}$ **(e)** $\dfrac{7x+24}{35}$ **(f)** $\dfrac{5x-37}{15}$

(g) $\dfrac{7x+14}{12}$ **(h)** $\dfrac{x^2-x+4}{2x-4}$ **(i)** $\dfrac{-x^2+8x-1}{x^2-1}$

(j) $\dfrac{2xy-x+36}{y^2-y-20}$

10 Students' own answers

11 (a) $A = \dfrac{1}{2}$ $B = \dfrac{-1}{2}$

(b) $A = \dfrac{4}{3}$ $B = \dfrac{-4}{3}$

(c) $A = \dfrac{6}{5}$ $B = \dfrac{9}{5}$

(d) $A = 9$ $B = {}^-7$

Pages 7 and 8   Draw a graph 1

1 Students' own answers
2 (a) $x = 2\cdot3$ and ${}^-1\cdot7$
  (b) Students' own answers
3 $y = 6$
4 $x = 2\cdot5$ and ${}^-2$
5 (a) $2x^2 - x - 4 = 3$ **(b)** $n = 3$
  (c) $x = 1$ and ${}^-0\cdot5$
6 (a) Re-arrange to $2x^2 - x - 4 = {}^-4$
  (b) $x = 0$ and $0\cdot5$
7 (a) Students' graph
  (b) (i) $x = 2\cdot8$ and ${}^-2\cdot8$
    (ii) $x = 3\cdot3$ and ${}^-3\cdot3$
    (iii) $x = 2\cdot2$ and ${}^-2\cdot2$
    (iv) $x = 4\cdot35$ and ${}^-4\cdot35$
8 (a)

x	-4	-3	-2	-1	0	1	2	3
y	-38	-19	-6	-3	2	-3	-14	-31

  (b) Students' graph
  (c) (i) $x = 0\cdot54$ and $-1\cdot2$
    (ii) $x = 0\cdot87$ and $-1\cdot5$
9 (a) $x = 0\cdot54$ and ${}^-1\cdot2$
  (b) $x = 0\cdot2$ and ${}^-0\cdot86$
  (c) $x = 0\cdot14$ and ${}^-0\cdot8$
  (d) $x = 0\cdot14$ and ${}^-0\cdot8$
10 (a) Students' graph
  (b) $x = 3$ and ${}^-1$
11 (a) $(3\cdot8, 3\cdot8)$ and $({}^-0\cdot8, {}^-0\cdot8)$
  (b) $x = 3\cdot8$ and ${}^-0\cdot8$
12 (a) (i) $x^2 - 2x - 3 = {}^-x$
    (ii) $x^2 - 2x - 3 = x + 1$
  (b) $x = 2\cdot3$ and ${}^-1\cdot3$
    $x = 4$ and ${}^-1$

Page 9   The factors of the matter

1 (a) $(x+1)(x+1)$ **(b)** $(x+2)(x+5)$
  (c) $(x+3)(x+4)$ **(d)** $(x+5)(x-10)$
  (e) $(x-4)(x-5)$
2 (a) $(3x-2)(x-5)$ **(b)** $(2x-1)(x+4)$
  (c) $(2x-2)(2x-10)$ **(d)** $(3x+2)(2x-7)$
  (e) $(4x-7)(x+3)$
3 (a) $(x+6)(x+5) = 0, x = {}^-6$ or ${}^-5$
  (b) $(x+8)(x+6) = 0, x = {}^-8$ or ${}^-6$
  (c) $(x+9)(x+3) = 0, x = {}^-9$ or ${}^-3$
  (d) $(x-7)(x-5) = 0, x = 7$ or 5
  (e) $(x+15)(x-4) = 0, x = {}^-15$ or 4
  (f) $(x+3)(x-12) = 0, x = {}^-3$ or 12
  (g) $(x-8)(x+7) = 0, x = 8$ or ${}^-7$
  (h) $x(x+5) = 0, x = 0$ or ${}^-5$
  (i) $(x+6)(x-6) = 0, x = 6$ or ${}^-6$

4 (a) $(2x-3)(x-1) = 0, x = 1$ or $1\cdot5$
  (b) $(3x+1)(x+1) = 0, x = {}^-1$ or $\dfrac{-1}{3}$
  (c) $(4x+1)(x-3) = 0, x = 3$ or $\dfrac{-1}{4}$
  (d) $(2x-5)(2x-5) = 0, x = 2\cdot5$
  (e) $(3x-1)(2x+5) = 0, x = \dfrac{1}{3}$ or ${}^-2\cdot5$
  (f) $(4x-3)(2x+5) = 0, x = 0\cdot75$ or ${}^-2\cdot5$
5 (a) $x^2 - 6x + 8 = 0$ **(b)** $x^2 + x - 12 = 0$
  (c) $x^2 + 10x + 21 = 0$ **(d)** $x^2 - 16 = 0$
  (e) $x^2 - 8x = 0$ **(f)** $x^2 - 6x + 9 = 0$
6 (a) $x^2 - 0\cdot25x - 0\cdot125 = 0$
  (b) $8x^2 - 2x - 1 = 0$
7 Students' own answers $(\alpha + \beta = {}^-b \ \ \alpha\beta = c)$

Page 10   Linear forms

Students' own answers

Pages 11 and 12   A square peg in . . .

1 $(x+3)^2 - 12 = x^2 + 6x + 9 - 12$
    $= x^2 + 6x - 3$
2 (a) $(x-4)^2 - 10 = x^2 - 8x + 16 - 10$
    $= x^2 - 8x + 6$
  (b) $(x+5)^2 - 2 = x^2 + 10x + 25 - 2$
    $= x^2 + 10x + 23$
  (c) $(x-1)^2 - 0\cdot5 = x^2 - 2x + 1 - 0\cdot5$
    $= x^2 - 2x + 0\cdot5$
  (d) $(x+6)^2 + 12 = x^2 + 12x + 36 + 12$
    $= x^2 + 12x + 48$
  (e) $(x+1)^2 + 2x = x^2 + 2x + 1 + 2x$
    $= x^2 + 4x + 1$
3 Students' own answers
4 (a) $(x+4)^2 - 26$ **(b)** $(x+6)^2 - 41$
  (c) $(x-6)^2 - 41$ **(d)** $(x-3)^2 + 1$
  (e) $(x+1\cdot5)^2$ **(f)** $(x-3\cdot5)^2 - 2\cdot25$
5 (a) $2(x+1\cdot5)^2 - 18\cdot5$
  (b) $3(x-2)^2 - 27$
  (c) $2(x-1\cdot75)^2 - 12\cdot125$
  (d) $4(x-0\cdot5)^2 + 19\cdot75$
  (e) $5(x+1\cdot2)^2 + 7\cdot8$
6 (a) $(3, 1)$ **(b)** It has no solutions.
7 (a) $(x-1)^2 + 2$ **(b)** Students' own answers
8 $-x^2 + 2x - 5 = -(x^2 - 2x + 5)$
    $= -((x-1)^2 + 4)$
    $= -(x-1)^2 - 4$
9 (a) $(x+3)(x+4)$ **(b)** $x = {}^-3$ or ${}^-4$
10 (a) (i) $x = {}^-2$ or ${}^-6$ **(ii)** $x = 7$ or 3 **(iii)** $x = 2$ or ${}^-8$ **(iv)** $x = {}^-2$ or ${}^-10$
  (b) Students' own answers
11 (a) $x^2 - 2x + 0\cdot5 = 0$
  (b) $(x-1)^2 - 0\cdot5 = 0$
  (c) $x = 1\cdot707$ or $0\cdot293$
12 (a) $x = 5$ or $1\cdot5$
  (b) $x = 2\cdot6 \ldots$ or 1
13 Students' own answers

Page 13   To the nth degree – revisited

1 (a)

Term	Value	1st difference	2nd difference
0	${}^-1$	3	
1st	2	3	0
2nd	5	3	0
3rd	8	3	0
4th	11	3	0
5th	14		

  (b) $-1 + n(3) + n(n-1)(0) = 3n - 1$

2 (a) and (b)

Term	Value	1st difference	2nd difference	3rd difference
0	0			
		3		
1st	3		2	
		5		0
2nd	8		2	
		7		0
3rd	15		2	
		9		0
4th	24		2	
		11		
5th	35			

(c) $0 + n(3) + \dfrac{n(n-1)^2}{2} = n^2 + 2n$

3 (a) $\dfrac{(n^2 + n)}{2}$

(b) $2n^2 - 3n + 1$

(c) $1 + 4n - 2n^2$

(d) $2n^3 - 3n^2 + n - 1$

Pages 14, 15 and 16   The Theorem of Pythagoras

1 **(a)** 5 cm **(b)** 12 cm **(c)** 7 cm
(d) 7·07 cm **(e)** 11·18 cm **(f)** 27·50 cm

2 29·2 km

3 13·42 cm

4 No

5 15 cm or 7·94 cm

6 **(a)** $x = 5$ cm, $y = 12$ cm **(b)** $x = 25$ cm, $y = 15$ cm
(c) $x = 5·74$ cm, $y = 11·53$ cm

7 **(a)** 8·94 cm **(b)** 10·25 cm

8 $\sqrt{x^2 + y^2 + z^2}$ cm

9 15·26 cm

10 **(a)** 7·42 cm **(b)** 22·25 cm

11 $\dfrac{y}{2} \sqrt{x^2 - \dfrac{y^2}{4}}$ cm²

12 14·35 cm

13 15·59 cm

14 Students' own answers

15 **(a)** Students' own answers **(b)** $x = 0$ or $4\frac{1}{2}$

16 **(a)** Students' own answers **(b)** $x = {}^-1·52$ or $0·38$
(c) Not possible

17 $x = 4$ cm

18 8·58 m

19 0·4 cm

20 3^2 not equal to $2^2 + 1^2$

21 Students' own answers

22 **(a)** $\sqrt{2x^2 - 40x + 400}$ **(b)** Students' own answers

23 **(a)** 1·732 **(b)** 2

24 **(a)** 1·732 units **(b)** 10·392 unit²

25 12·26 cm

26 Students' own answer

27 8·49 cm

28 Students' own answer

29 13

30 14·14

31 Students' own answers

32 $a^2 + b^2$ less than c^2 or similar

33 **(a)** Students' own answer **(b)** Students' own answer
(c) $^-2$ or 4

34 $(x - a)^2 + (y - b)^2 = r^2$

Pages 17 and 18   Trigonometry 1

1 **(a)** 73·3° **(b)** 5·9 cm **(c)** 45·6° **(d)** 6·11 cm
(e) 1·49 cm **(f)** $x = 6·69$ cm, $y = 30·98°$

2 032°

3 **(a)** 7·31 cm **(b)** 6·82 cm **(c)** 13·18 cm **(d)** 29°

4 **(a)** 14° **(b)** 164·9 m

5 **(a)** 2·51 cm **(b)** 26·6° **(c)** 6·44 m

6 16·2°

7 262·2 m

8 **(a)** 12·67 km **(b)** 11·24 km **(c)** 29° **(d)** 061°

9 10·26 cm

10 **(a)** 13·75 cm **(b)** 23·6° **(c)** 66·4°

Pages 19 and 20   Mensuration 1

1 **(a)** 61·7 m **(b)** 219·3 m² **(c)** 44

2 **(a)** Students' own answer
(b) Students' graph
(c) (i) 37·5 m² (ii) 2·8 and 7·2

3 **(a)** 534 cm² **(b)** 942·5 cm³ **(c)** 9·8 cm

4 6·495 cm²

5 600 cm³

6 **(a)** $1·09 \times 10^{12}$ **(b)** $1·09 \times 10^{12}$ **(c)** $3·41 \times 10^8$ km²

7 **(a)** Students' own answers
(b) Students' graph
(c) (i) 422 cm³ (ii) 1·45 or 8 cm (iii) $x = 4·5$ cm, $v = 631$ cm³

8 **(a)** 1400 cm³ **(b)** 6·94 cm

9 Students' own answer

10 **(a)** Students' own answer
(b) Students' own answer
(c) 864 m³

Page 21   Loci

1 **(a)** Students' sketch **(b)** Circle, radius 5

2 Sphere, radius 5

3 **(a)** Students' drawing **(b)** Semicircle or two of such

4 **(a)** Students drawing **(b)** Sector or two sectors of a circle

5 **(a)** Students' drawing **(b)** Sectors of circles

6 **(a)** **(b)** (i) 39·5 km
(ii) 41° or 42°

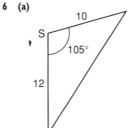

7 **(a)** Students' answer
(b) Students' answer
(c) Yes, $x = 9$, $y = 3$ for instance, i.e. when the radius to P is horizontal or vertical.

8   9

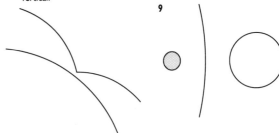

Page 22   Probability estimates

1 **(a)** 16 **(b)** 24

2 **(a)** 12 **(b)** 18

3 **(a)** 35 **(b)** 14

4 25

5 12

6 1000

7 **(a)** $\dfrac{13}{20}$ **(b)** $\dfrac{7}{20}$

8 **(a)** 1750 **(b)** 250

9 **(a)** $\dfrac{1}{3}$ **(b)** $\dfrac{1}{2}$

10 **(a)** $\dfrac{2}{5}$ **(b)** $\dfrac{3}{5}$

11 **(a)** $\dfrac{1}{20}$ **(b)** $\dfrac{19}{20}$

12 **(a)** $\dfrac{5}{16}$ **(b)** $\dfrac{11}{16}$

1 (a) $\frac{1}{4}$ (b) $\frac{5}{12}$ (c) $\frac{1}{3}$ (d) $\frac{1}{2}$

2 (a) $\frac{1}{6}$ (b) $\frac{7}{12}$ (c) $\frac{1}{3}$ (d) $\frac{3}{4}$

3 (a) $\frac{5}{7}$ (b) $\frac{2}{21}$ (c) $\frac{2}{7}$ (d) $\frac{2}{21}$

4 (a) $\frac{1}{2}$ (b) $\frac{1}{2}$ (c) $\frac{3}{3}$ (d) 0

5 (a) $\frac{1}{3}$ (b) $\frac{5}{12}$ (c) $\frac{1}{3}$ (d) $\frac{7}{12}$

6 (a) $\frac{1}{4}$ (b) $\frac{1}{5}$ (c) $\frac{11}{20}$ (d) $\frac{19}{40}$

   (e) $\frac{21}{40}$ (f) $\frac{3}{8}$

7 (a) $\frac{5}{12}$ (b) $\frac{3}{4}$ (c) $\frac{3}{4}$ (d) $\frac{1}{2}$

Page 24   Spreading about 1

1 (a) 4·17 and 2·54
   (b) 6 and 2·89
   (c) 5·2 and 0·54
   (d) 186·711 and 53·4
   (e) 3·35 and 0·328
   (f) 10·5 and 0·67
2 (a) 6 and 1·414
   (b) 18 and 1·414
   Each number in (b) is such that
   (b) = (a) + 12
   Hence mean in (b) is the mean in (a) + 12
   Standard deviations are equal. This is because the second set of numbers
   (b), is merely a linear shift of (a).

Pages 25, 26, 27 and 28   Histograms

1 (a)

Height	Frequency	Width	Frequency density
$140 \le x <150$	10	10	1
$150 \le x <160$	16	10	1·6
$160 \le x <165$	34	5	6·8
$165 \le x <169$	46	4	11·5
$169 \le x <175$	52	6	8·67
$175 \le x <181$	21	6	3·5
$181 \le x <190$	11	9	1·22
$190 \le x <205$	6	15	0·4
$205 \le x <225$	4	20	0·2

   (b) Students' histogram
2 Students' histogram
3 Students' histogram
4

Class interval	Frequency density	Class width	Frequency
$0 \le x <15$	0·6	15	9
$15 \le x <25$	1·7	10	17
$25 \le x <35$	3·0	10	30
$35 \le x <40$	4·6	5	23
$40 \le x <50$	2·0	10	20
$50 \le x <60$	0·5	10	5
$60 \le x <70$	0·5	10	5

   Total screws in sample = 109
5 122
6 The frequency density of class interval 230–250 is 1·75.
   Students' own histogram.
   Total sunflowers in competition = 191
7

Class	Frequency	Width	Frequency density
0–1·5	5	1·5	3·33
1·6–2·0	5	0·4	12·5
2·1–3·0	8	0·9	8·89
3·1–6·0	12	2·9	4·14
6·1–10	6	3·9	15·38

   Students' histogram

Pages 29, 30, 31 and 32   Beyond any doubt: proof

Students' own answers

Page 33   Some series summed

Students' own answers

Page 34   Straight to the boundary

1 (a) 21·5 cm   (b) 20·5 cm   (c) 20·5 cm to 21·5 cm
2 (a) 102 cm to 106 cm
   (b) 4 times the width/length interval
3 (a) $(x + 0.5)$ cm   (b) $(x - 0.5)$ cm
4 (a) $10(x + 0.5)$ cm $= (10x + 5)$ cm
   (b) $10(x - 0.5)$ cm $= (10x - 5)$ cm
   (c) $(10x - 5)$ cm to $(10x + 5)$ cm
5 (a) $(100x - 50)$ cm to $(100x + 50)$ cm
   (b) $(xy - 0.5y)$ cm to $(xy + 0.5y)$ cm
6 (a) 358·75 m^2 (b) 397·75 m^2
   (c) 358·75 m^2 to 397·75 m^2
   (d) The interval approximation is very wide.
7 (a) length 21·95 cm to 22·05 cm
       width 9·95 cm to 10·05 cm
       height 7·95 cm to 8·05 cm
   (b) 0·1 cm, 0·1 cm, 0·1 cm
   (c) 218·4025 cm^2 to 221·6025 cm^2
       174·5025 cm^2 to 177·5025 cm^2
       79·1025 cm^2 to 80·9025 cm^2
   (d) 32 cm^2, 3·0 cm^2, 1·8 cm^2
   (e) 944·015 cm^2 to 960·015 cm^2
   (f) 16 cm^2
   (g) 1736·2999 cm^3 to 1783·9001 cm^3
   (h) 47·6002 cm^3
8 Two approximations multiplied together give a bigger approximation.
9 Possible answers: Weighing the brick
                      Immersing in water and measuring the displacement

Pages 35 and 36   Sequences 1

1 Students' own answer
2 Students' own answer
3 (a) 1, 2, 3, 4, 5, 6
       3, 6, 9 , 12, 15
       25, 20, 15, 10, 5
       $^-$19, $^-$15, $^-$11, $^-$7, $^-$3
   (b) 2, 3, $^-$5, 4
   (c) 8, 24, $^-$10, 9
4 (a) The gradient rise per unit is constant.
   (b) 59
5 (a) and (d)
6 (a) nth term $= 6n - 1$
   (b) Students' own answers
7 (a) 7   (b) 138   (c) $5 + 7(n-1) = 7n - 2$
8 (a) 3, 10, 17, 24, 31, 38, 45, 52
   (b) $^-$2, 1, 4, 7, 10, 13, 16, 19
   (c) 1·4, 4, 6·6, 9·2, 11·8, 14·4, 17, 19·6
   (d) $^-$4·5, $^-$2·5, $^-$0·5, 1·5, 3·5, 5·5, 7·5, 9·5
   (e) 10, 6, 2, $^-$2, $^-$6, $^-$10, $^-$14, $^-$18
9 (a) $7n - 4$ (b) $3n - 5$ (c) $2·6n - 1·2$
   (d) $2n - 6·5$ (e) $14 - 4n$
10 (a) 4, 43, 407, $4 + 7(n - 1) = 7n - 3$
   (b) 3, 32, 305, $5 + 3(n - 1) = 3n + 2$
   (c) $^-$3, $^-$16, $^-$289, $11 - 3(n - 1) = 14 - 3n$
   (d) 5, 28, 483, $^-17 + 5(n - 1) = 5n - 22$
   (e) $^-$4, $^-$42, $^-$406, $^-6 - 4(n - 1) = ^-4n - 2$
11 (a) 12   (b) 4   (c) $4n - 2$
12 (a) 5   (b) 102   (c) $12 + 5(n - 1) = 5n + 7$
13 7, 12, 17, 22, 27, 32, 37, 42
14 (a) $11\frac{1}{2}$ (b) $9\frac{1}{4}$

Pages 37 and 38   Sequences 2

1 (a) 64, 128 (b) The previous term is doubled
2 2
3 Students' graph
4 Only graph (c)
5 (a) 3 (b) 486, 1458
6 (a) 2×3^{19} (b) 2×3^{100} (c) $2 \times 3^{n-1}$ (d) 2×3^0
7 (a) 2·5, 10, 40, 160, 640
  (b) 20, 10, 5, 2·5, 1·25
  (c) ⁻5, 17·5, ⁻61·25, 214·375, ⁻750·3125
8 (a) $2, 3 \times 2^{20}$, 3×2^{49}, $3 \times 2^{n-1}$
  (b) $4, 5 \times 4^{20}$, 5×4^{49}, $5 \times 4^{n-1}$
  (c) $6, 5 \times 6^{20}$, 5×6^{49}, $5 \times 6^{n-1}$
  (d) $\frac{1}{4}, 256 \times \frac{1}{4}^{20}$, $256 \times \frac{1}{4}^{49}$, $256 \times \frac{1}{4}^{n-1}$
  (e) $\frac{1}{3}, 81 \times \frac{1}{3}^{20}$, $81 \times \frac{1}{3}^{49}$, $81 \times \frac{1}{3}^{n-1}$
  (f) $^-2, 4 \times (^-2)^{20}$ $4 \times (^-2)^{49}$ $4 \times (^-2)^{n-1}$
  (g) $^-1, (^-1)^{20}$, $(^-1)^{49}$, $(^-1)^{n-1}$
9 (a) 112 (b) 896 (c) $7 \times 2^{n-1}$
10 (a) 4 (b) 49 152 (c) $3 \times 4^{n-1}$
11 (a) 1·5 (b) $ar^2 = 6$ (c) 2 or ⁻2
  (d) 3072 or ⁻3072 (e) $1·5 \times 2^{n-1}$ or $1·5 \times (^-2)^{n-1}$
12 (a) $ar^2 = 4·5$ (b) $ar^5 = 121·5$ (c) 3
  (d) 0·5 (e) 1093·5
13 (a) 3 or ⁻3 (b) 6 or ⁻6 (c) $\frac{2}{9} \times 3^{n-1}$ or $\frac{2}{9} \times (^-3)^{n-1}$

Page 39   How many terms?

1 16
2 (a) 60 (b) 15 (c) Add 1
3 Difference = 22, $\frac{22}{2} = 11$ 11 + 1 = 12 terms
4 (a) $\frac{75}{5} = 15$ 15 + 1 = 16 terms
  (b) 6, 11, 16, 21, 26, 31, 36, 41, 46, 51, 56, 61, 66, 71, 76, 81
5 (a) 24 (b) 17 (c) 52 (d) 15
6 (a) n (b) n (c) n
7 $\frac{(a + (n-1)d - a}{d} + 1 = \frac{a + nd - d - a}{d} + 1$
$= n - 1 + 1 = n$
8 (a) 4 (b) 83
9 (a) ⁻62·25 (b) ⁻51
10 (a) 10 years (b) £16 800

Page 40   The quadratic formula 1

1 (a) $(x + 3)(x + 4) = 0$, $x = ^-3$ or ⁻4
  (b) $x = ^-3$ or ⁻4
2 (a) $x = 0·697$ or ⁻4·303 (b) $x = 0·464$ or ⁻6·464
  (c) $x = ^-0·298$ or ⁻6·702 (d) $x = 5$ or ⁻1
  (e) $x = 9·583$ or 0·417 (f) $x = 0·162$ or ⁻6·162
  (g) $x = 5·464$ or ⁻1·464 (h) $x = 3·464$ or ⁻3·464
  (i) $x = 4$ or ⁻4
3 $x = 3·303$ or ⁻0·303
4 (a) $x = 0·499$ or ⁻4·449 (b) $x = 4·449$ or ⁻0·449
  (c) $x = 4·266$ or 0·234 (d) $x = ^-0·628$ or ⁻6·372
  (e) $x = 4·108$ or ⁻0·608 (f) $x = 2·117$ or 0·283
5 Students' own answers

Pages 41 and 42   Gradients

1 (a) 4
  (b) The velocity at that point is 4 m/s
2 (a) Students' graph
  (b) Gradient of tangent = 3 so velocity is 3 unit/s
  (c) $x = 0·5$
  (d) Gradient of tangent = ⁻3 so velocity is ⁻3 unit/s
  (e) Could be obtained by symmetry properties.
3 (a) Students' graph (b) 2 (c) ⁻6
4 (a) Students' graph (b) 10 (c) 20 m/s

5 (a) Students' graph (b) 62·5 m/s (c) 1
  (d) The acceleration at this point is 1 m/s². (e) (2·5, 62·5)
6 (a) 8 and 15 (b) 6 m/s²
7 Students' graph
8 (a) 2, 4 and 6 (b) 0
9 (a) $x = 0$
  (b) Because the graph is symmetrical.
  (c) ⁻2, ⁻4 and ⁻6
10 Students' graph
11 (a) Students' graph (b) Students' graph (c) $y = 2x$

Pages 43 and 44   Draw a graph 2

1 (a) Students' graph (b) Students' graph
  (c) (1·6, 2·6) and (⁻0·6, 0·4) (d) $x = 1·6$ and ⁻0·6
2 (a) $y = x + 6$ (b) Students' graph
  (c) $x = ^-2$ and 3 (d) $x = ^-1·56, 2·56$
3 (a) 2 and ⁻1 (b) $2x^2 - 2x - 4 = 0$
4 (a) $y = x^2 - 6$, $x = 3$ and ⁻2 (b) $y = x + 6$
5 (a)

x	⁻3	⁻2	⁻1	0	1	2	3
y	⁻4	3	2	⁻1	0	11	38

  (b) Students' graph (c) $x = ^-2·6, ^-0·4, 1$
6 (a)

x	⁻3	⁻2	⁻1	0	1	2	3
y	⁻27	⁻8	⁻1	0	1	8	27

x	⁻3	⁻2	⁻1	0	1	2	3
y	⁻23	⁻11	⁻3	1	1	⁻3	⁻11

  (b) Students' graph (c) $x = ^-2·6, ^-0·4, 1$
7 (a) Students' graph (b) $x = ^-2·6, ^-0·4, 1$
8 Students' answers. Possible answers:
  $y = x^3 - 1$ and $y = ^-2x^2 + 2x$ or
  $y = x^3 - 2x - 1$ and $y = ^-2x^2$
9 (a) Students' graph (b) $x = ^-2·5, 0·66, 1·83$
  (c) Students' answers
10 (a) (i) $x = 2$ (ii) $x = 1·8$ (b) Students' answers
11 (a) Possible arrangement::
  $y = x^3$ and $y = 2x - 1$ or
  $y = x^3 + 1$ and $y = 2x$
  Solution: $y = ^-1·63$ and 1
  (b) (i) $x = ^-1$ (ii) $x = ^-1·9$
  (c) $x = ^-1·55, ^-0·35, 1·88$

Page 45   The quadratic formula 2

1 (a) $x = 5$, or ⁻2 (b) $x = 5$ or ⁻2
2 (a) $a = 3, b = ^-8, c = 3$ (b) $x = 2·215$ or 0·451
3 $x = 1$ or ⁻3
4 (a) $x = 1·443$ or ⁻0·693 (b) $x = 0·370$ or ⁻2·703
  (c) $x = 3·886$ or ⁻0·386 (d) $x = 1·618$ or ⁻0·618
  (e) $x = ^-0232$ or ⁻1·434 (f) $x = 0·151$ or ⁻1·651
5 (a) $x = 1·123$ or ⁻7·123 (b) $x = 2$ or 0·5
  (c) $x = 7·123$ or ⁻1·123 (d) $x = 3·707$ or 2·293
  (e) $x = 10·522$ or ⁻0·522

Page 46   Rebounds

Students' own answers

Pages 47 and 48   Spring the trap

1 (a) 1540 square units
  (b) 1310 square units
  (c) 1425 square units
2 (a) 26·4 square units
  (b) 22·4 square units
  (c) 24·4 square units

3 (a) $29{\cdot}5 < 52{\cdot}5 < 79{\cdot}5$

(b) $32 < 50 < 68$

(c) $39{\cdot}5 < 48{\cdot}5 < 57{\cdot}5$

(d) The smaller the width of the rectangle the better the approximation.

4 (a) Answer as question **3**.

(b) (i) $43{\cdot}625 < 48{\cdot}125 < 52{\cdot}625$

(ii) $46{\cdot}22 < 48{\cdot}02 < 49{\cdot}82$

(iii) $47{\cdot}105 < 48{\cdot}05 < 48{\cdot}985$

(c) 48

5

Width	Area
1	$26 < 33{\cdot}5 < 41$
$0{\cdot}5$	$29{\cdot}375 < 33{\cdot}125 < 36{\cdot}875$
$0{\cdot}1$	$32{\cdot}255 < 33{\cdot}005 < 33{\cdot}755$
$0{\cdot}01$	$32{\cdot}925 < 33{\cdot}000 < 33{\cdot}075$

Pages 49 and 50   The trapezium rule

1 (a) 1425 square units

(b) The same approximation as question **1** of *Spring the trap*

2 792 square units

3 (a) Students' sketch   **(b)** 9 square units

4 792 square units and 9 square units

5 79·6 square units

6 (a) $x = 4$ or $^{-}2$

(b) 36 square units

Pages 51, 52 and 53   Vectors

1 (a) $\begin{pmatrix} 1 \\ 4 \end{pmatrix}$ **(b)** $\begin{pmatrix} 5 \\ ^{-}6 \end{pmatrix}$ **(c) (i)** $\begin{pmatrix} 6 \\ ^{-}2 \end{pmatrix}$ **(ii)** $\begin{pmatrix} ^{-}6 \\ 15 \end{pmatrix}$ **(iii)** $\begin{pmatrix} 4 \\ ^{-}16 \end{pmatrix}$

(d) 5·38   **(e)** 18·43°

2 (a) PR $= \begin{pmatrix} 6 \\ 8 \end{pmatrix} = 2$TS   **(b) (i)** 5   **(ii)** 10

3 (a) Students' own answer   **(b)** $\begin{pmatrix} ^{-}13 \\ 9 \end{pmatrix}$ **(c)** 250 square units

4 (a) $(1,4), (0,^{-}1), (5,^{-}2)$ **(b)** 26 square units   **(c)** 56·3°

5 (a) $(a, b) = (^{-}1,9)$ **(b)** P'($^{-}2,3$), Q'(2,4), R'(0,12), S'($^{-}4,11$)

6 (a) Students' diagram   **(b)** 13 N   **(c)** 022·6°

7 (a) x   **(b)** $-$x   **(c)** $-$y   **(d)** $\frac{1}{2}$y   **(e)** $\frac{1}{2}$(x+y)

8 (a) (i) $-$a   **(ii)** a   **(iii)** $-$b   **(iv)** c   **(v)** a + b   **(vi)** a + b + c

(b) (i) $\frac{1}{2}$a + b   **(ii)** b + c $- \frac{1}{2}$a   **(iii)** c $- \frac{1}{2}$a + $\frac{1}{2}$b

9 (a) Parallelogram   **(b) (i)** p + q   **(ii)** p − q

(c) (i) λ(p + q)   **(ii)** $(1 - \mu)$(p − q)   **(iii)** $(1 - \mu)$p + μq

(d) $\lambda = \mu = \frac{1}{2}$

10 Students' scale drawing as:

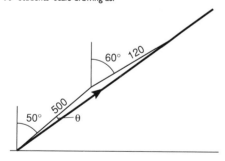

11 (a) (i) b − a   **(ii)** $\frac{3}{4}$a   **(iii)** $\frac{3}{4}$b   **(iv)** $\frac{3}{4}$(b − a)

(b) PQ parallel to BC, length of PQ = $\frac{3}{4}$ of length of BC

12 (a)

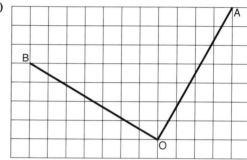

13 (a) (i) a + b   **(ii)** a + b + c

(b) (i) $\frac{1}{2}$(a + b + c)   **(ii)** $\frac{1}{2}$(a + b − c)   **(iii)** $\frac{1}{2}$(b + c − a)

14 (a)

(b) Rotation, 90°, clockwise about O

(c) (i) 8·06   **(ii)** 11·40

Page 54   Mensuration 2

1 (a) Students' explanation

(b) 2 could have dimensions of length

2 $x = 1, y = 2$ or $x = 2, y = 1$

3 A volume, B area, C length, D area, E volume, F length, G nonsense, H nonsense, I volume

4 The area and perimeter are numerically equal.

5 $a^2 + b$ is nonsense, unless we regard $b = 1 \times b$ so b = area of rectangle of length 1

6 Students' own answer

Pages 55, 56, 57 and 58   Trigonometry 2

1 (a) 10·83 cm^2 **(b)** 6·28 cm   **(c) (i)** 22·5°   **(ii)** 120·5°

2 Area is same, QA is same, angles reversed

3 (a) 4·09 cm   **(b)** 83°   **(c)** 7·67 cm   **(d)** 14·2 cm^2

4 Sin C greater than 1

5 (a) 14·35 cm   **(b)** 11·15 cm   **(c)** 17·46° and 120·54°

6 (a) Students' own answer

(b) Students' own answer

(c) 11·84 cm

7 (a) 76·29°, 103·71°   **(b)** 71·71°, 44·29°   **(c)** 27·75 cm, 24·91 cm

8 (a) 231·82 m^2 **(b)** 26·98 m   **(c)** 59·23°, 45·76°

9 (a) 184·96 km   **(b)** 153·07°   **(c)** 20·38 km

10 (a) 29·78°   **(b)** 78·22°   **(c)** 9·26 cm   **(d)** 20·7 cm^2

11 30·8°

12 38·94°, 31·59°, 109·47°

13 These ratios imply a straight line.

14 22·33°, 49·46°, 108·21°

15 Sin 50 : Sin 60 : Sin 70 = 0·766 : 0·866 : 0·940

16 (a) 33·2km   **(b)** 033·8°   **(c)** 7·1 km   **(d)** 303·38°

17 (a) 73·5 cm^2 **(b)** 9·2 cm   **(c)** 18·2 cm

(d) 30·7°   **(e)** 130°   **(f)** 5·47 cm

18 11·27 or 10·58 m

19 (a) 10·2 m   **(b)** 28·6°   **(c)** 5·56 m

20 (a) 65·45 km   **(b)** 3 hr 3 min p.m. or 1503

21 (a) Students' own answer

(b) Students' own answer

(c) Students' own answer

(d) 120°, 38·2°, 21·8°

22 (a) Students' drawing

(b) and **(c)** 46·85°

23 (a) Students' own answer
(b) $x = 1.475$
(c) 78·85° and 41·15°
24 (a) 27·92 km **(b)** 1558

Pages 59 and 60   Just the same

1   $A\hat{X}D = B\hat{X}C$ so two sides plus included angle
2   AC, BD meet at M.
   $\triangle$ABC and $\triangle$ADC, $\triangle$AMB and AMD, $\triangle$BMC and $\triangle$DMC
3   **(a)** three sides or two sides and included angle
   (b) (i) Yes **(ii)** Yes
4   2 sides and included angle
5   AC = 12 = PR, so 3 sides equal or hypotenuse and one side of 90° triangle
6   $B\hat{A}M = D\hat{M}A$, AB = DM, AM common, so two sides and included angle

Pages 61, 62 and 63   Similarity

1   **(a)** 6·67 cm **(b)** 6·25 cm **(c)** 16 cm **(d)** 10 cm
2   Worksheet 2
3   56 cm^2
4   37·5 cm^2
5   **(a)** 78·54 cm^2 **(b)** 452·39 cm^2
6   2·56
7   4 : 1
8   2·5
9   27
10 1·728
11 **(a)** 3 : 1 **(b)** 9 : 1
12 26·19 cm
13 **(a)** 8·6 cm **(b)** 6 750 000 cm^3
14 $V = k^{1.5}v$
15 **(a)** Students' own answer **(b)** Students' own answer
16 **(a)** around 170 cm **(b)** around 250 000 cm^3
   (c) around 14 cm **(d)** around 150 cm^3

Page 64   Painting cuboids

Students' own answers

Pages 65 and 66   Repeated Probability

1 **(a)** $\frac{2}{27}$ **(b)** $\frac{11}{216}$ **(c)** $\frac{7}{108}$
2 **(a)** $\frac{8}{27}$ **(b)** $\frac{2}{9}$ **(c)** $\frac{7}{27}$
3 **(a)** $\frac{27}{125}$ **(b)** $\frac{18}{125}$ **(c)** $\frac{32}{125}$
4 **(a)** $\frac{81}{676}$ **(b)** $\frac{137}{338}$ **(c)** $\frac{223}{338}$
5 **(a)** $\frac{8}{125}$ **(b)** $\frac{44}{125}$ **(c)** $\frac{54}{125}$
6 **(a)** $\frac{270}{2197}$ **(b)** $\frac{1000}{2197}$ **(c)** $\frac{1197}{2197}$
7 **(a)** $\frac{7}{27}$ **(b)** $\frac{8}{27}$ **(c)** $\frac{4}{9}$
8 **(a)** $\frac{9}{100}$ **(b)** $\frac{49}{100}$ **(c)** $\frac{31}{50}$
9 **(a)** $\frac{9}{64}$ **(b)** $\frac{3}{16}$ **(c)** $\frac{23}{32}$ **(d)** $\frac{1}{4}$
10 **(a)** $\frac{27}{1000}$ **(b)** $\frac{441}{1000}$ **(c)** $\frac{973}{1000}$

Pages 67 and 68   Without replacement

1 **(a)** $\frac{5}{21}$ **(b)** $\frac{15}{28}$ **(c)** $\frac{65}{84}$
2 **(a)** $\frac{1}{21}$ **(b)** $\frac{10}{21}$ **(c)** $\frac{17}{42}$
3 **(a)** $\frac{7}{44}$ **(b)** $\frac{21}{44}$ **(c)** $\frac{4}{11}$
4 **(a)** $\frac{8}{15}$ **(b)** $\frac{4}{15}$ **(c)** $\frac{11}{15}$
5 **(a)** $\frac{5}{22}$ **(b)** $\frac{15}{22}$ **(c)** $\frac{17}{22}$

6 **(a)** $\frac{1}{5}$ **(b)** $\frac{1}{3}$ **(c)** $\frac{8}{15}$
7 **(a)** $\frac{229}{2652}$ **(b)** $\frac{216}{613}$ **(c)** $\frac{99}{613}$
8 **(a)** $\frac{20}{117}$ **(b)** $\frac{88}{273}$ **(c)** $\frac{319}{819}$
9 **(a)** $\frac{61}{105}$ **(b)** $\frac{34}{105}$ **(c)** $\frac{34}{105}$
10 **(a)** $\frac{3}{10}$ **(b)** $\frac{1}{3}$ **(c)** $\frac{2}{3}$
11 **(a)** $\frac{7}{30}$ **(b)** $\frac{13}{40}$ **(c)** $\frac{13}{120}$
12 **(a)** $\frac{10}{143}$ **(b)** $\frac{691}{858}$ **(c)** $\frac{30}{143}$

Pages 69, 70 and 71   Cumulative frequency

1 **(a)**

Age (years)	Cumulative frequency
0–10	23
11–20	114
21–30	303
31–40	575
41–50	773
51–60	921
61–70	960
71–80	983
81–90	994
91–100	1000

(b) Students' cumulative frequency curve
(c) median ≏ 36·7
   lower quartile ≏ 27·7
   upper quartile ≏ 49·3
   interquartile range ≏ 21·6
   semi-interquartile range ≏ 10·8

2 **(a)**

Lifetime (hours)	Cumulative frequency
0–200	1
201–400	18
401–600	60
601–800	157
801–1000	193
1001–1200	208
1201–1400	210

(b) Students' cumulative frequency curve
(c), (d) median ≏ 692·7
   lower quartile ≏ 516·6
   upper quartile ≏ 800
   interquartile range ≏ 283·4
   semi-interquartile range ≏ 141·7
(e) 18·6%
(f) 23%

3 **(a)**

Mark	Cumulative frequency
0–10	1
11–20	3
21–30	18
31–40	47
41–50	114
51–60	149
61–70	170
71–80	185
81–90	196
91–100	200

(b) Students' cumulative frequency curve

(c), (d) median ≏ 48·4
lower quartile ≏ 40·9
upper quartile ≏ 60·8
interquartile range ≏ 19·9
semi-interquartile range ≏ 9·95
(e) 63%
(f) 63·5

4

Mark	Cumulative frequency
0–10	0
11–20	1
21–30	6
31–40	18
41–50	35
51–60	76
61–70	135
71–80	173
81–90	194
91–100	200

(a) median ≏ 64·6
lower quartile ≏ 54·2
upper quartile ≏ 74·4
interquartile range ≏ 20·2
semi-interquartile ≏ 10·1
(b) The second school has a higher median score. The spread of marks across the two schools is comparable.

Page 72   The errors aren't wrong

1 (a) £5000   (b) £6000   (c) £10 000
2 (a) £45 000   (b) £12 500
(c) (i) The largest amount divided by the smallest number of people
(ii) The smallest amount divided by the largest number of people

3 (a) $\frac{^-4}{3}$ (b) $\frac{3}{4}$ (c) AB

4 (a)

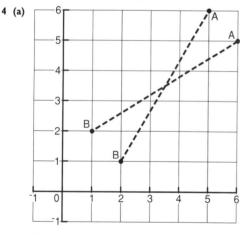

(b) $\frac{5}{3}$ (c) $\frac{3}{5}$

5 (a) 72   (b) 50   (c) 2·4   (d) 1·66 …
6 (a) 155·75 km   (b) 204·75 km
7 (a) 75·168 km/hr   (b) 74·831 km/hr   (c) 0·337 km/hr
8 Max speed 1·268 km/min   Min speed 1·232 km/min
Difference = 0·036 km/min
9 (a) 8·944 cm   (b) 8·832 cm
(c) 35·33 cm to 35·78 cm
(d) 688·9 cm^3 to 715·54 cm^3

Pages 73 and 74   More interesting 2

1 (a) 71   (b) 14·47   (c) $^-$20·63
(d) The investment is decreasing in value at a rate of 20·63%

2 (a) 12·25%   (b) 24·57%   (c) 25·89%
3 (a) 1·28 times   (b) 2·11 times   (c) 1·04 times
4 20 years
5 6·56%
6 (a) £462·73   (b) £4069·91   (c) £974·36
7 (a) 4·75%   (b) 13 years 11 months
8 (a) £344·58   (b) £344·58   (c) £1852·96
9 £995·72 × 0·45 = £448
10 £1732·74
11 (a) £1731·28   (b) Sally's by £1·46
12 15 years 6 months

Page 75   Come on be reasonable

1 (a) 43 685·25 cm^2 (b) 43 265·25 cm^2
(c) 43 265 cm^2 < area < 43 685 cm^2
(d) A reasonable approximation would be
43 475 cm^2 ± 200 cm^2 (other answers possible)
2 (a) 32·6 m/sec   (b) 32·33 m/sec
(c) 32·5 m/sec ± 0·1 m/sec (other answers possible)
3 $t = 35x + 20$
4 (a) 128·775 min   (b) 121·275 min
(c) 121 min < time < 129 min
125 min ± 4 min
5 Students' own answer
Longest   60·5 = 34·5x + 19·5
$x = 1·19$
Shortest   59·5 = 35·5x + 20·5
$x = 1·09$
Weight interval 1·09 kg < weight < 1·19 kg
Reasonable weight 1·14 kg ± 0·5 kg

Page 76   Some strange results

Students' own answers

Pages 77 and 78   Being rational

1 (a) $\frac{5}{1}$ (b) $\frac{3}{2}$ (c) $\frac{1}{10}$ (d) $\frac{1}{9}$ (e) $\frac{^-4}{1}$ (f) $\frac{^-1}{3}$ (g) $\frac{^-17}{4}$
2 Students' own answer
3 Students' own answer
4 (a), (b) and (c) all rational, (d) and (e) irrational
5 irrational
6 $x^2 + 6x + 9 = (x + 3)^2$ hence square root = z + 3
7 (a) 3, 4 and 5, 12 plus others   (b) 1, 1 and 1, 2 plus others
8–15   Students' own answers
16 (a), (b), (c) and (d) irrational, (e) rational

Pages 79 and 80   Iteration

1 (a) Students' own answer
(b) Students' own answer
(c) 9·4813
2 (a) Students' own answer
(b) 7·6458
3 (a) Students' own answer
(b) 2·1345
4 (a) Students' own answer
(b) (i) $x_{n+1} = \sqrt{6x_n + 2}$ (ii) $x_{n+1} = 6 + \frac{2}{x_n}$
(iii) $x_{n+1} = \frac{x_n^2 - 2}{6}$
(c) (i) and (ii) converge (iii) does not
(d) 6·32
5 (a) Students' own answer
(b) Students' own answer

(c) **(i)** $x_{n+1} = \sqrt{10 + \dfrac{1}{x_n}}$ **(ii)** $x_{n+1} = 0{\cdot}1(x_n^{\,3} - 1)$

     (iii) $x_{n+1} = \dfrac{10}{x_n} + \dfrac{1}{x_n^{\,2}}$

(d) only **(i)** converges   **(e)** $2{\cdot}21$

6 (a) Students' own answer

   (b) Students' own answer

   (c) Students' own answer

   (d) $2{\cdot}0903$ correct to 4 decimal places

Pages 81 and 82   Swings and roundabouts

1 (a) $U_9 = {}^-254$ $U_{10} = {}^-510$ $U_{11} = {}^-1022$ $U_{12} = {}^-2046$

   (b) $U_{100} = 2U_{99} - 2$

2 (a) $U_n = 2U_{n-1} - 2$

   (b) $U_{n+1} = 2U_n - 2$

3 (a) $U_1 = 4,\ U_2 = 6,\ U_3 = 14,\ U_4 = 26,\ U_5 = 50,\ U_6 = 98$

   (b) They are diverging in opposite directions one positive, one negative

   (c) The number 2 is repeated

4 (a) $^-1{\cdot}5$

   (b) $U_1 = 1$

       $U_2 = {}^-1{\cdot}5$

       $U_3 = {}^-2{\cdot}75$

       $U_4 = {}^-3{\cdot}375$

       $U_5 = {}^-3{\cdot}6875$

       $U_6 = {}^-3{\cdot}84375$

5 (a) $U_7 = {}^-3{\cdot}921875$

       $U_8 = {}^-3{\cdot}9609375$

       $U_9 = {}^-3{\cdot}9804688$

       $U_{10} = {}^-3{\cdot}9902344$

   (b) $U_{50} = \dfrac{U_{49}}{2} - 2$

6 (a) $U_n = \dfrac{U_{n-1}}{2} - 2$ **(b)** $U_{n+1} = \dfrac{U_n}{2} - 2$

7 The difference between successive terms is decreasing each time.

8 (a) $U_1 = 3$

       $U_2 = 4$

       $U_3 = 4{\cdot}5$

       $U_4 = 4{\cdot}75$

       $U_5 = 4{\cdot}875$

       $U_6 = 4{\cdot}9375$

       $U_7 = 4{\cdot}96875$

   (b) Converging

   (c) Possible limit 5

   (d)

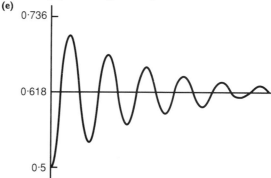

9 (a) Input ⟶ -2 ⟶ $\div\, 0{\cdot}5$ ⟶ Output

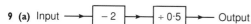

   (b) $U_1 = 2{\cdot}5$

       $U_2 = 1$

       $U_3 = {}^-2$

       $U_4 = {}^-8$

       $U_5 = {}^-20$

       $U_6 = {}^-44$

   (c) Diverging

(d)

10 (a) $U_{n+1} = \sqrt{1 - U_n}$

   (b) $U_1 = 0{\cdot}5$

       $U_2 = 0{\cdot}7071067$

       $U_3 = 0{\cdot}5411961$

       $U_4 = 0{\cdot}6773506$

   (c) $U_5 = 0{\cdot}5680223$

       $U_6 = 0{\cdot}65725$

       $U_7 = 0{\cdot}5854484$

       $U_8 = 0{\cdot}6438567$

       $U_9 = 0{\cdot}5967773$

       $U_{10} = 0{\cdot}6349981$

       $U_{11} = 0{\cdot}6041538$

       $U_{12} = 0{\cdot}629163$

   (d) Converging. The convergence is very slow.

   (e)

11 (a) $7, 6{\cdot}5, 6{\cdot}25, 6{\cdot}125, 6{\cdot}0625, 6{\cdot}03125, 6{\cdot}015625, 6{\cdot}0078125$

   (b) 6

   (c) $6, 6, 6, 6, \ldots$

   (d) 6 is the solution to the equation

       $x = \dfrac{x}{2} + 3$

12 (a) Diverging positively

   (b) Approaches zero

   (c) Diverging positively

   (d) Fixed solution

13 $x = 0$ or $0{\cdot}5$

Pages 83 and 84   That's the law

1 Students' graph and comments

2 Straight line graph

3 (a)

T^2	4	9	16	25	36	49
D	50	75	110	155	210	275

   (b) The straight line confirms Andrew's theory.

   (c) $m = 5, c = 30$

   (d) $D = 5T^2 + 30$

   (e) $145{\cdot}2$ m

4 (a)

S	12	33	61	98	142	194
t^2	16·6	60·0	114·5	190	279	380

(b) $a = 2, d = {}^-8$
(c) $t^2 = 2S - 8$
(d) $S = 16.5, t = 13.85$

5 (a) Plot P against $\sqrt{Q}$
(b)

$\sqrt{Q}$	2	3	4	5	6	7
P	3.5	4.8	6.1	7.6	9.1	10.4

(c) $m = 1.4, c = 0.6$
(d) $P = 1.4\sqrt{Q} + 0.6$
(e) $P = 6.54$
(f) $Q = 27.9$

6 (a)

P^3	1.33	13.8	46.6	74.1	166
C	34	72	170	252	530

(b) $a = 3, b = 30$
(c) $C = 3P^3 + 30$
(d) £3840
(e) £452

7 (a) $A = m\,\dfrac{1}{S} + c$
$\uparrow\quad\uparrow\quad\uparrow\quad\;\uparrow$
$y = m\;\;x\;\; + c$

(b)

$\dfrac{1}{S}$	1	0.4	0.33	0.25	0.2
A	10.5	4.5	3.8	3.3	2.5

$m = 10\quad c = 0.5$

8 (a) Students' own answer
(b) $S = m(T^2 + 3T) + c$
$= m((T + 1.5)^2 - 2.25) + c$
$= m(T + 1.5)^2 - 2.25m + c$
$S = m(T + 1.5)^2 + k$
(c) $y = mX + c$ where $X = (T + 1.5)^2$
(d)

$(T + 1.5)^2$	7.3	16.8	29.2	36	57.7	75.7	81
S	2.6	22.6	48.6	62.8	108	146	157

(e) Students' straight line graph
(f) $m = 2.1, k = {}^-12.7$
(g) (i) $S = 2.1(T + 1.5)^2 - 12.7$
(ii) $S = 2.1T^2 + 6.3T - 8$

Pages 85 and 86 Keep your distance

1 (a) 18 m/s **(b)** 163 m
2 (a) 10 seconds
(b)

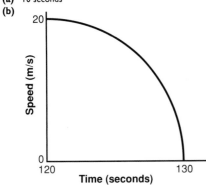

(c) 133 metres

---

3 (a)

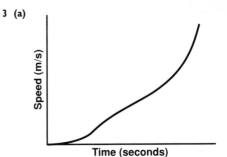

(b) 5 m/s^2 **(c)** 138 m
4 Using widths of 10 sec, volume = 1380 litres
5 36.66… metres
6 (a) (i) 48.125 **(ii)** 48.02 **(iii)** 48.005
(b) Answers should be similar to those obtained earlier.
7 Area = 3.141 59
8 (a) With width of 0.0001, area = 3.141 59
(b) With width of 0.0001, area = 3.141 59
(c) Students' own answer
9 (a) $v = t^2 + 2t$
(b)

Time	0	1	2	3	4	5	6
Speed	0	3	8	15	24	35	48

(c) (i) 6 m/s^2 **(ii)** 8 m/s^2
(d) 108 metres **(e)** 60 metres

Page 87 Let's get out of the joint

1 (a) The volume trebles.
(b) The volume is 0.25 of the original.
2 The volume increases by a factor of 4.5
3 $V \propto \dfrac{t}{p}$
4 (a) 0.75
(b) 1.5
(c) V increases by a factor of 2
(d) 960 m^3
5 $V \propto \dfrac{v^2}{l}$
6 (a) W decreases by a factor 0.81
(b) W decreases by a factor 0.91
(c) W decreases by a factor of 0.74
7 20% increase in voltage
8 $X = 13.416$ to 3 decimal places

Page 88 Functions 1

1 (a) 15 **(b)** 15 **(c)** ${}^-0.75$ **(d)** 35
2 (a) 6 and $^-6$ **(b)** 10 and $^-10$
(c) 2.5 and $^-2.5$
3 (a) $^-12$ **(b)** 0 **(c)** $x = 1$ and $^-2$
4

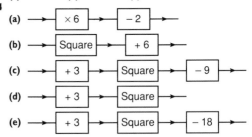

5 (a) 47 **(b)** $x = {}^-4$ twice
6 (a) $2x^2 - 1$ **(b)** $gf(x) \neq fg(x)$
7 (a) 15 **(b)** 26 **(c)** 35
(d) $10x + 25$ **(e)** $6x - 3$ **(f)** $4x + 14$
8 (a) $(2x^2 + 1)^2 = 4x^4 + 4x^2 + 1$
(b) $2((x + 2)^2)^2 - 1 = x^4 + 4x^3 + 12x^2 + 16x - 15$
(c) $(x^2 + 4x + 6)^2 = x^4 + 8x^3 + 28x^2 + 48x + 36$

Pages 89 and 90   Graphs of $y = f(x)$

1 (a) $y = {}^-2x + 1$ **(b)**
  (c) $y = {}^-2x - 2$

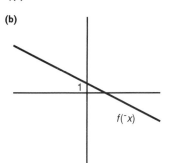

  (d) Reflection in the y-axis

2 (a) $y = (x - 2)^2$
  (b) and **(c)**

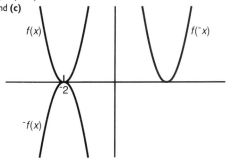

  (d) $y = -(x - 2)^2$ and $y = (x + 2)^2$

3 (a)

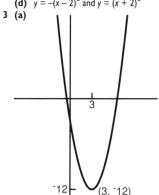

  (b) $y = x^2 - 6x - 3$
  (c) Students' sketch
  (d) $y = x^2 - 6x + 5$

4 (a)

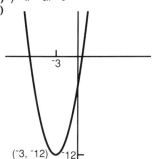

  (b) (i) $y = (x + 3)^2 - 13$
    (ii) $y = -(x + 3)^2 - 12$
   (iii) $y = (x - 3)^2 - 16$
   (iv) $y = -(x + 3)^2 - 20$

5 (a)

x	0	1	2	3	4	5
$f(x)$	0	${}^-5$	${}^-8$	${}^-9$	${}^-8$	${}^-5$
$f(x+3)$	${}^-9$	${}^-8$	${}^-5$	0	7	16

  (b) Students' graphs

6 (a) $x^2 - 9$ **(b)** $(x - 0)^2 - 9$
  (c) Translation $\begin{pmatrix} {}^-3 \\ 0 \end{pmatrix}$

7 (a) Translation $\begin{pmatrix} 1 \\ 2 \end{pmatrix}$ **(b)**

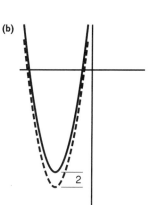

8 (a) $(2, {}^-4)$ maximum   **(b)** $(0, {}^-4)$ maximum
  (c) $(4, 4)$ minimum   **(d)** $(2, 8)$ minimum
  (e) $(2, 0)$ maximum   **(f)** $(4, 10)$ minimum
  (g) $(4, {}^-10)$ maximum
9 (a) Translation $\begin{pmatrix} {}^-3 \\ 20 \end{pmatrix}$ **(b)** $y = f(x - 3) + 20$

Page 91   Reflect on the problem

1 $y = -3x - 1$
2 (a) $f(x) = 3x + 1$ $-f(x)$
    $(0, 1) \longrightarrow (0, {}^-1)$
    $(1, 4) \longrightarrow (1, {}^-4)$
    $(2, 7) \longrightarrow (2, {}^-7)$
    $(3, 10) \longrightarrow (3, {}^-10)$
    $(4, 13) \longrightarrow (4, {}^-13)$
    $(x, y) \longrightarrow (x, -y)$
3 (a) $y = -3x + 6$ **(b)** $y = -(x + 4)^2 + 1$
  (c) $y = \dfrac{-12}{x}$ **(d)** $y = x - 6$

4 (a) The x coordinate changes to ^-x.
    The y coordinate remains the same.
  (b) $x \longrightarrow -x, \quad y \longrightarrow y$

5 $y = \dfrac{x - 1}{3}$

6 $f(x) = 3x + 1$ $Image$
   $(0, 1) \longrightarrow (0, 1)$
   $(1, 4) \longrightarrow (4, 1)$
   $(2, 7) \longrightarrow (7, 2)$
   $(3, 10) \longrightarrow (10, 3)$
   $(x, y) \longrightarrow (y, x)$
7 (a) The x coordinate maps to y.
    The y coordinate maps to x
  (b) $x \longrightarrow y \quad y \longrightarrow x$
8 $x = 3y + 1$
  $x - 1 = 3y$
  $\dfrac{x - 1}{3} = y, \quad y = \dfrac{x - 1}{3}$

9 (a) $y = \dfrac{x + 1}{6}$ **(b)** $y = \sqrt{x - 4}$

  (c) $y = 6 - x$ **(d)** $y = \dfrac{12}{x}$
  (e) $y = \sqrt{x} - 2$ **(f)** $y = \sqrt{x + 21} - 3$
10 (a) 23, 20, 2, 3, 36, 28, 6
  (b) 4, 4, 4, 4, 4, 4, 4
  (c) Students' own answer

Page 92   Functions 2

1 (a) $\dfrac{x}{3}$ **(b)** $\dfrac{x - 1}{2}$ **(c)** $3x - 2$
2 (a) 4   **(b)** 12

174

3 (a) $\dfrac{2x-1}{3}$ (b) $3-x$ (c) $\dfrac{4-3x}{2}$

4 (a) $\dfrac{x-2}{4}$ (b) $3-2x$ (c) $\dfrac{4}{x}$

  (d) $\dfrac{x+1}{x-1}$ (e) $\dfrac{4-2x}{x-2}$ (f) $\dfrac{3-4x}{3x+2}$

5 (a) 6   (b) ⁻1   (c) $\dfrac{1}{3}$

  (d) $\dfrac{x-5}{3}$ (e) $\dfrac{x-3}{2}$ (f) $\dfrac{1}{x}$

  (g) $\dfrac{3}{x-5}$ (h) $\dfrac{1-5x}{3x}$ (i) $\dfrac{2}{x+3}$

6 (a) ⁻0.5, $\dfrac{x-7}{6}$

  (b) 1.5, $\dfrac{x+4}{6}$

  (c) ⁻0.5, $\dfrac{x-7}{6}$

  (d) $f^{-1}g^{-1} = (gf)^{-1}$

7 (a) Students' own answers $(f^{-1}g^{-1}) = (gf)^{-1} = \dfrac{\sqrt{x-4}}{3} - 1$

  (b) $(fg)^{-1} = 3(x^2+4)+1 \neq f^{-1}g^{-1}$

  (c) $gg^{-1} = x$, the identity

Page 93   The School Council

Students' own answers

Page 94   Mensuration 3

1 (a) 9.08 cm   (b) 45.38 cm²   (c) 5.98 cm²
2 (a) 85.94°   (b) 48 cm²
3 (a) 20.52 m   (b) 20.94 m   (c) 314 m²   (d) 24.7 m²
4 2.56 m²
5 (a) 1840.8 cm³   (b) 1190.38 cm²

Pages 95, 96, 97 and 98   Trigonometry 3

1 (a) Students' table   (b) Students' graph   (c) 180°
2 (a) Students' graph   (b) 180°
3 (a) Students' graph   (b) 90°
4 (a) Students' graph   (b) 120°, 120°, 60°
  (c) 1 and ⁻1, 1 and ⁻1, infinite   (d) specific multiples of 30°
5 (a) Students' graph   (b) 90°, 90°, 45°
  (c) 1 and ⁻1, 1 and ⁻1, infinite; all at specific multiples of $22\tfrac{1}{2}$°
6 (a) Students' graph   (b) Students' own answer
  (c) Students' own answer   (d) specific multiples of 90°
7 (a) Students' graph   (b) Students' own answer
  (c) ⁻3   (d) specific multiples of 45°
8 (a) Students' graph   (b) (i) 2 (ii) ⁻2
  (c) specific multiples of 30°
9 (a) Students' graph
  (b) 5 and ⁻5   (c) specific multiples of 30°
10 (a) 4   (b) ⁻4   (c) specific multiple of 18°
11 (a) n (b) ⁻n (c) specific multiples of $\dfrac{90°}{m}$
  (d) Students' own answer
12 (a) Students' graph
  (b) 1.41   (c) ⁻1.41   (d) 45° and ⁻135°
  (e) Students' graph
13 (a) Students' graph
  (b) 11.5°, 168.5°, ⁻348.5°, ⁻191.5°
14 (a) Students' graphs
  (b) 63.4°, 243.4°
15 (a) Students' graphs
  (b) Students' own answer   (c) 53.5°
16 (a) Students' graphs
  (b) 0°, around 130°, around ⁻130°
17 75.5°, ⁻75.5°, 284.5°
18 (a) Students' graphs
  (b) about 38°, 142°

19 (a) Students' own answer
  (b) Students' own answer
  (c) Students' own answer
  (d) 38.17°, 141.83°, ⁻218.17°, ⁻321.83°
20 (a) Students' own answer
  (b) 64.4°, 243.4°
21 ⁻150°, ⁻30°, 210°, 330°, 90°, 270°
22 (a) Students' own answer
  (b) 46°, 134°
23 (a) 45°   (b) 30°   (c) 30°   (d) $22\tfrac{1}{2}$°
24 30°, 90°

Pages 99 and 100   Trigonometry 4

1 Students' own answers
2 (a)–(c) Students' own answers
  (d) $\sqrt{3}$ (e) $\dfrac{\sqrt{3}}{2}$
3 Students' own answers
4 (a) 30°   (b) 56°   (c) 45°
5 Students' own answers
6 (a) $\dfrac{\sqrt{3}}{2}$ or 0.866   (b) 0.6

Pages 101, 102 and 103   Spreading about 2

1 (a) 2.24, 1.78   (b) 7.08, 1.2   (c) 3, 2.09
  (d) 2.418, 0.149   (e) 52.83, 1.423
2 31.1, 8.5
3 (a) 23.9   (b) 11.6   (c) Students' histogram
4 (a) 9.51   (b) 4.18   (c) Students' diagram

Page 104   Changing probabilities

1 $\dfrac{9}{32}$

2 (a) $\dfrac{7}{100}$ (b) $\dfrac{3}{100}$

3 (a) $\dfrac{17}{75}$ (b) $\dfrac{187}{1125}$

4 $\dfrac{27}{50}$

5 (a) $\dfrac{7}{18}$ (b) $\dfrac{61}{216}$

6 (a) $\dfrac{5}{8}$ (b) $\dfrac{7}{20}$

7 (a) $\dfrac{7}{30}$ (b) $\dfrac{1}{120}$

Pages 105 and 106   Spreading about 3

1 (a) 37.9, 1.27   (b) 135, 13.3   (c) 99.38, 0.155
2 (a) 35.83, 15.5   (b) 15.13, 6.09

Page 107   It all adds up

1 (a) 4   (b) 42   (c) 42   (d) They all add up to 42.
2 (a) 10 terms   (b) 5 sets   (c) 5 × 42 = 210
3 (a) 12 terms   (b) 35   (c) 35   (d) 6 pairs
  (e) 6 × 35 = 210
4 Students' own rule
5 (a) 21 × 84 = 1764   (b) 9 × 89 = 801   (c) 31 × 43 = 1333
  (d) 6 × ⁻37 = ⁻222
6 (a) 2   (b) 3   (c) 24 terms   (d) 440
7 (a) 500   (b) 9300
8 (a) 2.5   (b) 575   (c) 25 terms

Page 108 It all disappears

1 (a) $x + y + 200$ (b) $x - y$
2 (a) $a - b$ (b) $a - h$ (c) 1st term − last term
3 $3S = 6 + 18 + 54 + 162 + \ldots + 1458 + 4374$
4 (a) $2S$ (b) 4372
5 (a) $2S = 4372$
  (b) $S = 2184$
  (c) $2 + 6 + 18 + 54 + 162 + 486 + 1458 = 2184$
6 (a) $r = 2$
  (b) $2S = 10 + 20 + 40 + 80 + \ldots + 1280 + 2560$
  (c) 2555
  (d) $S = 2555$
  (e) $S = 2555$
7 (a) $r = 5$
  (b) $rS = 5 + 25 + 125 + 625 + \ldots + 78\,125$
  (c) $4S = 78\,124$
  (d) $S = 19\,531$
8 (a) ar^{n-1}
  (b) $rS = ar + ar^2 + ar^3 + \ldots + ar^{n-1} + ar^n$
  (c) $rS - S = ar^n - a$
  (d) $rS - S = a(r^n - 1)$
    $S(r - 1) = a(r^n - 1)$
    $S = \dfrac{a(r^n - 1)}{r - 1}$
9 (a) $r = 4$ (b) 6825
10 $S = 2557.5$

Page 109 Close encounters of the nth kind

1 (a) $U_1 = {}^-1.5$
  $U_2 = {}^-0.8$
  $U_3 = {}^-1.1111$
  $U_4 = {}^-0.947\,368\,4$
  (b) $U_5 = {}^-1.027\,027$
  $U_6 = {}^-0.986\,666$
  $U_7 = {}^-1.006\,711\,4$
  $U_8 = {}^-0.996\,655\,5$, limit $= {}^-1$
  (c) ${}^-1 = \dfrac{1}{{}^-2}$

2 (a) $2 = \dfrac{2}{1}$
  (b) $U_1 = 2.5$
  $U_2 = 1.3333$
  $U_3 = 6$
  $U_4 = 0.4$
  $U_5 = {}^-3.3333$
  $U_6 = {}^-0.461\,5384$
  $U_7 = {}^-1.368\,4211$
  $U_8 = {}^-0.844\,444\,44$
  (c) $U_9 = {}^-1.084\,3373$
  $U_{10} = {}^-0.959\,5375$
  (d) Same limit of ${}^-1$

3 (a) $x = \dfrac{2}{x - 1}$
    $x(x - 1) = 2$
    $x^2 - x = 2$
    $x^2 - x - 2 = 0$
  (b) $x^2 - x - 2 = 0$
    $x^2 = x + 2$
    $x = \sqrt{x + 2}$
  (c) $U_1 = 2.5$
  $U_2 = 2.121\,320\,3$
  $U_3 = 2.030\,103\,5$
  $U_4 = 2.007\,511\,8$, limit $= 2$
  (d) This arrangement gives the second solution to the equation.
4 (a) Students' own answer
  (b) $U_1 = 3$
  $U_2 = 7$
  $U_3 = 47$
  $U_4 = 2207$
  $U_5 = 4\,870\,847$
  (c) A diverging sequence

5 (a) Students' own answer
  (b) $U_{n+1} = \sqrt{7 - U_n}$
  (c) $U_1 = 2$
  $U_2 = 2.236\,068$
  $U_3 = 2.182\,643\,4$
  $U_4 = 2.194\,847\,7$
  $U_5 = 2.192\,065\,7$
  $U_6 = 2.192\,700\,2$
  $U_7 = 2.192\,555\,5$
  (d) limit $= 2.193$ to 3dp
  (e) Students' own answer
6 (a) $x = \dfrac{7}{x + 1}$
    $U_{n+1} = \dfrac{7}{U_n - 1}$
  (b) $U_1 = 1$
  $U_2 = 1.75$
  $U_3 = 2.545\,4545$
  $U_4 = 1.974\,359$
  $U_5 = 2.353\,4483$
  $U_6 = 2.087\,4036$
  $U_7 = 2.267\,2773$
  (c) This arrangement converges to the same limit.
7 (a) Students' own answers
  (b) $U_{n+1} = \dfrac{1}{U_n{}^2 - 1}$, $U_{n+1} = (1 + U_n)^{\frac{1}{3}}$
  (c) $U_1 = 1.3$ ... $U_1 = 1.3$
  $U_2 = 1.449\,2754$ ... $U_2 = 1.320\,061$
  $U_3 = 0.908\,7612$ ... $U_3 = 1.323\,8224$
  $U_4 = {}^-5.742\,0755$ ... $U_4 = 1.324\,5478$
  $U_5 = 0.031\,2779$ ... $U_5 = 1.324\,6856$
  $U_6 = {}^-1.000\,9793$ ... $U_6 = 1.324\,7118$
  $U_7 = 510.336\,38$ ... $U_7 = 1.324\,7168$
  Solution is $x = 1.325$ to 3 dp

Page 110 Special prices

Students' own answers

Pages 111 and 112 Logging on

1 (a) $n = 1.5$ (b) $n = {}^-1$ (c) $n = {}^-4$ (d) $n = {}^-4.5$
  (e) $n = 2$ (f) $n = 3.25$
2 (a) 10^4 (b) 10^5 (c) 10^3 (d) 10^{-2}
  (e) 10^{-6} (f) 10^{-4}
3 $n = 2$
4 (a) $n = 3$ (b) $n = 6$ (c) $n = 2$ (d) $n = 0.75$
  (e) $n = 2$ (f) $n = \dfrac{{}^-1}{15}$ (g) $n = 2$ or ${}^-2$
5 10 years
6 11 years
7 (a) £15000 (b) £16441.04 (c) 9 years
8 (a) £6407.23 (b) 2.4 years (2 years 5 months)
9 (a) 10.4 years (b) 16 years (c) never
10 (a) £21600 (b) 10 years
  (c) Students' own answer
    The problem could be solved using a graphical method, trial and improvement or an algebraic method:
    answer approximately 9.315 years.

Page 113 Transforming equations

1 (a) $x = 4$ or ${}^-6$ (b) $x = 4$ or ${}^-6$
2 Students' explanation. Suggested explanation:
  Factorise the x^2 term and the x term.
  Express as difference of two squares $(y + a)(y - a)$ where $a =$ half of the coefficient of x
3 (a) $x = {}^-2$ or ${}^-4$ (b) $x = 5.742$ or ${}^-1.742$
  (c) $x = 2.324$ or ${}^-10.324$ (d) $x = 1.193$ or ${}^-4.193$
  (e) $x = 5.0$ or 0.334 (f) $x = 0.351$ or ${}^-2.851$
  (g) $x = 1.593$ or 0.157 (h) $x = 2.0$ or 1.667
4 Using $y = x + 2$ leaves the equation $y^2 = {}^-4$ which has no real roots.

176

Page 114 'e' by gum

This piece of work generates the transcendental number 'e'.

1. £2.00
2. (a) 50p (b) £2.25
3. (a)

Time interval of interest payments	Value of the £1 after one year
Annually	£2·00
6 monthly	£2·25
4 monthly	£2·370 370 4
3 monthly	£2·441 406 2
Monthly	£2·613 035 3
Weekly	£2·692 597
Daily	£2·714 567 5

(b) The limit of the sequence is 'e' (2·718 281 8)
(c) Justified by graphs/further extension of table, etc.

Pages 115, 116, 117 and 118   Much ado about a circle

1. Worksheet 3
2. Worksheet 4
3. Worksheet 5
4. Worksheet 6
5. Students' drawing
6. (a) 40° (b) 52° (c) 130° (d) 20°
7. Students' answer
8. Students' answer
9. (a) 8 cm (b) 2 cm (c) 2 cm (d) 6 cm
   (e) 5·25 cm (f) 9·80 cm
10. (a) Students' answer
    (b) $x = 4$ cm or $x = {}^-9$ cm but the second result is not physically possible
11. (a) Students' answer
    (b) $x = 7·83$ cm or $x = {}^-3·83$ cm but the second result is not physically possible

Pages 119, 120, 121 and 122   Transformation geometry 1

1. (a) Students' drawing
   (b) P'Q'R' is $({}^-2, 1)$, $({}^-5, 1)$, $({}^-5, 3)$
   (c) P"Q"R" is $(1, {}^-2)$, $(1, {}^-5)$, $(3, {}^-5)$
2. (a) (13, 3) (b) $x = 6$
3. T: $\begin{pmatrix} x \\ y \end{pmatrix} \rightarrow \begin{pmatrix} x \\ y \end{pmatrix} + \begin{pmatrix} 5 \\ 2 \end{pmatrix}$
4. (a) (i) (2, 5) (ii) $({}^-1, 2)$ (iii) $({}^-5, {}^-1)$ (iv) $({}^-7, {}^-6)$
   (b) (i) $(5, {}^-2)$ (ii) (6, 1) (iii) $(2, {}^-3)$ (iv) $(a + 5, b - 2)$
5. (a)

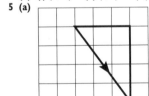

(b) 5 units (c) 53·1°
6. (a) Students' drawing
   (b) (i) (9, 9), (18, 9), (18, 27) (ii) (1,1), (2,1), (2,3)
   (iii) $({}^-6, {}^-6)$, $({}^-12, {}^-6)$, $({}^-12, {}^-18)$
   (iv) $({}^-1\frac{1}{2}, {}^-1\frac{1}{2})$, $(2, {}^-1\frac{1}{2})$, $(2, {}^-4\frac{1}{2})$
   (v) $(4\frac{1}{2}, 4\frac{1}{2})$, $(9, 4\frac{1}{2})$, $(9, 13\frac{1}{2})$ (vi) $({}^-4, {}^-4)$, $({}^-8, {}^-4)$, $({}^-8, {}^-12)$
7. (a) 2 (b) (1, 1)
8. (a), (b) Students' drawings (c) 3 (d) 9s
9. 4 and $^-4$

Page 123 and 124   Transformation geometry 2

Students' own answers

Page 125   More on Circles

1. (a) 40° (b) 63° (c) 63° (d) 62°
   (e) 96° (f) 104°
2. 6.5 cm
3. (a) 37° (b) 53°
4. 82°
5. (a) 46° (b) 52° (c) 23° (d) 134°
6. (a) 8 cm (b) Students' answer
7. (a) Students' answer (b) 6·45 cm or 1·55 cm

Page 126   Bravo Brazil

Students' own answers

Pages 127, 128 and 129   Trigonometry 5

1. (a) (i) 14·14 cm (ii) 21·21 cm (b) (i) 70·5° (ii) 27·3°
   (c) 666·7 cm^3 (d) 512·8 cm^3 (e) 75·96°
2. (a) 49·5 m (b) 53·4 m (c) 37·3 m (d) 52·9°
3. (a) Students' own answer
   (b) (i) 18 cm (ii) 29·2 cm
   (c) 2520 cm^3 (d) 6·72 cm (e) 77·4°
4. (a) 13 cm (b) 25 cm
   (c) (i) 22·6° (ii) 62·5 cm (iii) 10·2°
   (d) (i) 15·81 cm (ii) 18·4°

Page 130   Trigonometry 6

1. (a) 16·64 cm (b) (i) 16·55 cm (ii) 19·21 cm
   (c) (i) 25·0° (ii) 38·7° (iii) 54·85°
2. (a) Students' own answer
   (b) Students' own answer
   (c) 16·9 cm
3. (a) Students' own answer
   (b) Students' own answer
   (c) Students' own answer
   (d) (i) 97·2° (ii) 70·7° (iii) 51·3°
4. (a) 51·3° (b) 3·12 m (c) 2·40 m (d) 120°

10

10. (a) (i) $1·1^2 = 1·21$ (ii) $1·1^4$ (iii) $1·1^9$
    (b) (i) $1·1^4$ (ii) $1·1^8$ (iii) $1·1^{18}$
    (c) $1·1^{n-1}$
    (d) (i) $1·1^{2(n-1)}$ (ii) $1·1^{2n}$ (iii) $1·1^{2(n+p-1)}$
    (e) $1 + 1·1^2 + 1·1^4 + ... + 1·1^{18}$
    (f) $\dfrac{1·1^{2n} - 1}{0·21}$

11. $(1, {}^-2)$, $(1, {}^-5)$, $(7, {}^-5)$
12. (a) (i) (1, 0), $(1, {}^-3)$, $(7, {}^-3)$ (ii) (2, 1), $(2, {}^-2)$, $(8, {}^-2)$
    (iii) (5,4), (5,1), (11,1) (iv) $(5, {}^-4)$, $(5, {}^-7)$, $(11, {}^-7)$
    (b) Students' own answer
    (c) $(a{-}b{+}1, a{+}b{-}2)$, $(a{-}b{+}1, a{+}b{-}5)$, $(a{-}b{+}7, a{+}b{-}5)$
13. $(a - b + y, a + b - x)$
14. $(\text{Cos } \Theta, \text{Sin } \Theta)$
15. Students' own answer
16. (a) $(2a{-}p, q)$ (b) $(p, 2b{-}q)$ (c) (q, p) (d) $({}^-q, {}^-p)$
17. (a) Horizontal (b) $y = \frac{1}{2}(q + r)$
18. (a) $k = \sqrt{n}$ or $k = n^{\frac{1}{2}}$ (b) $n = k^2$
19. Students' own comments
20. Rotation, anti-clockwise through 36·9°

1 (a) $\frac{2}{15}$ (b) $\frac{1}{3}$ (c) $\frac{12}{25}$

2 (a) $\frac{1}{8}$ (b) $\frac{1}{4}$ (c) $\frac{3}{4}$ (d) $\frac{43}{64}$

3 (a) $\frac{9}{100}$ (b) $\frac{63}{10\,000}$ (c) $\frac{1325}{5000}$

4 $\frac{13}{25}$

5 (a) $\frac{9}{25}$ (b) $\frac{4}{25}$ (c) $\frac{12}{25}$ (d) $\frac{21}{25}$

6 $\frac{19}{49}$

7 (a) $\frac{5}{33}$ (b) $\frac{35}{66}$ (c) $\frac{21}{22}$

8 (a) $\frac{7}{15}$ (b) $\frac{3}{10}$

9 (a) $\frac{12}{25}$ (b) $\frac{13}{25}$

10 $\frac{1}{5525}$

11 $\frac{1}{12}$

12 (a) $\frac{3}{7}$ (b) $\frac{16}{35}$

13 (a) $\frac{1}{8}$ (b) $\frac{7}{8}$

14 (a) $\frac{20}{63}$ (b) $\frac{56}{81}$

15 (a) $\frac{27}{343}$ (b) $\frac{40}{49}$ (c) $\frac{64}{343}$ (d) $\frac{108}{343}$

16 (a) $\frac{14}{27}$ (b) $\frac{5}{27}$

17 (a) $\frac{1}{8}$ (b) $\frac{1}{2}$

18 (a) $\frac{1}{25}$ (b) $\frac{6}{25}$ (c) $\frac{6}{125}$ (d) $\frac{6}{125}$

19 (a) $\frac{64}{729}$ (b) $\frac{304}{729}$ (c) $\frac{189}{729}$

20 (a) $\frac{1}{21}$ (b) $\frac{3}{7}$ (c) $\frac{57}{252}$

Page 134   Linear programming

1 (a) 27   (b) 32   (c) 40
2 (a) 0   (b) 0   (c) 11
3 60
4 (a) Students' drawing
   (b) $\frac{165}{7} = 23\cdot57$ (c) 100
5 (a) $c \geq 0$, $a \geq 0$, $c + a \leq 300$, $c \leq 240$, $c \geq 3a$
   (b) Students' drawing
   (c) £3c + 5a
   (d) £1050

Pages 135 and 136   Sampling

Students' own answers

Pages 137, 138 and 139   Histogram and distributions

1 (a) 50%   (b) 16%   (c) 95%   (d) 25
2 (a) 61   (b) 49   (c) 37%
3 Approximately 65 minutes
4 800 per day
5 48·64, 13·78
6 32·33, 16·59
7 75·5, 15·88
8 37·83, 11·81

Page 140   The germ of an idea

1 (a) 64   (b) 4096

2

Time in minutes	0	10	20	30	40	50	60
Number of bacteria	2^0	2^1	2^2	2^3	2^4	2^5	2^6

3 (a) Number $= 2^{n/10}$
   (b) 32768
4 (a) 3 hours 20 mins
   (b) $1\,000\,000\,000 = 10^9$
5 2^n
6 (a) 32   (b) 1024   (c) $1\cdot15 \times 10^{18}$

Page 141   That's the way it grows

1 (a) 18·5%   (b) 32·5%
   (c) 18·75% (d) 37·5%
2 17 days
3 (a)

Date	1700	1750	1800	1850	1900	1950	2000
A	120	168	235	329	461	645	904
B	120	220	320	420	520	620	720
C	120	120	120	216	389	700	1260

(b) and (c)

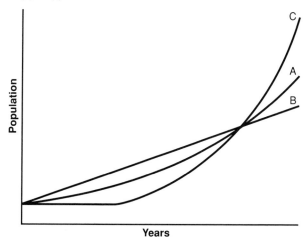

4 (a) 1935   (b) A(390), B(470), C(290)
   (c) A from 142 to 764 = 622
       B from 170 to 670 = 500
       C from 120 to 940 = 820
5 A(1710), B(920), C(4080), all to nearest 10

Page 142   It's half a life

1 Students' table and graph
2 5000
3 (a)

Time in seconds	0	1	2	3	4
Number of bacteria	20000	5000	1250	312	78

(b) Students' graph
4 (a) 2500   (b) 625   (c) 156
5 0·5 seconds
6 (a)

Time after switch on	0	2	4	6	8	10
Amount of moisture removed	4	2·4	1·44	0·864	0·52	0·31

(b) Students' graph
(c) (i) 2·71 hours   (ii) 1·115 kg

7 (a)

Year	Population of village
1800	200
1850	300
1900	450
1950	675
1970	540
1990	432
2000	345

(b) Students' graph
(c) 1913 and 1977
(d) 2060

Pages 143 and 144   The roots of all evil

1 **(a)** $x = {}^-2$ or $^-4$ **(b)** $x = {}^-3$ or $^-5$
  (c) $x = {}^-2$ or $^-3$
2 **(a)** $^-6, 12$ **(b)** $5, 7$ **(c)** $^-12, {}^-15$ **(d)** $4, {}^-9$
  (e) $^-1·5, 0$ **(f)** $0, {}^-9$
3 **(a)** $x^2 - 20x + 64 = 0$ **(b)** $x^2 - 20x - 64 = 0$
4 Students' own answer
5 **(a)** $\alpha + \beta = 3$ $\alpha\beta = {}^-7$ **(b)** $2\alpha + 2\beta = 6$
  (c) $\alpha\beta = {}^-28$ **(d)** $x^2 - 6x - 28 = 0$
6 **(a)** $x^2 - 6x - 27 = 0$ **(b)** $x^2 - 6x - 27 = 0$
7 $x^2 - 5x - 3 = 0$
8 **(a)** $\alpha + \beta = 2$ $\alpha\beta = {}^-4$ **(b)** $^-0·5$
  (c) $^-0·25$ **(d)** $x^2 + 0·5x - 0·25 = 0$
9 $\alpha + \beta = \dfrac{-b}{a}, \alpha\beta = \dfrac{c}{a}$

10 **(a)** $^-2, {}^-3$ **(b)** $3, 5$ **(c)** $\dfrac{1}{2}, {}^-1$ **(d)** $0, 2$ **(e)** $0, \dfrac{-16}{9}$

11 **(a)** 2 **(b)** 4 **(c)** 4 **(d)** 3 **(e)** $\dfrac{1}{8}$

12 **(a)** $x^2 + 3x - 4 = 0$ **(b)** $4x^2 - x + 4 = 0$

13 **(a)** $\alpha + \beta = \dfrac{-3}{2}, \alpha\beta = \dfrac{-n}{2}$ **(b)** $n = \dfrac{-9}{8}$

  (c) $x^2 + \dfrac{27}{32}x - \dfrac{729}{4096} = 0$

Pages 145 and 146   Let's bisect this equation

1 **(a)** When $x = 3, y = {}^-1$
            $x = 4, y = 4$
  (b) Students' table   **(c)** Students' table
  (d) $x = 3·828$ or $x = {}^-1·828$ **(e)** Students' own answer
2 **(a)** When $x = 2, y = {}^-6$
            $x = 3, y = 3$
  (b) Students' table giving $x = 2·777$
  (c)   **(d)** One solution

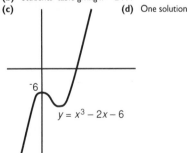

$y = x^3 - 2x - 6$

3 **(a)** $^-2 < x < {}^-1$ **(b)** $x = {}^-1·427$
4 **(a)** 3 solutions   **(b)** $^-3 < x {}^-2, {}^-1 < x < 0$
  (c) $x = {}^-2·617$ or $^-0·383$ or 2
5 **(a)** $^-8·322$ or $1·322$ **(b)** $^-2·440$ or $^-0·1836$ or $1·123$
  (c) $x = {}^-1·754$

Pages 147 and 148   Points in space

1 Students' own answer
2 **(a)** A(4, 0, 0) B(4, 5, 0) C(0, 5, 0) D(0, 5, 2) E(0, 0, 2) F(4, 0, 2) G(4, 5, 2)
  (b) (i) 6·40   **(ii)** 6·71   **(iii)** 4·47
  (c) (i) 17·3°   **(ii)** 17·3°   **(iii)** 26·6°
3 11·2
4 **(a)** 7·48   **(b)** 10·34   **(c)** 17·29
5 **(a)** $(4, 7, 4)$ **(b)** $(1\frac{1}{2}, 6\frac{1}{2}, {}^-\frac{1}{2})$ **(c)** $(1, 4\frac{1}{2}, {}^-3\frac{1}{2})$
6 **(a)** $(4, 0, 0)$ **(b)** $(8, 6, 0)$ **(c)** $(4, 6, 0)$

  (d) $(4, 3, 15)$ **(e)** $(4, 1\frac{1}{2}, 7\frac{1}{2})$ **(f)** 15·81 units

  (g) 53·1°   **(h)** 71·6°   **(i)** 78·7°
  (j) 29·3°   **(k)** 22·6°   **(l)** 61·2 unit^2
  (m) 240 unit^3
7 $(5, 3, 7)$ or $(3, 2, 4)$
8 $(8, 4, 7)$ or $(4, 2, 5)$
9 $(x_1 + \dfrac{k}{k+1}(x_2 - x_1),\ y_1 + \dfrac{k}{k+1}(y_2 - y_1),\ z_1 + \dfrac{k}{k+1}(z_2 - z_1))$

10 **(a)** B(5, 1, 1) C(5, 3, 1) D(1, 3, 1) E(1, 3, 9) F(1, 1, 9) G(5, 1, 9) H(5, 3, 9)
  (b) 8·25   **(c)** 9·16   **(d)** 64·1°   **(e)** (5, 2, 9)

  (f) $(3, 2, 9)$ **(g)** $(4, 2\frac{1}{2}, 7)$

Pages 149, 150, 151, 152 and 153   Transformation geometry 3

1 Worksheet 7
2 **(a)** $(1, 4)$ **(b)** Students' drawing
  (c) $(9, 4)$ **(d)** Students' own answer
3 Worksheet 8
4 Students' own answers
5 Students' own answers
6 Rotation, about origin, anticlockwise through 53·1°
7 $\begin{pmatrix} x \\ y \end{pmatrix} \rightarrow \begin{pmatrix} x \\ y \end{pmatrix} + \begin{pmatrix} 2 \\ 1 \end{pmatrix}$

8 S: $\begin{pmatrix} x \\ y \end{pmatrix} \rightarrow \begin{pmatrix} x \\ y \end{pmatrix} + \begin{pmatrix} 3 \\ 5 \end{pmatrix}$

9 **(a) (i)** $(^-6, {}^-1)$ **(ii)** $(^-5, 0)$ **(iii)** $(^-3, {}^-5)$ **(iv)** $(^-8, {}^-7)$ **(v)** $(^-9, 2)$
  (b) $(21, 23)$
10 **(a)** Students' own answer
  (b) Translation of double distance
  (c) If n is even, translation through n times the distance for T
     If n is odd, glide reflection through n times that for T
11 Worksheet 9
12 Students' drawings
13 **(a)** All clockwise rotations about the origin through:
    (i) 360°   **(ii)** 450°   **(iii)** 45°   **(iv)** $^-90°$ **(v)** $90n°$
  (b) $b - a =$ a multiple of 4
14 Worksheets 10 and 11
15 **(a), (b)** Students' drawing
  (c) Anti-clockwise, 90°
  (d) Students' own answer
16 Rotation, 180°, about (0, 2)
17 Worksheet 12
18 **(a), (b), (c)** Students' drawings
  (d) Rotation, 90°, anti-clockwise, about (6, 6)
  (e) Rotation, 90°, clockwise, about (6, 6)
19 **(a), (b), (c)** Students' drawings
  (d) Rotation, 90°, clockwise, about (3, 3)
20 **(a)** Students' drawing
  (b) Rotation, 90°, anti-clockwise, about (5, $^-5$)
21 Rotation, 90°, anticlockwise, about $(^-6, 8)$

Page 154   You cannot be real

1 **(a)** $x = 0·1623$ or $^-6·1623$
  (b) $x = 3·225$ or $0·775$
  (c) $x = 0·921$ or $^-2·171$
2 **(a) (i)** $x = {}^-1$ or $^-3$ **(ii)** $x = {}^-2$ twice   **(iii)** No real solution
  (b) (i) $x^2 + 4x + 4 = 0$ **(ii)** $x^2 + 4x + 5 = 0$ **(iii)** $x^2 + 4x + 3 = 0$
3 **(a)** No real roots   **(b)** 2 real roots   **(c)** 2 real roots
  (d) equal roots   **(e)** equal roots   **(f)** no real roots

4 (a) 0   (b) 6·25, $x = 2·5$ twice
5 (a) 10 or ⁻10
   (b)

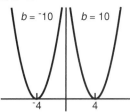

$b = ⁻10$ $b = 10$

⁻4   4

6 (a) $b^2 – 4ac = b^2 – 4(b – 1)$
$= b^2 – 4b + 4$
$= (b – 2)^2$
which is ≥ 0 for all values of b
   (b) For equal roots $(b – 2)^2 = 0$
$b = 2$
Solutions when b is 2 are $x = ⁻1$ twice.

Pages 155, 156, 157, 158 and 159
Transformation geometry 4 : matrices

1 (a) $\begin{pmatrix} ⁻1 & 0 \\ 0 & ⁻1 \end{pmatrix}$ (b) $\begin{pmatrix} 0 & 1 \\ 1 & 0 \end{pmatrix}$ (c) $\begin{pmatrix} 2 & 0 \\ 0 & 2 \end{pmatrix}$ (d) $\begin{pmatrix} 0 & 1 \\ ⁻1 & 0 \end{pmatrix}$

   (e) $\begin{pmatrix} 0 & ⁻1 \\ ⁻1 & 0 \end{pmatrix}$

2 The origin moves, so matrices cannot be used.
3 (0, 3), (0, 5), (⁻2, 5)
4 A'(6, 12), B'(9, ⁻3), C'(⁻6, 15)
5 (a) Reflection in $y = x$ (b) P'(3, 2), Q'(1, 5), R'(2, ⁻1)
6 (a) $\begin{pmatrix} \frac{\sqrt{3}}{2} & -\frac{1}{2} \\ \frac{1}{2} & \frac{\sqrt{3}}{2} \end{pmatrix}$ (b) $\begin{pmatrix} 0·259 & ⁻0·966 \\ 0·966 & 0·259 \end{pmatrix}$

   (c) $\begin{pmatrix} ⁻0·259 & ⁻0·966 \\ 0·966 & ⁻0·259 \end{pmatrix}$

7 Students' own answer
8 (a) $\begin{pmatrix} \frac{1}{2} & \frac{\sqrt{3}}{2} \\ -\frac{\sqrt{3}}{2} & \frac{1}{2} \end{pmatrix}$ (b) $\begin{pmatrix} \frac{\sqrt{3}}{2} & \frac{1}{2} \\ -\frac{1}{2} & \frac{\sqrt{3}}{2} \end{pmatrix}$

   (c) $\begin{pmatrix} 0·259 & 0·966 \\ -0·966 & 0·259 \end{pmatrix}$

9 $\begin{pmatrix} \frac{1}{\sqrt{2}} & -\frac{1}{\sqrt{2}} \\ \frac{1}{\sqrt{2}} & \frac{1}{\sqrt{2}} \end{pmatrix}$, $\begin{pmatrix} 0 & ⁻1 \\ 1 & 0 \end{pmatrix}$

10 $\begin{pmatrix} \frac{1}{\sqrt{2}} & \frac{1}{\sqrt{2}} \\ -\frac{1}{\sqrt{2}} & \frac{1}{\sqrt{2}} \end{pmatrix}$

11 Anti-clockwise rotation, about origin through 60°
12 Clockwise rotation, about origin through 53·13°
13 $\begin{pmatrix} \frac{12}{13} & -\frac{5}{13} \\ \frac{5}{13} & \frac{12}{13} \end{pmatrix}$

14 $\begin{pmatrix} \frac{24}{25} & \frac{7}{25} \\ -\frac{7}{25} & \frac{24}{25} \end{pmatrix}$

15 $\begin{pmatrix} ⁻0·38 & ⁻0·92 \\ 0·92 & ⁻0·38 \end{pmatrix}$

16 A'(4, 3), B'(1, 7), C'(⁻3, 4)
17 (a) Reflection in x-axis   (b) $\begin{pmatrix} 1 & 0 \\ 0 & ⁻1 \end{pmatrix}$
   (c) They are the same.
18 (a) $\begin{pmatrix} 0 & 1 \\ 1 & 0 \end{pmatrix}$ (b) $\begin{pmatrix} 0 & 1 \\ 1 & 0 \end{pmatrix}$

19 (a) $\begin{pmatrix} \frac{\sqrt{3}}{2} & -\frac{1}{2} \\ \frac{1}{2} & \frac{\sqrt{3}}{2} \end{pmatrix}$ (b) $\begin{pmatrix} \frac{\sqrt{3}}{2} & \frac{1}{2} \\ -\frac{1}{2} & \frac{\sqrt{3}}{2} \end{pmatrix}$

20 (a) $\begin{pmatrix} 3 & 0 \\ 0 & 3 \end{pmatrix}$ (b) $\begin{pmatrix} \frac{1}{3} & 0 \\ 0 & \frac{1}{3} \end{pmatrix}$

21 (a) $\begin{pmatrix} k & 0 \\ 0 & k \end{pmatrix}$ (b) $\begin{pmatrix} \frac{1}{k} & 0 \\ 0 & \frac{1}{k} \end{pmatrix}$

22 Worksheet 13
23 (a) A = Reflection in $y = x$, B = Reflection in y-axis
   (b) Rotation about origin, through 90°, clockwise
   (c) $\begin{pmatrix} 0 & ⁻1 \\ 1 & 0 \end{pmatrix}$

24 (a) Rotation about origin through 90° clockwise
   (b) $\begin{pmatrix} 0 & 1 \\ ⁻1 & 0 \end{pmatrix}$

   (c) Each is the inverse of the other.

25 (a) A = $\begin{pmatrix} 0 & ⁻1 \\ 1 & 0 \end{pmatrix}$, B = $\begin{pmatrix} ⁻1 & 0 \\ 0 & 1 \end{pmatrix}$

   (b) Reflection in $y = x$
   (c) $\begin{pmatrix} 0 & 1 \\ 1 & 0 \end{pmatrix}$

26 Worksheet 14
27 (a) (i) A = 90° rotation, anti-clockwise about the origin
        (ii) B = Reflection in y-axis
   (b) (i) Vertices at (⁻1, ⁻2), (⁻, ⁻5), (⁻3, ⁻5)   (ii) Reflection in $y = ⁻x$
   (c) $\begin{pmatrix} 0 & ⁻1 \\ ⁻1 & 0 \end{pmatrix}$

28 (a) 90°, clockwise rotation about origin
   (b) Vertices of T' at (1, ⁻2), (1, ⁻5), (3, ⁻2)
   (c) $\begin{pmatrix} 0 & ⁻1 \\ 1 & 0 \end{pmatrix}$

   (d) (i) $\begin{pmatrix} ⁻1 & 0 \\ 0 & ⁻1 \end{pmatrix}$ (ii) $\begin{pmatrix} 0 & ⁻1 \\ 1 & 0 \end{pmatrix}$ (iii) $\begin{pmatrix} 1 & 0 \\ 0 & 1 \end{pmatrix}$

   (e) $M^{-1} = M^3$ Rotation of 90° anti-clockwise = rotation of 270° clockwise

Pages 160, 161, 162 and 163   The road to success

1 Students' own answers
2 (a) SACDGF (10 units)
   (b) Ⓢ ① ④ ⑤ ⑧ ⑨ (23 units)
3 Ⓢ ② ③ ⑤ ⑦ ⑨ Ⓕ ⟶ 7 + 11 + 6 + 10 + 16 = 50 units
4 (a)

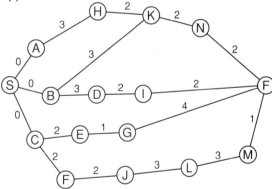

   (b) S C F J L Finish   (11 days)
5 (a)

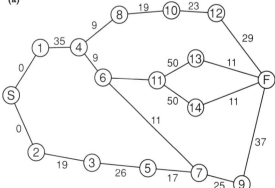

   (b) (i) Ⓢ ② ③ ⑤ ⑦ ⑨ Finish   (ii) 124 hours

Heinemann Educational,
a division of Heinemann Educational Books Ltd
Halley Court, Jordan Hill, Oxford OX2 8EJ

OXFORD LONDON EDINBURGH
MADRID ATHENS BOLOGNA PARIS
MELBOURNE SYDNEY AUCKLAND SINGAPORE TOKYO
IBADAN NAIROBI HARARE GABORONE
PORTSMOUTH NH (USA)

First published 1995

95 96 97 98 99 10 9 8 7 6 5 4 3 2 1

ISBN 0 435 52987 0

Designed and produced by VAP Group Ltd, Kidlington, Oxford

Illustrated by Jane Bottomley and Trevor Mason

Printed in Great Britain by the Bath Press, Avon

The authors and publishers would like to thank the following for permission to use photographs:
p. 63 Granada Television Ltd. and p.126 Allsport USA/David Cannon
Cover photo: The Science Museum